Buying & Selling Farmland

D1597529

Buying & Selling Farmland

A Guide to Profitable Investment
Dwight W. Jundt

Doane Agricultural Service, Inc. / 8900 Manchester Road / St. Louis, Missouri 63144

Library of Congress Catalog Card Number: 80-67887
ISBN: 0-932250-10-6

Printed in U.S.A.

The Author

Dwight Jundt is President of Jundt Associates, Inc., headquartered in Fort Lauderdale, Florida. They represent builders, chains, and investors in the acquisition and sale of sites on both coasts of South Florida.

He is Vice President and Director of Florida Operations of The Lyon Realty Company, a subsidiary of The William Lyon Company, based in Newport Beach, California. As such, he is developing 900 acres in Broward County for the construction of 4,300 homes and commercial and office space. The William Lyon Company builds about 1,500 homes per year in several California locations.

Born on a farm near Creighton, Nebraska, he was graduated from the University of Nebraska in 1955 with a Bachelor of Science degree in Agricultural Economics. He was with Doane Agricultural Service, St. Louis, as manager of their appraisal and real estate departments until 1969. He then formed the St. Louis company of Land Dynamics, Inc., selling it in 1973 and moving to Fort Lauderdale.

He is a licensed real estate broker in Florida, Illinois, Texas, Oklahoma, Nebraska, Missouri, Kansas, and Arkansas.

Jundt was President of the National Farm and Land Institute in 1973, and served as a member of the Executive Committee of the National Association of Realtors in 1975 and 1976. He is an accredited member of the American Society of Farm Managers and Rural Appraisers.

He is a Certified General Contractor in the State of Florida. Currently on the Board of Directors of the Builders Association of South Florida, he has served two years on their Executive Committee.

Jundt has lectured at over 200 seminars and institutes since 1962. He is a contributing author to the "Real Estate Handbook" recently published by Dow Jones-Irwin.

*This book is dedicated to my mother and
father who exemplify the millions of
land owners whose roots bind our land
together; and to my daughters for their
appreciation of those ties to the land.*

PREFACE

This book is about land ... farmland. More specifically, it deals with the techniques of buying and selling farmland plus includes general procedures for operating the property. Books on general real estate are fairly common. Indeed, over a million people in this country hold licenses to sell real estate. Yet, probably less than a thousand deal exclusively with farmland transactions, a miniscule percentage when compared to the enormity of the dollars involved in land transactions annually.

The search for a perfect investment is a fantasy that never fails to bring a gleam to the eyes of those with capital to spend. Land is perpetually on the list of investment recommendations, albeit always with the qualification that while the rewards are great, so are the risks to the uninformed.

This book does not portray land as a perfect investment. Rather, for those inclined to own farmland for one reason or another, I have tried to reduce the unknowns. To those current farmowners who have woven their way through many land transactions, I apologize if portions of the book seem basic. To the newcomer, I apologize for using terminology not always understandable.

No claims are made by the author that this book is without bias. It is the product of one who grew up on a farm; studied vocational agriculture in high school; agricultural economics in college; and has been involved in the purchase, sale, operation and development of land his entire life. I believe that the proper use of all land, whether for crops, housing, industry, or recreation, is vital to the strength and health of our nation. I'm conservative and believe that overregulation by government at all levels results in high taxes, burdensome costs, and curtailment of common sense decisions that the American people are capable of making in a relatively free economy.

Anyone who is capable, and has the inclination to own land, should– which brings us to land promotions. Most highly promoted lot sales schemes are among the great wrongs perpetrated on the American public. By capitalizing on the inborn and proper desire of people to own a piece of land, promoters have taken millions of acres of swamp, desert, mountains, and range country, divided them into small plots, and sold them at from 10 to 100 times what they are worth, and what the promoter paid for the land. Based on what this writer has seen, a general rule for the public should be that any mailing piece, on slick paper with pretty pictures, offering to pay your way to look at a lot at some distant location, should be viewed with suspicion, and disposed of as quickly as possible.

There is no doubt that owning land is a great hedge against inflation, and a solid asset in times of recession or economic uncertainty. Very seldom has great wealth been accumulated without the inclusion of land in an investment portfolio. This has always been true, and always will be. But treat land with the respect it deserves–a complicated resource, the use of which requires knowledge, study, and care.

Acknowledgment is given to the staff of Doane Agricultural Service, Inc. for their assistance in providing certain factual data, and constructive comments in the preparation of the manuscript. Thanks are also due to Doane for their confidence in asking me to write the book in the first place.

Apologies are due my friends for the many excuses I've made for not spending time with them these seemingly interminable months. I admit now that I didn't spend that much time writing. My defense is that when I wasn't writing, I was thinking about it. To my publisher, thank you for your patience. I know there were times you didn't think this book would ever be finished. Well, you had a lot of company, especially me.

Dwight W. Jundt
Ft. Lauderdale, Florida

Contents

CHAPTER 1

Land: For Labor, Leisure, Heritage and Profit

Land best embodies those traits comprising the personality of America. Something about the ownership of land inherently appeals to the basic nature of our citizenry. Perhaps the freedom and independence of our heritage is brought more clearly into focus by open space. A forest, waving fields of grain, snowcapped mountains, and lush green pastures evoke exotic mental images.

A recent study posed the question: What are the ideal surroundings in which to rear a family? Over 70% answered: On a farm or ranch, or in the country. Parents associate a foundation stemming from the land with the traits of honesty, strength, fairness, and compassion.

Nearly every wealthy man sought land ownership when he became financially able. Television and movie personalities, sports celebrities, and Presidents go back to the land as a retreat and as a way of life.

References to land invade our vocabulary: earth-to-earth, dust-to-dust. Wars are fought to protect territory. Television programs focus on tales of the Old West, and heroes of pioneer days. City street gangs wage war over their "turf". Struggling suburbanites labor for a house on a larger lot. Estate is equated to luxury: estate-sized lots, a country estate. A King has his Kingdom, Presidents have their Camp David, George Washington had his Mt. Vernon.

Americans are particularly close to their land because it is as varied in type and temperament as they are. A few hours in a plane will whisk one from prairie to canyon, field to forest, snowcapped mountains to wave-swept beaches, and tundra to tropics. It's no wonder, then, that the ownership of land is a status desired by so many persons.

Those of us who had the great and good fortune to grow up on a farm or ranch, or in a small town close to nature, never quite abandon those roots, no matter how citified our present world becomes. Many hunters are not drawn to the fields and forest for meat, or for the sport of the

hunt . . . it's the solitude of the land. Autumn leaves make us reflective
and melancholy; the first buds of spring bring renewed vitality.

Nature is associated with peace and tranquility. The favorite childhood bedtime stories are associated with animals of the farm or forest.
Mother Goose remains perennially popular. Henny Penny, the Three
Bears, Bambi, Lassie, Black Beauty, and Peter Rabbit all make up part
of our folklore of the land. People go to sleep counting sheep–not tall
buildings.

And so this book is about land; how to best acquire it, own it, and if
we must–sell it. Land for some means labor, and an occupation. Others
own land as part of their heritage. The pursuit of leisure and relaxation
will always motivate buyers. Whatever the reason for acquiring a property, most will find that profit is part and parcel of land ownership. But
not least important is a sense of pride in owning part of American history. Land is our legacy!

LAND VALUES

For almost 50 years, land prices have been on a continuous climb. The
law of supply and demand dictates that well chosen land will always be
an attractive investment. The reason is obvious: the supply of land is fixed, but increasing population, industrial activity, rising personal incomes, and higher standards of living mean intensified use of land.

For centuries land has been a primary source of subsistence and
wealth, as well as the reason for many great conflicts between peoples
and nations. Given human nature, there is no reason to believe these factors will be any less forceful in the future.

Rising Land Prices

Charting trends in land values is not an idle economic exercise. A recent
study of a rural county showed an increase of 443 millionaires in residence–all obtaining that status by virtue of owning farmland that had
rapidly increased in value. Over 2,000,000 people in the United States
own substantial income-producing farms. Several million more own
land ranging from a few acres to a few hundred acres. The investment
represented is staggering–perhaps a trillion dollars.

Land values in the United States are low, compared to their productive capacity, when analyzed against other parts of the world. Tech-

nology never stands still. As new production innovations are introduced into agriculture, they are capitalized into increased land values.

Factors directly tied to land price increases include:

Increase in population
Conversion of farmland to urban uses
General inflation
Increased productivity
Generally higher level of commodity prices
Limited supply of land
Improved machinery encouraging farmers to expand their operations, thus competing for available land

Indirect factors also support land prices.

Government Support. The government of the United States could not possibly let agriculture face bankruptcy. If Lockheed and Chrysler were thought to be worth supporting, just let this country be threatened with a food shortage. A very small percentage of the people feed all of the rest of America.

Influence on Foreign Policy. The productivity of the United States farm operator is keenly recognized by both political parties as a major strength of the United States in the world balance of power. The government is strongly committed to maintaining product prices to encourage ample food and fibre supplies. The importance of food in the export market increases annually.

Outside Investors. Foreigners buy land in the United States because of our political stability. Resident predictors of doom may talk of our runaway inflation, slowing productivity and energy crises, but investors in other countries still view our system as the beacon of the world. While we seem to come under criticism from abroad, most foreign visitors wonder at our self-castigation and criticism. That's the reason why a piece of America is as good as gold–maybe better.

Attitudes in Good Times and Bad. A critical factor in the future price trend of land is the attitude of the people buying it. When people believe that inflation will continue they look to land as a hedge. As long as the farmer wants to expand his operations he will take a bullish approach when nearby land comes up for sale. The investor who looks at land as a secure place to put his money for both returns and appreciation will continue to have a strong affect on land that comes up for sale.

Land In U.S. Underpriced Relative To World Prices. Finally, agricultural land values in the United States are low, compared to their productive capacity, when measured against other parts of the world. Most developed countries expect a lower return to farmland, and view land as an asset much like gold–in short supply and great demand.

Dollar Returns To Land Still Important

While the rate of return on land has seemingly been ignored during periods of steady appreciation, profits are only partially related to the individual prices on farm products. Because farmers have steadily increased their productivity through the use of larger machinery and other technology, they have been able to increase their overall returns, even though commodity prices have not been keeping pace with costs.

However, product prices tend to be cyclical. In each cycle there is a point at which the returns become so marginal that they do not support additional land price increases. Then, land prices tend to level off until the next upward cycle, or until other factors come along to provide additional impetus. Lenders become concerned with the impact that higher land prices and heavy debt have on a farmer's cash flow. Notwithstanding inflation and appreciation, over any period of time, those who purchase land will continue to look to earning potential as a major factor in determining its value.

Historical Trends In Land Values

Since 1935, average land values in the United States have increased consistently. Dynamic increases were recorded during the 4 years from February 1, 1976 to February 1, 1980.

12 Months Ending	% Price Increase
February 1, 1977	17%
February 1, 1978	9%
February 1, 1979	15%
February 1, 1980	14%

This 4 year increase raised the average per acre value in the United States from $390 to $640. The Corn Belt and Lake States land increased over 60% during these years.

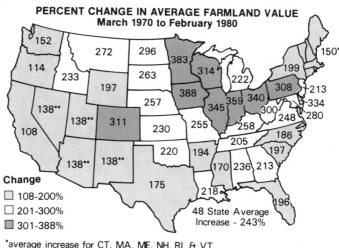

PERCENT CHANGE IN AVERAGE FARMLAND VALUE
March 1970 to February 1980

Change
- ☐ 108-200%
- ☐ 201-300%
- ■ 301-388%

48 State Average
Increase - 243%

*average increase for CT, MA, ME, NH, RI, & VT.
**average increase for AZ, NM, NV, & UT.

Averages only indicate trends, however. At the start of the 1980s, prime land in the Corn Belt was not infrequently selling in excess of $4,000 per acre. These prices are obviously averaged out with many sales of farmland between $400 and $2,000 per acre. Large acreages of ranches, cut-over timberlands, and pasture selling at under $200 per acre bring the average land price in the country to $639 per acre estimated for 1980.

The following illustrations depict the movement in farmland values since 1940.

Farmland as an investment. As land has proven to be a more reliable and rewarding investment than the stock market, other capital sources have sought a medium through which to participate in farmland ownership. "Mutual funds" of land have been proposed by private and institutional agencies. While many private investment syndicates have been formed, no major, publicly held, farmland ownership companies have been launched. Some public and congressional resistance has discouraged major corporate ownership, but efforts by these organizations will continue as farmland remains one of the most stable long term investments in the United States.

Farm Real Estate Values: Average Value Per Acre, March 1, 1940-1980

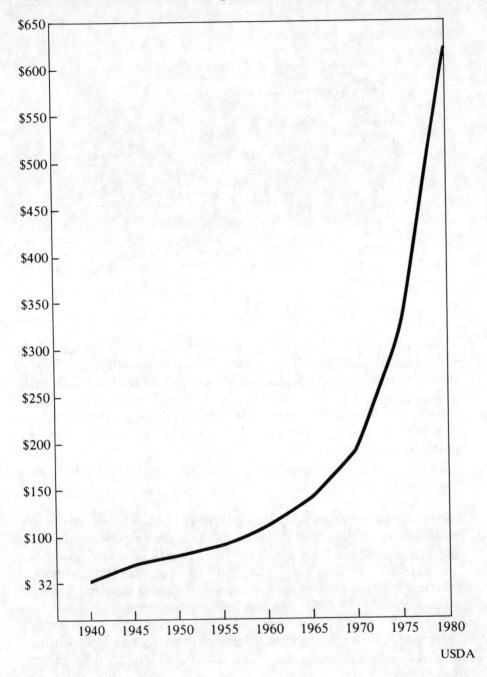

USDA

Farm real estate values: Average value per acre of land and buildings by State grouped by farm production region, 1970-80

STATE	March 1, 1970	March 1, 1972	March 1, 1974	Feb. 1, 1976	Feb. 1, 1978	Feb. 1, 1980[1]
NORTHEAST						
Maine[2]	161	217	302	369	441	524
New Hampshire[2]	239	339	493	610	729	866
Vermont[2]	224	298	410	500	597	710
Massachusetts[2]	565	687	875	1,040	1,242	1,475
Rhode Island[2]	734	971	1,334	1,623	1,939	2,304
Connecticut[2]	921	1,108	1,395	1,647	1,962	2,331
New York	273	323	445	549	589	681
New Jersey	1,092	1,224	1,582	2,004	2,057	2,400
Pennsylvania	373	419	621	815	1,092	1,370
Delaware	499	566	810	1,155	1,500	2,018
Maryland	640	732	980	1,278	1,578	2,249
LAKE STATES						
Michigan	326	370	521	604	860	1,089
Wisconsin	232	274	389	490	690	928
Minnesota	226	241	338	521	730	1,008
CORN BELT						
Ohio	399	439	627	856	1,263	1,713
Indiana	406	435	592	878	1,303	1,723
Illinois	490	522	720	1,052	1,581	1,929
Iowa	392	414	597	903	1,268	1,706
Missouri	224	261	384	446	602	816
NORTHERN PLAINS						
North Dakota	94	98	144	228	273	352
South Dakota	84	87	119	163	227	292
Nebraska	154	170	242	355	385	536
Kansas	159	174	253	330	380	498
APPALACHIAN						
Virginia	286	345	501	620	732	942
West Virginia	136	173	262	375	403	519
North Carolina	333	396	551	637	694	885
Kentucky	253	295	385	504	671	879
Tennessee	268	302	415	495	608	743
SOUTHEAST						
South Carolina	261	313	418	486	543	629
Georgia	234	290	424	476	564	682
Florida[3]	355	403	608	726	838	1,097
Alabama	200	236	331	404	452	639
DELTA						
Mississippi	234	242	340	381	464	629
Arkansas	260	296	406	465	571	829
Louisiana	321	380	469	538	669	984
SOUTHERN PLAINS						
Oklahoma	173	194	263	332	402	522
Texas	148	173	241	267	317	411
MOUNTAIN						
Montana	60	68	96	132	168	218
Idaho	177	205	287	368	445	553
Wyoming	41	48	70	94	105	127
Colorado	95	116	175	219	274	388

(continued)

Farm real estate values (continued)

STATE	March 1, 1970	March 1, 1972	March 1, 1974	Feb. 1, 1976	Feb. 1, 1978	Feb. 1, 1980[1]
MOUNTAIN						
New Mexico[4]	42	49	73	81	93	112
Arizona[4]	70	86	110	114	125	150
Utah[4]	92	128	171	212	248	297
Nevada[4]	53	66	85	87	97	116
PACIFIC						
Washington	224	238	308	420	528	615
Oregon	150	186	234	265	303	320
California	479	494	570	668	761	1,123
48 STATES	196	219	302	385	488	640

[1]Preliminary. [2]Average rate of change for the 6 New England States was used to project the dollar values. [3] Values are based on an index estimated from the average of the percentage change in Georgia and Alabama index values. [4] Starting November 1978 the average rate of change for these States was used to project the dollar values.   USDA

Farmland vs. Other Investments

For years farmland has not only been an excellent hedge against inflation but ranks well with other investment opportunities. Compare the rapid climb in land values, shown in the following charts, with the rate of inflation and the up and down pattern of the common stock market. An equal amount invested in 1967 in average U.S. farmland and average corporate common stocks would result in a land portfolio worth more than three times the stock portfolio.

Land Price Gain Exceeds Inflation

While much of the land price increase is due to inflation, a comparison to the consumer price index clearly indicates that increases in the real value of land have exceeded the rate for other consumer items.

NUMBER, SIZE AND OWNERSHIP OF U.S. FARMS

The operation and ownership of farms in the United States is widely diversified. The significance of this broad spectrum of control is that no mass selling or buying occurs in any one year, and there are no sudden fluctuations in the market. Manipulation of the market is not possible.

Since most farms are owner-operated, and there is a tendency for farmers to increase the size of their operations for greater efficiency, the demand constantly increases as the available supply of land decreases slightly. For example, in 1940, excluding Hawaii and Alaska, there were

FARMLAND VS. CONSUMER ITEMS
Index - (1967= 100)

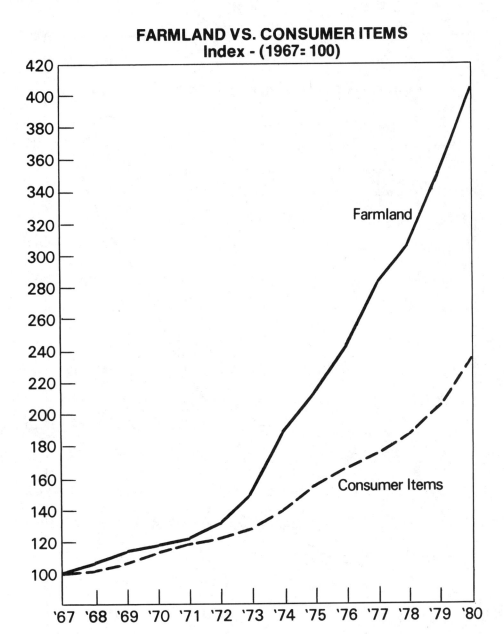

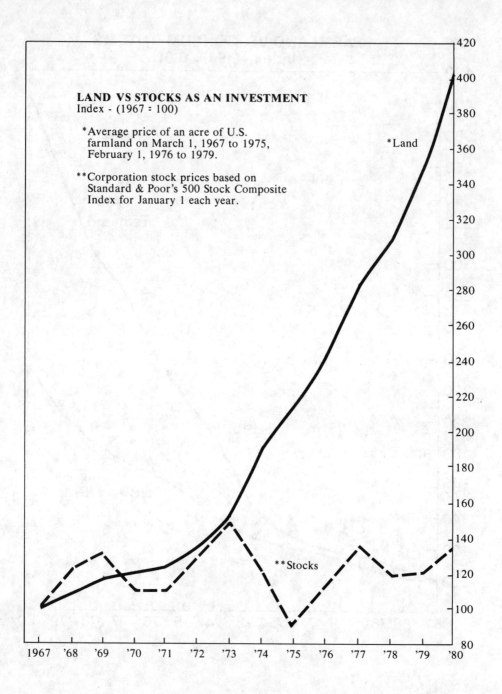

LAND VS STOCKS AS AN INVESTMENT
Index - (1967 = 100)

*Average price of an acre of U.S.
 farmland on March 1, 1967 to 1975,
 February 1, 1976 to 1979.

**Corporation stock prices based on
  Standard & Poor's 500 Stock Composite
  Index for January 1 each year.

*Land

**Stocks

6,096,000 farms, containing 1,061,000,000 acres, or an average of 174 acres per farm. In 1970, there were 2,726,000 farms containing about 1,060,000,000 acres, or an average of 389 acres per farm. In 1974, according to the Census of Agriculture, there were 2,450,000 farms, containing about 1,000,000,000 acres, or an average of 408 acres per farm.

Looking further at the 1974 figures, if small farms (under $2,500 annual gross sales) are excluded, there were 1,680,689 farms. The operators were:

Full owner-operators	900,729
Own part - rent part	558,170
All tenant	221,790
Total	1,680,689

In 1978, the U.S. Department of Agriculture conducted a comprehensive survey of land ownership in the United States. Of the total of about 2.3 billion acres in the U.S., roughly 60%, or about 1.25 billion acres, were in private hands. Federal, state and local governments own the remaining 40% of the land in the country.

The government survey put total farm and ranchland (excluding Alaska) in 1978 at 871 million acres. The table below shows how this privately-held agricultural land was owned.

Type of Ownership: U.S. Farm and Ranch Land*

Owner type	Ownership units		Acres owned	
	Thous.	Pct.	Million acres	Pct.
Sole proprietor	2,740	44.0	319.0	36.6
Husband-Wife	2,807	45.1	324.9	37.3
Family partnership	365	5.9	105.9	12.2
Nonfamily partnership	78	1.2	16.3	1.9
Family corporation	83	1.3	53.5	6.1
Nonfamily corporation	37	.6	21.2	2.4
Miscellaneous	116	1.9	30.1	3.5
Total	6,226	100.0	870.9	100.0

*Excluding Alaska.
Source: 1978 Landownership Survey (USDA).

Diversity Of Ownership Gives Market Anonymity

Ownership of farmland is centered in individuals, primarily owner-operators. Traditionally, there is little interchange in the land market between regions of the country. The stock exchanges instantly reflect the current market status of stocks. The commodity exchanges provide a means to compare relative product prices. But there is no central "exchange" that monitors comparative prices for land. It is possible for an expert supplied with appropriate documentation, however, to accurately chart land values on a relative scale, and thus predict where land is relatively underpriced and should increase in value most rapidly. Value judgments can be made based on productive capacities and opportunities of one area versus another. Except for private studies, such information is not available to the general public.

GEOGRAPHICAL SELECTION OF LAND BY AREA

Land represents a significant portion of the world's assets; it is a curious phenomenon, therefore, that most farms and ranches are bought by persons within a 10-mile radius of the property. That fact notwithstanding, the areas available for purchase are vastly different from one another. The person buying solely for investment, or the operator willing to relocate, is well advised to give close examination to the alternatives that exist.

The success of an individually tailored land investment program is chiefly dependent upon the selection of the right property. Every newspaper in the United States offers numerous land parcels for sale. Over a million real estate licensees would enthusiastically show you land they have for sale in over 3,000 counties, and every parcel is different. The classification of regions that follows provides a general guide to land suited for specific farming uses.

Production Regions and Types of Farming

A broad classification of production regions helps in the classification of the major types of farming found in particular parts of the country. One should realize that categorization by regions is oversimplified and represents partial images of complex farming situations. Wide variations in the type of farming are found in each region. Some of these variations have little in common with the predominant type found in that region.

Although the United States Department of Agriculture has slightly different classifications, for purposes of this discussion the regions and dominant farming types have been classified as follows:

FARM PRODUCTION REGIONS

Production Regions	Predominant Type of Farming
Northeast and Lake States	Dairy
Corn Belt, Northern Plains	Corn, Wheat, General Farming
Appalachian	General Farming and Tobacco
Delta States, Southeast	Cotton, Soybeans, Citrus
Southern Plains	Cotton, Soybeans, Livestock
Mountain	Livestock, Wheat
Pacific	Dairy, Specialty Crops

Northeast and Lake States

Dairying is the main farm enterprise in these states. The region has rougher, less productive soils than the Corn Belt, but the cool climate is well adapted to the production of pasture and forage. The proximity of the area to centers of population makes the dairy operation particularly well adapted. Milk is expensive to ship long distances and is generally produced within 200 miles of where it is consumed.

The operation of dairy farms has become highly specialized. Gone are the days when nearly every farmer kept cows and chickens, not only for his own use, but to supplement income by the sale of cream and eggs. Now, nearly every farmer buys dairy and poultry products in the same manner as any urban consumer.

Most commercial dairy farms are family-operated, with the utilization of some outside labor. Milk production is a labor-intensive enterprise, requiring early and long hours, every day of the week. A high degree of management is required for an efficient dairy, and seldom can it be a successful operation with the use of hired labor only. Consequently, dairies seldom make satisfactory investment properties.

Almost half of the land in this region is wooded. Some of it has been used for farming in the past and could be farmed again.

The region is so far north as to have a short growing season. Although oats, barley, and wheat can be grown in most of the region, many of the fields are small and quite stony because of the rough terrain. Modern, large scale machinery is difficult to use in these areas.

Many other major farming types can be found in this region. The southern portions of Minnesota, Michigan, and Wisconsin contain many large row-crop farms which more nearly identify with the Corn Belt. The production of poultry, fruit, potatoes, and truck crops is extremely important in many of the areas of this region.

In addition, much of the land in these areas has been diverted from farming to urban or estate type use, and has reduced the amount of farmland available for production. The high concentration of population in these states ensures a constant demand for land of all types.

Corn Belt and Northern Plains

The Corn Belt contains the most uniform type of agricultural production in the country. Within the limits of these regions is found the most productive land of any area of equal size in the world. Thus, it is a favorite area of domestic and foreign investors alike. Land prices have generally increased faster in this region during the last decade.

Land found in the Corn Belt is normally level or generally rolling. The soils are deep, rich and fertile, and well adapted to the production of corn, soybeans, and other row crops. The climate is favorable, with good rainfall in most years, and the growing season is adequate for the production of most feedgrain crops. Over 50% of the world's output of corn is grown in the Corn Belt and Northern Plains.

Because of the abundance of feed crops, the production of cattle and hogs, as well as poultry, is also very important in this region. The unique features of the Corn Belt have contributed to a greater use of modern technology. The fields are well adapted to the use of large machinery, insecticides and herbicides, and other modern technology. As a consequence, farms have become larger, and the number of farms fewer each year. Since good land attracts good operators, a high level of management and technology is found in this region.

While the southeastern portion of the Northern Plains identifies with the Corn Belt, the soils of much of the Northern Plains area are less productive than those found in the Corn Belt and the annual precipitation is much lower. Much winter wheat is grown in these areas. Since the advent of center-pivot sprinklers, irrigation has become a very important factor in portions of Nebraska and Kansas.

Cattle production, both in terms of cow-calf and feedlot operations, is important to agricultural production in Nebraska and Kansas. The ideal location of these states between the feeder calf producing regions of the West, and the feedgrain production regions of the Corn Belt, has made the Northern Plains a leader in the production of fat cattle.

Appalachian Region

While much of this region is mountainous and wooded, it is still an important segment of agriculture. The wide range of soils, topography, and climate makes it almost impossible to generalize this area. Tobacco of all types is one of the most important crops. Lumber and other forest products are major commodities. Corn, small grain, and hay are grown as feed for hogs, sheep, and cattle. Cotton and soybeans are also important crops found in this area. Since the climate and rainfall is conditioned to a long growing season, it is one of the best pasture regions in the country. However, farms and fields are often small and make the returns low as compared with farms in many other areas.

Delta States and Southeast

The Delta states and the northern states of the southeast region have long been known as the Cotton Belt. Cotton requires a long growing season and rather high temperatures. Mechanization and other technological changes have vastly increased the yields and changed the economics of cotton production.

Arkansas has two distinct regions. The Mississippi Delta region of the east is highly productive for cotton, rice, and soybeans. The western region is heavily timbered and has value for resort purposes, as well as timber production. Most crop production in western Arkansas is restricted to the Red River Valley.

As important as cotton is to these regions, many changes have occurred in the last decade. The timber was removed from hundreds of thousands of acres of delta land during the mid-1960s, and this land was transformed primarily to the production of soybeans and wheat. The importance of soybeans in the world market has reduced the reliance upon cotton as the primary cash crop of these regions.

Timber production, however, continues to be an important cash crop in many of the southeastern states and supplies the large demands for construction in the South. In addition, the "Sun Belt," as this area is often referred to, has boomed with industrial uses and population expansion. This has changed the nature of agriculture as well.

Because of high land prices in the Corn Belt, many farmers accustomed to a higher input of technology moved to the Delta States and Southeast. As a consequence, general farming is taken much more seriously.

Florida is probably the most unique state of the southeastern region. While thought of as a resort state, agriculture is an important segment of the economy. The production of timber, cattle, citrus, and vegetable crops is critical to the production of the state. It is possible to acquire large tracts in North and Central Florida, and outside investments are prevalent.

Southern Plains

This region is made up of Texas and Oklahoma. Included are highly specialized cotton farms, soybean, rice, and timber production, and the traditional cattle country. Both the production of calves from cowherds, and feeder cattle from hundreds of feedlots, contributes substantially to the agricultural economy. The southern portion of Texas is important in the production of citrus and vegetable crops.

Oklahoma displays diversity in types of farming. Cattle, wheat and milo dominate the lower-rainfall areas in the western portion, while the eastern edge is more typical of Midwestern general farming.

Texas contains nearly every type of agricultural enterprise that can be found in the country. In the southeast portion of this vast state cotton is king, while further north dryland wheat and milo predominate. Much of the Southwest region consists of huge cattle operations where land has a low productivity and scant rainfall and the grazing is sparce. Drouth and shortage of range feed are frequent hazards of the rancher.

Mountain

The Mountain region is primarily made up of grazing land. The lower country includes a complex of desert and semi-desert grasses and shrubs, which are used mainly as winter, or spring and fall grazing. Higher elevations slope primarily into oak brush and timber types. The rangeland is sometimes required to be used seasonally, therefore livestock must be moved long distances at different times of the year. Much of the rangeland in this area is federally owned.

As with other regions, it is difficult to generalize because where irrigation can be used, the southern portions of the Mountain region are important in the production of citrus and vegetable crops. The northwestern region is important for the production of many grain crops, potatoes, and sugar beets, particularly where irrigation can be utilized.

Pacific

The most important crops of this region are the specialties of fruits, nuts, vegetables, and citrus found in California. This is not to overlook the districts of Washington and Oregon which constitute the chief wheat-growing region of the west. Timber production is a major crop as well, and general farming can be found in much of the Pacific region.

Regions Overlap

Because of the diversity found in all farm production regions of the country, a footnote is necessary. While the predominant crops of each region have been mentioned, it must be noted that within each region are found many overlapping types of production. For example, every region has pockets of specialty production. California produces some of the finest cotton in the country. Michigan produces some of the finest potatoes in the country. Colorado sugar beet production has a substantial impact on the region. Production of alfalfa for dehydration is important to the economy of Nebraska. These pockets of production illustrate the great diversification of agriculture in this country.

LAND INVESTMENT SUMMARY

Well selected farm or ranchland provides annual income, tax benefits, and substantially increased value for the future. In addition, land ownership may give the owner a large measure of pleasure and satisfaction. There is every reason to believe that long term capital appreciation will continue to accrue to land holdings. It is a tangible asset, absolutely essential to the survival of mankind.

Three basic tenets for successful land investment are:

1. Buy it right: make an informed purchase decision.
2. Manage it right: achieve maximum income and appreciation.
3. Sell it right: realize full market value.

The prudent local land buyer, be he an expanding farmer or investor, is generally well informed as to values in his community. Over 60% of farm properties are purchased by local residents. This buyer is not particularly concerned, or knowledgeable, as to whether on a pure value basis his money would be better spent 100 or 1,000 miles away.

The Central Illinois farmer paying $4,000 per acre for choice land doesn't know, or perhaps care, that he may be able to purchase land nearly as productive in Mississippi for less than half the price.

The Nebraska rancher may pay $2,000 per animal unit carrying capacity for pasture, while in Missouri or Arkansas similarly productive land may be $1,000 per unit. But if he has always ranched in Nebraska, even if he is aware of the inequity, chances are that he will still buy land in Nebraska.

An investor, without location bias, can take advantage of inequities in value/price. There are always areas of the country undervalued in relation to their capacity to produce and appreciate in value.

CHAPTER 2

Finding Your Land

The buyer's odds of being rewarded with an exceptionally profitable land purchase are enhanced many times if he will take the time and make the effort to seek out the right property. An intelligent, informed decision is a direct result of this effort. An uninformed decision may result in a profit if the buyer is lucky, or if general inflation pushes up the price. But there is no need to leave major investment decisions to chance. Many land buyers shop and compare more intensively to buy a car than to buy land costing 50 times more. If more buyers viewed the purchase of land with the same comparative nature, they would make better decisions, resulting in more profitable investments. Follow these guidelines:

1. Know every similar property for sale in the market area of interest.
2. Research every property that has sold. Learn the price and terms of the deal.
3. Compare the features of the "for sale" and "sold" properties.

GATHERING INFORMATION

Remember that the soundness of the initial decision in buying is the most important determinant when it comes to making a profitable sale months or years later.

Our office frequently represents buyers on an exclusive basis for acquisition because of the research we put into a recommendation for purchase. Why should an individual seeking out his own property with his own money make less effort?

In harmony with the three guidelines listed above, we acquire for our clients the following packages of key information for a given county:

1. A complete set of aerial photographs, topographic maps, high-way maps, zoning maps, and, if available, ownership plat books.

2. A complete list of owners' names and addresses, together with a description of their property. This information is available through commercial sources or from the county records, particularly the assessor's offices.

3. A compilation of all similar properties that have sold within the past three years, including price, terms, size, etc. This is available from county records, news sources, individuals, or commercial sources.

4. Information on all similar property for sale. While we do this primarily through direct contact with the owners, individual buyers can do it through brokers, "for sale" signs, classified ads, and other inquiries.

After the above information is collected, a personal inspection of the properties that have sold, and are for sale, is mandatory. With the facts at hand, every viewing of property helps establish a basis of comparison for making an intelligent decision. There is no shortcut. The buyer or his consultants must go through this process, or make uninformed decisions.

General Information Sources

Area In Which To Buy. If completely open as to the area of the country in which to buy, then substantial study is needed. Consultation with one of the national agricultural firms is in order. However, from bias, personal preference, necessity, family, or scientific study of geographical areas, you will probably have determined not only the region of the country you want to buy in, but probably the state. Most buyers have narrowed the area to one or two counties that appeal to them.

Size Needed. As an example, let's assume the decision is to buy a ranch capable of supporting a minimum of 300 mother cows for a cow-calf operation. Ranches are normally described as being capable of carrying a certain number of "animal units" (AUs). A 300 cow herd is going to require approximately 15 bulls and 30 to 45 replacement heifers, plus some horses, so the carrying capacity will need to be closer to 350 AUs.

In certain areas of the country 10 acres of land will provide feed to carry one AU year-round, thus indicating a need for about a 3,500 acre ranch. Ranches in the arid Southwest may require 100 acres or more per AU, meaning a ranch of 35,000 acres. On the other hand, as little as 1,000 acres or less might carry the herd in some areas where improved pasture is supplied with irrigation and fertilizer and is under close management.

Seeking Out Property. Assuming the area settled on will require 7,000 acres for the herd, how do we find it, and buy it at less than the going market price (or at worst, no higher than market)?

First, allow enough time. Remember, this will be a purchase in excess of $500,000. Take three months to decide--not full time, of course. And remember that a good decision right now will make at least $100,000 difference in future profits.

Drive Around. Using detailed state and county highway maps, drive all the main roads; check out the main towns. Make note of "for sale" signs, ranch brokers, banks, and government agricultural offices.

Use Local Tools. Subscribe to the main local papers. Check their real estate ads, sale notices, and generally get a feel for the area.

From phone books, get the names of real estate brokers and auctioneers, and write for information on properties of the type you are interested in. Understand that you may be obligating yourself to a broker you might not want to work with.

Some buyers don't want to work with brokers for one reason or another. In that case, contact bankers, lawyers, feed and fertilizer distributors, and equipment dealers. How? Walk into their offices and tell them you're interested in buying some property!

Run ads in the local papers, labelled "Principals Only", telling of your interest.

Visit the County Agricultural Agent's Office. He may know of available property. He may advise you to look at some areas--stay away from others. He may tell you of bad water supplies, hail belts, water rights problems, drouth areas, soil condition problems, or a myriad of other existing conditions. He'll have production brochures applicable to the area. Whether or not all of the information is used, at least it's available as a reference.

Technical Information Sources

County Highway Maps. Preparatory to arriving in the community, write to the State Highway Department for county highway maps. They may also be obtained at the County Courthouse. Try the county engineer's office or the county clerk's office. These maps are normally prepared by each State Road Department in cooperation with the U.S. Department of Transportation, and may also be obtained from the Federal Highway Administration of the Bureau of Public Roads.

These general highway maps provide a wealth of information. Included on the map are legal descriptions with townships, ranges, sections, survey numbers; city limits, with populations of each city; all federal, state and county roads; rivers and topographical bench marks; as well as schools, churches, recreational facilities, and similar information. These maps work particularly well if you shade in the properties being considered, thus giving their general location in proximity to each other, and major demographic features.

Ownership Maps (Also Called Plat Books or Atlases). In many states private map companies have prepared map books showing the boundary of each property, along with the name of the owner, and the number of acres in the property. Also shown are roads, cities, and certain demographic features. Occasionally, mailing addresses are given. These books are extremely valuable for locating various parcels of property. In certain areas, not only are the ownership maps available, but the properties are superimposed on aerial photographs matching the ownership maps.

In the absence of ownership maps, be certain to check the assessor's office, and other public records in the county courthouse, to ascertain whether they have other records that will give you access to similar information.

Soil Maps. The Department of Agriculture began making soil surveys about 1900. Evolution in knowledge of soil-plant relationships caused many changes in the older maps. Ordinarily, the soil scientists used aerial photographs as a basis for plotting the soil boundaries. Field checks were made as to what actual soils were found, and identification symbols were placed on the maps.

The United States Department of Agriculture has prepared a soil map on virtually all of the more productive agricultural land in the United

BEAVER

TOWNSHIP 83 NORTH - RANGE 28 WEST OF 5TH P.M.

AMAQUA   TWP.

Sample Page From A Plat Book

PAGE 14

States. Recent publications include an aerial photo of all the land, with the actual soil boundaries mapped on the photos.

Copies of available published maps and reports may be obtained through the State Extension Service or Soil Conservation Service Offices. Files of unpublished maps are maintained in the local Soil Conservation Service Offices and may be examined there.

The principal technical uses of soil surveys are to interpret the capabilities of the soil for agricultural use, adapted crops, estimated yields of crops under defined systems of management, and the presence

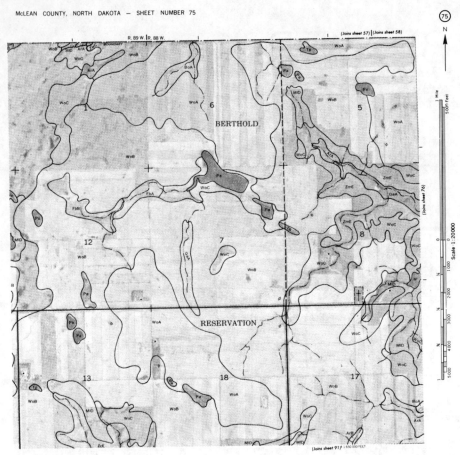

Soil Map

of particular problems. More recent soil surveys include information on the engineering uses of the soils, including percolation. Soils are now also examined as wildlife habitat, and with respect to suitability for recreational development. The publications also contain substantial demographic information. Climate, transportation, markets, water supply, natural resources, physiography, and drainage are all discussed in these soil survey reports.

Topographic Maps. The U.S. Department of the Interior publishes the Geological Survey, more commonly known as *topographic maps.* Although not yet complete, a series of standard topographic maps to cover the United States, Puerto Rico, Guam, American Samoa, and the Virgin Islands are being made. Maps are published in scales of one inch equals 2,000 feet, one inch equals 1 mile, and one inch equals 2 miles.

MC LEAN COUNTY, NORTH DAKOTA

*—Range productivity and composition—*Continued

Soil and map symbol	Range site	Potential production		Common plant name	Compo-sition
		Kind of year	Dry weight		
			Lbs/ac		*Pct*
Cabba part _____	Shallow.	Favorable _____	1,700	Little bluestem _____	20
		Normal _____	1,400	Western wheatgrass _____	20
		Unfavorable _____	1,150	Prairie sandreed _____	10
				Needleandthread _____	10
				Green needlegrass _____	5
				Plains muhly _____	5
				Bluebunch wheatgrass _____	5
[1]ZmE: Zahl part _____	Thin upland.	Favorable _____	2,300	Little bluestem _____	20
		Normal _____	1,900	Western wheatgrass _____	10
		Unfavorable _____	1,500	Needleandthread _____	10
				Sideoats grama _____	5
				Plains muhly _____	5
				Porcupinegrass _____	5
				Blue grama _____	5
				Penn sedge _____	8
Max part _____	Silty.	Favorable _____	2,650	Western wheatgrass _____	20
		Normal _____	2,250	Needleandthread _____	15
		Unfavorable _____	1,850	Green needlegrass _____	10
				Prairie junegrass _____	10
				Blue grama _____	10
				Kentucky bluegrass _____	5
				Penn sedge _____	5
[1]ZpE: Zahl part _____	Thin upland.	Favorable _____	2,300	Little bluestem _____	20
		Normal _____	1,900	Western wheatgrass _____	10
		Unfavorable _____	1,500	Needleandthread _____	10
				Sideoats grama _____	5
				Plains muhly _____	5
				Porcupinegrass _____	5
				Blue grama _____	5
				Penn sedge _____	8
Max part _____	Silty.	Favorable _____	2,650	Western wheatgrass _____	20
		Normal _____	2,250	Needleandthread _____	15
		Unfavorable _____	1,850	Green needlegrass _____	10
				Prairie junegrass _____	10
				Blue grama _____	10
				Kentucky bluegrass _____	5
				Penn sedge _____	5
Parnell part _____	Wetland.	Favorable _____	5,700	Prairie cordgrass _____	30
		Normal _____	5,200	Northern reedgrass _____	20
		Unfavorable _____	4,800	Reed canarygrass _____	20
				Slough sedge _____	10
				Switchgrass _____	5
[1]ZwC: Zahl part _____	Thin upland.	Favorable _____	2,300	Little bluestem _____	20
		Normal _____	1,900	Western wheatgrass _____	10
		Unfavorable _____	1,500	Needleandthread _____	10
				Sideoats grama _____	5
				Plains muhly _____	5
				Porcupinegrass _____	5
				Blue grama _____	5
				Penn sedge _____	8
Williams part _____	Silty.	Favorable _____	2,350	Western wheatgrass _____	25
		Normal _____	1,950	Needleandthread _____	15
		Unfavorable _____	1,550	Green needlegrass _____	7
				Prairie junegrass _____	5
				Blue grama _____	13
				Kentucky bluegrass _____	5

[1] This mapping unit is made up of two or more dominant kinds of soil. See mapping unit description for the composition and behavior characteristics of the mapping unit.

Topographic maps provide insight into the character of the property being studied. Aside from the obvious advantage of being able to determine the contour or slope of the property, other information is included. Physical features, such as roads, railroads, cities and towns are shown. Section, township, range and survey information is shown to allow the location of a specific property.

The maps are printed in 3 colors. Water features are shown in blue

and the features of relief, such as hills, mountains, and valleys are shown
by brown contour lines. Green shows woodland areas, with red for highway classification, urban areas, and United States landlines. Most
topographic maps are available either with or without green woodland
overprint. Further information concerning maps may be obtained from:
The Map Information Office, Geological Survey, Washington, D.C. 24202.

Each state has an index to assist in the selection of the particular
topographic map required. Maps for states west of the Mississippi River,
(including all of Louisiana and Minnesota), should be ordered directly
from: *The Distribution Section, Geological Survey, Federal Center, Denver,
Colorado, 80225.*

Maps for states east of the Mississippi River, (including Puerto Rico
and the Virgin Islands), should be ordered from: *Distribution Section,
Geological Survey, 1200 South Eads Street, Arlington, Virginia 22202.*

The prices are reasonable, about $1.00 for each standard quadrant
map, and discounts are allowed on orders over a certain amount. Also,
local book, map or office supply stores may sell topographic maps at
slightly higher prices.

Aerial Photographs. The importance of aerial photographs to a detailed
inspection of a property is nearly equal to that of the actual inspection of
the property. All agricultural areas have been photographed from above
for the Department of Agriculture by private companies. Many areas
have been photographed on a repetitive schedule, averaging a new flight
about every 7 years.

The ability to interpret the details shown on an aerial photograph
allows one to discover many different kinds of information. Physical
features such as ditches, erosion, boundaries, creeks, ponds, and roads
can easily be observed. Distances can be measured, using the scale
shown. The land can be categorized by use, such as cropland, pasture,
and timberland. Building locations are apparent to the point of reveal-
ing even the shape and relative size of the building. Electric transmis-
sion lines can be seen on aerial photographs. The size of timber can be
estimated. The miles of fences and location of corrals in relation to
pasture and building areas, important in considerations of operational
ease, can be determined.

The trained eye can spot unusual soil conditions such as wet spots,
muck conditions, and sandy areas. The comparison of a recent photo
with one from several years earlier allows measurement of the growth
that has taken place.

Topographic Map

Aerial Photograph

Aerial photos of any rural property in the United States can be obtained by writing one of the two Aerial Photo Laboratories maintained by the U.S. Department of Agriculture. Requests for photos on land in the western part of the United States, including Texas and Oklahoma, and north through the Dakotas should be addressed to: *Western Aerial Photograph Laboratory, Compliance and Appeals Division, A.S.C.S.– USDA, 2505 Parley's Way, Salt Lake City, Utah 84109.*

Requests for photos in all other states should be addressed to: *Eastern Aerial Photography Laboratory, Compliance and Appeals Division, A.S.C.S.–USDA, 45 South French Broad Avenue, Asheville, North Carolina 28801.*

Cost of a 24 x 24 inch aerial on a scale of one inch equals 660 feet is under $10. Photos on smaller scales may also be obtained. The scale of one inch equals 660 feet is equivalent to eight inches to the mile, so each aerial photo will include a total of nine sections. Request forms may be obtained from the county offices of the U.S. Department of Agriculture.

LEGAL DESCRIPTIONS

By using one of the three methods of describing land, each parcel can be identified and distinguished from all others. The description of every land parcel is as unique and different as a set of fingerprints. The methods used for describing land in the United States have an interesting evolution.

Metes and bounds is one of the first methods used to describe real property. Known earlier as the "tomahawk," this system relies on natural features as points of reference. It is still used in much of the eastern United States, particularly south of the New England states.

The most widely used system is known as *rectangular survey,* and is used in 30 states located principally west and south from Ohio, including Alaska and excluding Hawaii.

The use of *plats* is common in urban areas where a larger parcel of land previously described by one of the other systems is further subdivided into lots.

Shortly after the United States had won her freedom, the country turned to land as a resource. The theory of the public domain took shape, primarily as a way to raise money. In addition to the Thirteen Colonies, 541 million acres of land had been acquired from England.

This acquisition became the original public domain. No less a personage than Thomas Jefferson was appointed chairman of a committee to plan for administration of the public domain.

One of the provisions of the 1785 Ordinance ordered the survey of land, to be followed by public sale. Under this ordinance, one section (640 acres) of each township was set aside for the support of public education--the beginning of the concept of free public schooling. Some of these original set-aside sections are still owned by school districts.

The United States Public Land Survey that began with the 1785 Ordinance has had a continuing impact upon the configuration of the American countryside. It called for precise measurements patterned after the New England system called *rectilinear survey*. The township was the basic surveying unit--an area 6 miles by 6 miles, making 36 sections--each a mile square. These sections were in turn divided into quarter sections, and less.

Metes and Bounds

A metes and bounds description of a tract of land always starts at a given point called the "point of beginning." The outline of the tract is then followed by using certain measurements and reference points such as trees, stakes, stones, roads, and rivers until you arrive back at the "point of beginning." Obviously, such landmarks as trees and roads are not permanent, and some property descriptions appear to be out-of-date, or inexact. Unfortunately, these old descriptions are perpetuated in land transactions by the usual custom of copying verbatim the description as it appears in previous deeds and mortgages.

In plotting metes and bounds descriptions, all directions are oriented from either north or south. Obviously, there are four quadrants. Any direction from 0 to 90 degrees and 270 to 360 degrees is referred to as being so many degrees either east or west of north. Conversely, any direction that we would normally think of as being between 90 degrees and 270 degrees is referred to as being so many degrees east or west of south. Following is a typical example of a metes and bounds description showing how it would be plotted.

"Beginning at the maple tree on the property line of the old Jones Farm and its intersection with the Summer Creek road; thence S 67 degrees W 593', thence N 24 degrees W 642'; then N 15 degrees E 265'; thence S 35 degrees E 490'; thence S 66 degrees E 500' to the point of beginning, containing 5.46 acres more or less."

The readings given can be used to draw the tract. The reading S 67 degrees W means the line is 67 degrees west of the North-South line in the south half of the arc. The same procedure would be followed for the next part of the description until all boundaries are plotted.

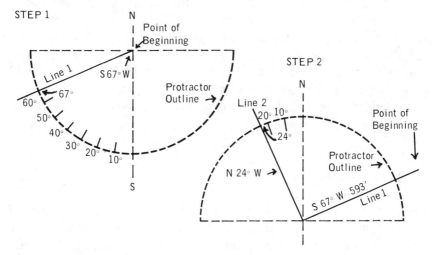

Using a protractor, start at the point of beginning and draw the first line. Measure the distance given. Draw the next line, etc., until the last drawn line reaches the point of beginning. The following illustrates the property drawn from the metes and bounds description.

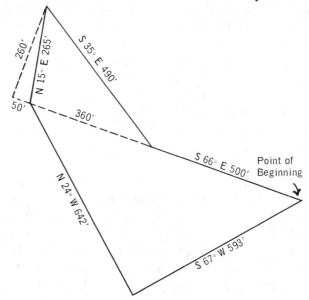

The dotted lines in the illustration are for the purpose of computing acreage by the use of triangles. The area of a triangle is found by multiplying the height times one-half the base. Thus, in the upper left hand corner of the field, we have to go out another 50 feet to get a right angle so as to measure the altitude of the triangle. The area of the smaller triangle formed is subtracted from the total computed area.

Directions by degrees are given in degrees, minutes, and seconds. One degree has 60 minutes of measurement separating the degree mark from its neighbor on either side. Each minute is then divided into 60 seconds. The symbols for degrees, minutes, and seconds always follow the number in the approximate place that symbols for feet and inches are placed when used. Ten degrees is written 10°; ten minutes as 10'; ten seconds as 10''.

Rectangular Survey

In areas where rectangular survey is used, land is divided into townships, sections, quarter sections, quarter-quarter of sections. The starting point is meridians and base lines. The meridians used in survey have no connection with the global geographical meridians--the lines which run through the North and South Poles, marking off the areas of the earth in longitude. Meridians used in survey or legal descriptions of land are arbitrarily chosen north and south lines from which measurements are made to the east or west. Base lines are arbitrarily chosen lines running east and west from which measurements are made to the north or south. Each meridian has its own base line intersecting it.

The following map shows the area covered by rectangular survey and the names of 21 of the 34 principal meridians and their base lines. The heavy lines indicate the boundaries of the areas measured from each principal meridian. Land in eastern Kansas, for instance, is measured from the sixth principal meridian, not the fifth. The boundary is the Missouri-Kansas border.

Legal descriptions of property identify the location in relation to meridian and base line, measured in units of one township, or one range. A township is 6 miles square, that is, 6 miles east and west and 6 miles north and south. The term range is used to represent the distance east or west from the meridian, one range equaling the width of one township, or approximately 6 miles. In a legal description, the word township represents the distance north or south from the base line, each township being equal to approximately 6 miles. Sometimes the word 'tier' is used in place of townships.

A legal description of a farm might read in part "... township 9 north, range 12 east of the Black Hills meridian." This would mean that it is 12 ranges or about 72 miles east of the meridian and 9 townships or 54 miles north of the base line.

Map showing area covered by rectangular survey with meridians and base lines. Meridians indicated on map by number are identified as follows: 1—First; 2—Second; 3—Third; 4—Fourth; 5—Fifth; 6—Sixth; 7—Michigan; 8—Louisiana; 9—Indiana; 10—Black Hills; 11—Principal; 12—Boise; 13—Salt Lake; 14—New Mexico; 15—Gila and Salt Rivers; 16—San Bernardino; 17—Mt. Diablo; 18—Willamette; 19—Copper River; 20—Fairbanks; 21—Seward.

Townships and Sections

A regular township is rectangular in form with boundaries 6 miles apart, enclosing an area of 36 square miles, which is subdivided into sections of one square mile, or 640 acres. Certain sections in each township are normally fractional, that is, they contain more or less than 640 acres; and there are also fractional townships which contain less than 36 sections. Fractional townships normally occur on natural boundaries; lakes, rivers, etc. Fractional sections occur because it is impossible for two parallel lines to run due north and remain square. The northern end of a township will therefore be narrower than the southern end. Convergence increases as one moves northward from the equator to the North Pole. A township at latitude 33 degrees near the northern boundary of Louisiana will be 31.1 feet narrower on the north end than the south end; at latitude 41 degrees near the south border of Iowa the convergence increases to 41.6 feet; at Minneapolis, 47.9 feet.

To correct for this, guide meridians were set up every 24 miles east and west of the principal meridians and standard parallels at 24 mile intervals north and south of the base lines. These correction lines take care of the convergence caused by the shape of the earth. Thus, inspection of a survey map of a large area such as the state of Iowa shows some irregular county boundary lines which are the result of correction lines. The illustration shown below is an example. The guide meridians are offset; the standard parallels are not.

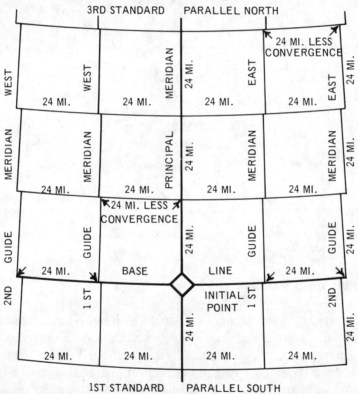

Each full township contains 36 sections and they are numbered starting with 1 in the northeast corner, section 6 in the northwest corner; immediately below section 6 is section 7 and the numbering continues back and forth across the township to section 36 in the southeast corner (see the following illustration). The convergence problem is still with us though, so some sections will not be precisely 640 acres. It was decided early that all excesses and deficits would be thrown to the sections on the north and west boundaries of the township. This provides the greatest number of sections of uniform size within a township. Likewise, within each fractional section, the deficit is thrown to the north or west

			6 Miles		
6	5	4	3	2	1
7	8	9	10	11	12
18	17	16	15	14	13
19	20	21	22	23	24
30	29	28	27	26	25
31	32	33	34	35	36

40 acre tracts, depending on which boundary of the township the section is on. If section 1 of a township was short 20 acres, for example, each of the four 40 acre tracts along the northern boundary would contain only 35 acres. This solution provides for both the greatest number of standard 160 acre quarter sections and 40 acre quarter-quarter sections within the section.

Division of a Section

Sections are divided using quarters or halves. Since the standard section is square and contains 640 acres it is a simple matter to convert it to 4 square tracts containing 160 acres each and these quartered to give 4 square tracts containing 40 acres each. Each 40 acres can be further subdivided into 4 square 10-acre tracts.

Likewise, sections, quarter sections, and quarter-quarter sections can be broken down into halves for tracts of 320, 80, 20, 5 and lesser acreages and combinations of quarter and halves to arrive at any other sizes. The following figure illustrates this.

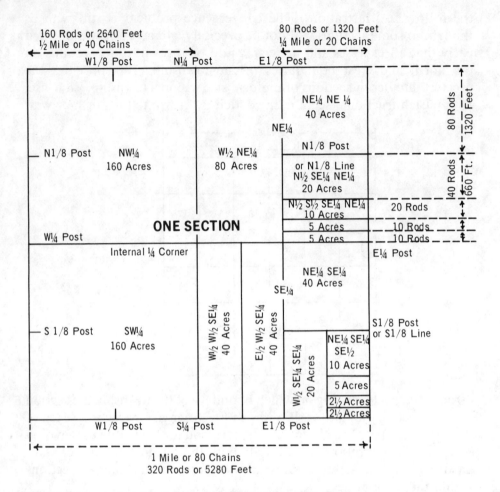

Reading Legal Descriptions By Rectangular Survey

A legal description of a farm is no more than its address. Of all the farms in the United States, no two have the same legal description. One method, description by metes and bounds, has been explained earlier in this chapter. Metes and bounds are used mainly in the eastern part of the United States--which was largely settled before the system of rectangular survey was inaugurated.

Description by rectangular survey is tied to a map on which the property is accurately shown. It is much less subject to error. A typical description might read: SW¼ SW¼ sc. 4, township 45 north, range 25 west of the fifth principal meridian.

A cardinal rule in reading rectangular survey descriptions is to work backward. The first objective is to find the fifth principal meridian. (Refer to the earlier figure showing the location of various meridians used in rectangular survey.) The fifth principal meridian is a north and south line running through eastern Arkansas, Missouri, and Iowa. The farm, then, is located in one of 6 possible states: Arkansas, Missouri, Iowa, Minnesota, North Dakota, and eastern South Dakota. Continuing to read backward from the description the phrase "range 25 west" indicates that the farm is west of the fifth principal meridian; furthermore, that it is 25 ranges, or roughly 150 miles west of it. A range is the width of one township or 6 miles. Next in the description reading backward is Township 45 north. This means it is 45 townships or 270 miles north of the base line which runs east and west through Arkansas.

Once the township is found in west-central Missouri, locate section 4. We know from the illustration of a township shown above that section 4 will be located along the northern boundary of the township. Reading backward again we see "SW¼ SW¼" which means the southwest quarter of the southwest quarter of the section. The southwest quarter of the section will contain 160 acres and the southwest quarter of it will contain 40 acres. The location of this 40 acres will be in the extreme southwest corner of the section. If the tract were not a full 40 acres, the description would have been "SW fr. ¼ SW¼"--the "fr." denoting a fractional unit. Often, the legal description will give the acreage at the end such as, "containing in all, 38 acres more or less according to government survey."

THE PLAT SYSTEM

Of particular importance in urban areas and subdivisions, plats are designed to encompass streets, lots, and blocks. Using this system, a tract of land that may have earlier been described by metes and bounds, or rectangular survey, is now described in a more detailed manner. Typically, a subdivider or developer will have engineers design site plans or maps of real property.

The maps will show the manner in which the property is to be subdivided and will locate the individual lots with respect to a street, block, and lot number. These maps or site plans are called plats, and a record is kept of each subdivision plat in the records of the city or county where the property is located.

For example, "Lot 5, Block 2, of John Doe's Second Subdivision in the City of Miami, Florida", might describe a portion of a subdivision by plat of real property located in that area. Many jurisdictions now require that a recorded plat be filed and approved prior to the issuance of building permits, or the sale of lots.

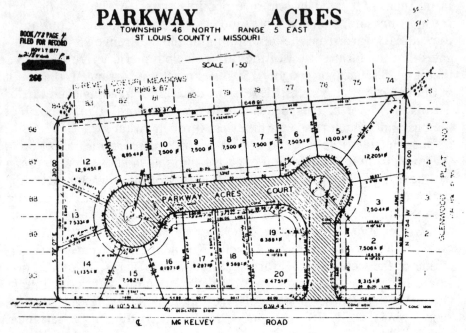

A typical platted subdivision

CHAPTER 3

Estimating Land Values

In 1955, an experienced farm and ranch appraiser, Charles H. Everett, was co-authoring RURAL APPRAISALS*, the first complete text on the subject. In describing the "Economic Basis Of Value", the author said:

"Land, or any object, has value because it is useful, and because it is scarce. Air is useful, but there is plenty of it, so it has no value. In the early development of the United States there was plenty of land to be had for the taking. It had very little value and there was very little attempt to appraise land."

"When most of the 'free' land in the United States had been taken up and it became 'scarce', its usefulness or utility became important. Land came to have value and interested persons needed to measure that value, or *appraise* the land."

Author's personal note: That same year, Mr. Everett hired a 20-year-old agricultural economics graduate from the University of Nebraska. This set me on the path of appraising land throughout the United States and some other countries for about ten years. Taught were the values of research, judgment, and long hours. The first two traits were well retained.

All Buyers Make An Appraisal

In a manner of speaking, everyone who considers the acquisition of land goes through some mental process to justify the purchase. Most value judgments would probably fall into one of three broad classifications:

*Earl F. Crouse, A.R.A. and Charles H. Everett, A.R.A., *Rural Appraisals* (Englewood Cliffs, New Jersey: Prentice-Hall, Inc., 1956), p.1.

1. Casual observation (also called a hunch).
2. Informal but informed.
3. Formal, with documentation, or the true appraisal.

Persons associated with appraisal work will claim that I have omitted perhaps the most common classification: the SWAG, which in polite terms could be explained as the "Sophisticated Wild...Guess." I would respond that some elements of this are found in all value estimates.

Value Estimates By Casual Observation

Included in this group which we can call casual observers of land values, are most buyers and sellers, some bankers, attorneys and real estate salesmen, and a few professional appraisers.

At the risk of sounding trite, most have just enough information to be dangerous. Their memories may be too long, too short, or incomplete. The two main dangers in relying on their estimates are:

1. Their lack of basic factual information. Most opinions from this group sound like: "I heard that the Mecke Farm brought $1,200 per acre, and half of it is too sandy to farm. That makes this place worth $1,900 per acre." The following errors could be involved:

- The heresay may have been erroneous.
- We don't know the terms or conditions.
- The soils data may be bad.

2. Imprecise examination of all relevant data. Even if all the data on the one sale proved to be correct, it is only one transaction. The examination of ten other comparable sales may all point to a different conclusion. Documentation and research is the key to a good appraisal. With land requiring so large an investment, all information relating to value should be studied.

Many investment failures have occurred when respected and talented professionals in fields other than real estate values take it upon themselves to advise clients for or against purchases. For example, while many attorneys or bankers may be otherwise bright people, they often fail to limit their advice to legal or financial matters. Real estate people and land appraisers have the same problem when they get beyond their field of experience.

Informed But Informally Presented Value Estimates

In every community are those participants or players who have been involved in a specialized field of real estate, let's say land, for many years. They know the sales that have occurred, and why. They may be buyers, sellers, bankers, brokers, lawyers ... I know some who have worn the hats of at least four of those occupations. If they can be found, if their time is for sale; and if they are willing to do so, they can probably tell you values within 10% on all land in their area.

Chances are that these informal "appraisers" won't always document what they say. They aren't interested in writing reports and, in most cases, don't hold themselves out as consultants. They use their tediously-acquired information for their own accounts or business. Their experience, however, is invaluable and represents highly reliable data because they are generally involved in the marketplace on a personal and day-to-day basis.

Formal Value Estimates

The serious appraiser is a student of his work. Appraising has become a specialized activity for many practitioners. Standards of practice have evolved from the translation of experience into educational forums. While differences of opinion exist among appraisers and their organizations as to the proper techniques, the differences are often in semantics.

Although there are a number of appraisal organizations, the two most prominent in the appraisal of land are:

1. American Institute of Real Estate Appraisers of the National Association of Realtors (Member, Appraisal Institute).

The appraiser who holds the Institute's designation, M.A.I., has proven his ability and experience through many hours of education, testing, and demonstration appraisals. He is governed by a rigid set of ethics and is skilled in appraisal techniques. As in most professions, appraisers specialize in certain areas. You should select one who is experienced and skilled in appraising the type of property you are selling.

2. The American Society of Farm Managers and Rural Appraisers. As the name implies, members of this organization specialize in the management and appraisal of agricultural property. The designation used by their accredited appraisers is A.R.A. (Accredited Rural Appraiser). As with the M.A.I., this appraiser has demonstrated his proficiency and skill through rigid training and examination.

A roster of the organizations' accredited members may be obtained by contacting: *American Institute of Real Estate Appraisers, 430 N. Michigan Avenue, Chicago, Illinois 60611;* or *American Society of Farm Managers and Rural Appraisers, P.O. Box 6857, Denver, Colorado 80206.*

Fair Market Value

Appraisals may be required for a number of purposes. In an attempt to standardize the measurement of value, many appraisers now use a common definition of Fair Market Value which has been handed down by several courts. It is as follows:

> "Fair Market Value is the highest price, estimated in terms of money, which the property will bring if exposed for sale on the open market, with a reasonable time allowed to find a buyer who has knowledge of all uses and purposes to which the property is best adapted, and for which it is capable of being used."

While many appraisers take the position that there is only one value for any given property at any given time, there are often restrictive conditions or assumptions attached to the appraisal. These conditions may very well affect the value estimate. Zoning would be a prime example. If an appraiser assumes that the existing zoning of a property, such as agricultural, is the most likely use of that property, he will find a much different value from the appraiser who is equally confident that the property may be rezoned to residential development, and determines the value upon that higher level of zoning.

The definition given above also fails to consider the terms of the possible sale of the property. For example, if the property is to be sold for all cash, its value (price) may be as much as 30% less than a property which can be sold for 20% down with a purchase money mortgage at a reasonable interest rate. Consequently, all of the assumptions of the appraiser should be formally and clearly spelled out in a foreword to the appraisal.

Appraisal Procedure

Once an appraiser has been employed to make an appraisal, an inspection of the subject property is of prime importance. He must consider all of the factors affecting the value such as soils, topography, land use, and improvements. In addition to physical features, he must consider where the property is located, features such as roads, neighborhood, size, salability, and other economic conditions affecting the property.

The appraiser must utilize all of the tools described in the previous chapter on "Finding Your Land". For example, aerial photos allow the appraiser to determine the acreages of tillable land, woodland, pasture, and the general layout of the property. Special features such as creeks, wet spots, and fences can be most practically observed by using aerial photos.

Soil maps will be used extensively by appraisers to help determine topography, limitations on crop adaptation, and potential crop yields. Productivity of the farm, a major factor of value, will be derived from analyzing the soil types.

A thorough analysis of the buildings on the property will be required by the appraiser. Not only must he understand the probable cost to replace such buildings, but he must have a knowledge of the current uses to which the buildings may be put. He will consider not only the physical depreciation to the buildings, but their functional and economic obsolescence, which may limit the value of many of the existing buildings.

ESTIMATING VALUE

Three approaches to value are used by most professional appraisers. They are: *cost approach, income approach, market data approach.*

Cost Approach

In determining the value by use of the cost approach, the appraiser will attempt to estimate the cost of the improvements on the property. Normally he will apply current cost factors for reconstructing the improvements or similar improvements with the same utility. Technically, there are two types of cost analyses. One is based on the cost of reconstructing the improvements as they exist, and a deduction is then made for physical, functional, and economic obsolescence.

By comparison, replacement cost is the cost of providing a building which will provide comparable utility but may assume the employment of modern construction methods and does not attempt to reproduce unusual features found in the existing buildings. Of course, the appraiser must be cognizant of the value that a potential buyer will place upon the buildings, and for this reason he must be well-acquainted with market conditions in the area.

Once the value that the improvements contribute to the property has been determined, the value of the land must be approached separately. This is normally the current market value of the land when considered as unimproved. On a farm or ranch property, this will consist of dividing the property into the various classes of land such as level cropland, rolling cropland, pasture, timber, and waste.

Land that has value for urban purposes may be considered as frontage versus rear land, or divided into classes by use such as commercial, multi-family, single-family residential, or industrial. Here again, the land may be carved into net buildable acres, deducting the area necessary to provide services to the land such as collector streets, easements, and dedications. To determine the cost approach of a farm, an appraiser will make the following type of breakdown:

Improvement Summary

Type	Size	Square Feet	Present Cost	Less Depreciation	Present Value
House	30 x 50	1,500	$45,000	40%	$27,000
Garage	24 x 24	576	5,700	40%	3,420
Barn	50 x 80	4,000	32,000	50%	16,000
Machine Shed	40 x 80	3,200	24,000	20%	19,200
Well	600' depth,	8" casing	4,000	30%	2,800
Fences	6 miles		12,000	50%	6,000
TOTAL PRESENT VALUE					$74,420

Land Summary

Type Of Land	Acres	Price Per Acre	Total Value
Best Cropland	100	$2,000	$200,000
Other Cropland	100	1,500	150,000
Pasture	50	500	25,000
Timber	40	300	12,000
Farmstead	5		
Roads and Waste	5		
TOTAL LAND	300 acres	1,290 per acre average value	$387,000
Value of Improvements			74,420
TOTAL PROPERTY VALUE		$1,538	$461,420

Since the contribution of value by the buildings is determined from a knowledge of what the market will pay, and the values allocated to each land class must necessarily come from a study of properties which have been sold and are offered for sale, it is clear that the cost approach is really another way of examining the property based upon market influence, and thus is clearly related to the market data approach discussed later.

Income Approach

The income approach is often known as the *capitalization approach*. Here, an attempt is made to determine the value of the property based upon the net income which the property should produce under normal conditions.

INCOME APPROACH

Income:

Crop	Acres	Per Acre Yield	Total Production	Owner's Share	Price	Total Value
Corn	150	130 bu.	19,500 bu.	9,750 bu.	$3.00	$29,250
Soybeans	50	35 bu.	1,750 bu.	875 bu.	5.00	4,375
Pasture	50 ⎫					
Timber	40 ⎬ Cash rented					5,000
Farmstead	5					
Roads/Waste	5 ⎭					
Total	300					$38,625

Expenses:

Taxes	$ 4,500
Insurance	800
Maintenance	2,800
1/2 Seed	1,900
1/2 Fertilizer	3,000
1/2 Chemicals	900
Management (5% of gross)	1,880
	$15,780

$15,780

Net Income $22,845

Net Income Capitalized (divided) by 5%, $\dfrac{\$22,845}{.05}$ = Indicated Value Of $456,900

Often, only the most skilled and experienced appraisers are competent to accurately determine the net income. On farms, the net income is normally estimated on the basis of a lease to a tenant who will pay a share of the income to the landlord. The process requires an estimate of crop acreages, yields, and prices, as well as the cost of producing these products. The net income is then capitalized, or divided by an appropriate interest rate, to arrive at a value for the property.

The interest or capitalization rate used should represent what owners of farmland are typically receiving on their investments. In other words, it is that rate which attracts capital to the type of investment considered in the appraisal.

Obviously, the income approach is subject to a wide swing of values because of the variables necessary to mathematically determine the income, expenses, and capitalization rate. One of the more useful purposes of the income approach on land, or farms and ranches particularly, is to give the potential buyer some estimate of how much income he may expect to derive from the property, thus helping him determine what his cash flow position will be, and help him determine whether he can afford to buy the property. The income approach is used primarily in the evaluation of real estate such as highly improved urban properties like office buildings, shopping centers, or other properties where the income stream is readily predictable, backed up by long term leases. On those properties, the income approach is a much more reliable indication of value.

Market Data Approach

Also known as the *comparable sale method,* this approach calls for a comparison of the property with similar properties that have recently changed hands. The appraiser must attempt to accumulate all information available on properties that have sold in recent years, normally not to exceed the past 5 years. To derive the pertinent facts from a comparable sale property, the appraiser must analyze the property that sold in some detail. Not only must he know the price and terms, but he must dissect the sale to best determine what elements of the sale contributed to value. Obviously, the more similar that the sale property is to the property being appraised, the more weight that can be placed on the sale.

Many appraisers make adjustments for properties that are not alike by adjusting for appreciation, location, tillable land, improvements, and any other factors that are major differences between the properties. By analyzing the sale to determine how much the building has contributed to the selling price, he will be assembling data which is useful in the cost approach. Likewise, by analyzing the net income of the property that has been sold, he will have to extract the capitalization rate necessary for use in the income approach. The appraiser who works primarily in a relatively small area will normally establish a system which provides him with a continuous flow of information on properties that have sold and are for sale, and this will be an inventory of data to draw from.

The Final Value Estimate

If the appraiser has utilized all three approaches to value, in his final analysis he will weigh the accuracy of the information that went into each approach. Obviously, if he has handled all of the information correctly, the values indicated by the three approaches should be quite similar. Since the information retrieved through properties which have been sold apply to the other two approaches, the market data approach is by far the most important in the valuation of farm property. The income and cost approaches will have substantial validity on certain types of property and are good cross-checks to be certain that all factors relating to value have been considered.

Appraising For Condemnation Purposes

Certain governmental agencies have the power of eminent domain. The Fifth Amendment to the Constitution of the United States provides . . . "nor shall private property be taken for public use without just compensation." Condemnation appraisals are often required for determining the loss in market value to owners due to the construction of highways, pipelines, lake projects, and other public takings of property.

The approach to establish just compensation under condemnation appraisal is similar to that required for any other appraisal. If there is only a portion of the property taken, the appraiser then must look at the property before the taking and after the taking. The difference represents the compensation to the owner and the cost to the taking agency.

SPECIAL VALUATION TECHNIQUES AND CONSIDERATIONS

Buyers, sellers, and others keenly interested in determining land values, have developed individual techniques and philosophies. The limitless types of land and situations require ingenuity to zero in on what they consider to be the appropriate price for their purpose.

The fascination of dealing in land comes from the results obtainable from the application of special knowledge and foresight. Ten people may look at the same parcel of property and see different uses, values, shortcomings, and opportunities.

To the uninformed, buying, operating, developing, and selling land may be speculation. The student of land takes the speculation out of land ownership. The user of property will frequently have unique considerations that apply to his purpose only. Thus, the value to one person justifiably may be totally unrelated in the view of another.

Value For Farm Expansion—Buy or Lease?

Expanding owners must evaluate land values in terms of the peculiar benefits to them. Their ability to use income from other land to cover the payments for additional acreage is a major factor in the decision.

Due to inflation, most owners who have owned land for some years have built substantial equity in their current holdings. I've often observed that there are many wealthy farmers who are landowners; there are very few wealthy farmers who are tenants on land owned by others. For example, an Iowa farmer who purchased an "average" 400 acre parcel at age 30 in 1960 would have paid $230 per acre, or $92,000.

The same "average" farm in 1980 is worth over $1,500 per acre, or more than $600,000. Chances are that he now owns the property free and clear. If he now wants to add 200 acres to his property at $1,500 per acre, he can easily obtain an overall loan of $500 per acre (one-third of value) on the entire 600 acres, and pay cash for his addition. It is likely that the income from the entire property will carry the debt service of the loan. On the other hand, it is impossible for a tenant on the same 400 acres to have saved enough money to acquire either the land he has been farming, or land for expansion.

A farm economist would recommend the following steps to assist a farmer in evaluating the wisdom of an expansion.

Step 1. Determination of Gross Returns
Step 2. Determination of Variable Costs
Step 3. Determination of *Increased* Fixed Costs
Step 4. Determination of Minimum Desired Return for Labor and Management
Step 5. Determination of Average Net Returns to Land
Step 6. Determination of Land Value

Most farm economists, however, tend to ignore appreciation in value as a valid determinant in making a decision to add land. Without assuming continued inflation, the analysis above would nearly always give a negative purchase response. For purposes of illustration only, assume that land costing $1,500 per acre would yield a net return, before debt service, of 6%, or $90 per acre. On a 200 acre or $300,000 expansion, the net income available for principal and interest payments would be $18,000. If all the money were borrowed on a 20-year loan, at 8% interest, with equal annual principal payments, the first year payment would be $39,000, leaving an apparent negative result of $21,000.

Let's reexamine the situation, however. The two assumptions are: 1) the buyer is in the 40% tax bracket, and 2) he believes land will continue to increase in price through a combination of scarcity and inflation at 12% per year.

Of the $39,000 payment, $24,000 was interest, deductible against other income. Therefore, the actual cash flow cost of interest is 60% of $24,000, or $14,400. The principal amount of $15,000 is debt reduction, or equity buildup. If the value increase is 12%, or $36,000, the owner's net worth change is:

Equity increase from debt reduction	$15,000
Equity increase from increased price	36,000
Total	$51,000
Less actual interest cost	14,400
Increase in net worth	$36,600

(This increase will some day be realized and taxed at favorable capital gain rates.)

Value Due to Proximity to Urban Areas

Population centers have a substantial impact on surrounding land values. While there is not an exact relationship applicable to all situations, it is possible to establish demand formulas.

As related to value, the effect of urban areas is demonstrated in several ways:

1. Farm buildings are salable with small acreages for use as weekend second homes, or full time occupancy to the commuter breed. From World War I through the 1960s, as the number of

farmers decreased and farms became larger, literally millions of farmsteads were destroyed or allowed to fall into disrepair. With the recent wave of back-to-the-land attitudes, farm homes are in great demand if near a town or city.

2. Land for recreational use continues to increase in demand. Small tracts for hunting and fishing are particularly desirable.

3. Land for subdividing second home developments is needed.

4. Related commercial and industrial urban uses accelerate demand.

5. Investors interested in land purely for agricultural production purposes prefer a location within a reasonable drive of their primary homes and businesses.

The ripple effect of a city of 1,000,000 population may be demonstrated in the manner shown on the next page, assuming the first 20-mile radius to be fully urbanized.

The Ripple Effect on Land Values

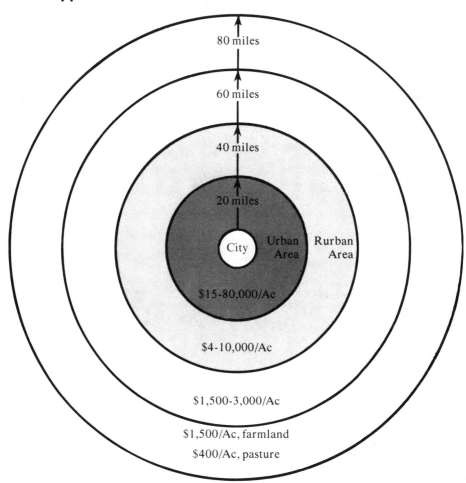

CHAPTER 4

Getting the Most Net Dollars for Your Land

For whatever reason, decisions to sell property are often hard to make. Sentiment is sometimes involved. It isn't easy to say goodby to something you've been as closely associated with as the soil.

My father owned our farm for more than 40 years. Mom gave birth to three sons in that farmhouse they had remodeled many times and always intended to replace. Every corner of every field, the trees planted, the pets buried, the ponds fished--all hold the memories of a lifetime. They're hard to view as an asset on a balance sheet.

The land has been benevolent; it's been sadistic. It has yielded to the floods and drouths and then brought forth the bounty to feed and to provide for loved ones. But now, for one reason or another, it's time to relinquish title. For most people, the sale of their land is the largest transaction in which they will ever be involved. It's only fair that the seller is interested in netting the most possible dollars from the sale. That's what this chapter is about.

Economic conditions may dictate the proper time to sell property. While economic cycles are difficult to interpret, the past indicates broad general guidelines which may be applied. For example, from about 1973 to 1980 was a period of rapid increase in land prices. Obviously, the time to sell was closer to 1980 than earlier 1973. Many landowners tripled their equity in that period of time.

A period of rapidly escalating inflation nearly always precedes a rapid climb in land prices. As inflation occurs in a continuing fashion, investors and farmers become caught up in the syndrome of never-ending spirals of increasing land values.

While inflation may be the most important factor affecting land prices, farm enlargement or expansion is another key reason. As the cost of producing crops and livestock increases, the only way in which a set amount of overhead can be held to a reasonable level is to spread that cost over a larger operation. More efficient methods of operation and increased size of machinery, along with other labor saving devices, have accelerated the trend to farm enlargement.

The cycle of increasing land prices tends to feed on itself. As the demand becomes more feverish, the rise is fueled by a scarcity of property for sale because owners don't want to sell prematurely.

Optimism about commodity prices is also certain to point prices higher. Increased profits have almost always been capitalized into higher land prices.

To those students of monetary matters, farm real estate investments have performed particularly well in recent years. The rate of return of farm real estate has far exceeded returns from the ownership of common stock including returns from capital appreciation, as well as earnings. World affairs also have an impact as the strong export demand for U.S. farm products is weighed by producers. If an owner is fortunate enough to have a choice, and be blessed with the ability to analyze the economic side of the question, the obvious time to sell is after the boom has been in progress long enough to get the prices up, but before the boom is over and there is no longer an active buyer market.

Q. What is the right time of year to sell my farm?

A. More practical than attempting to predict the best economic period is selecting the best time of year to sell. Without being facetious, the best time to sell is when you have a buyer who wants to buy!

Seriously, you may be approached by a buyer before you have decided to sell. Before you say "No," think about your future plans. If you have been considering a sale anyway, it's easier when you have a motivated buyer.

Many sellers are often disturbed because someone actually wants their farm at the price that is being asked. Their first reaction may be that they have underpriced the property. Buyers are just as unpredictable as sellers. When something strikes their fancy, they may make an impulsive decision to buy. Perhaps they have been frustrated in looking for property for months and yours looks like the answer to their needs. For whatever reason, if you are satisfied that the price is right, don't be frightened by finding a buyer quickly. In most cases, the first prospects are the best buyers.

There is no single time of year that is better than another. By the nature of the business, an operating farm is most likely to sell after the crop season is over. Most buyers are going to want to take over the property well in advance of the next crop season so that time is available to arrange for seed, fertilizer, equipment, tenants, and other necessary inputs. Similarly, for the seller, year-end is an appropriate time to wind up the operations. This is not to say, of course, that farms cannot be sold with growing crops in place; they often are.

Livestock operations are apt to be less critical as related to a particular time of year, although cow-calf operations will normally be more readily available after the feeder calves have been sold.

Property that is suitable for a second home or country estate reaches its peak salability in spring. There is something about the greening of trees and blooming of flowers that brings out the desire of city dwellers to acquire a place in the country. This desire may be lessened by the hot days of summer, but will revive for a short period with the colors of autumn. It is almost impossible to get northern buyers seriously interested in second home property from the middle of November until after January 1.

Buyers of investment or development properties really have no seasonal period. With the exception of the holiday season previously mentioned, they are likely buyers year-round.

Q. How can I be sure I'm not leaving money on the table....? Or how do I know what my land is worth?

A. There is an old saying, "The worth of a thing is the price it will bring." After several years as an appraiser, I reached a point where I was sure that I was able to establish the exact market value of a property. I was convinced that with all I knew about soils and production, comparable sales, capitalization rates, and building costs, I must certainly be able to tell an owner what his property was worth. The several professional appraisal organizations have definitions of market value that include such terms as ready, willing, and able; informed buyer and informed seller; acting of their own free will; and fully informed as to the factors of value. Then I realized that no matter how good the appraiser, unless he acts as the buyer or seller, he doesn't have the final say about the property worth.

I came to realize that if 5 buyers looked at the same piece of property, I would have five substantially different offers to purchase. For example, I might have thought that a piece of property was worth $250,000, but if I had 5 serious buyers, I might end up with offers ranging all the way from $200,000 to $300,000. The conclusion here is that there is no such thing as a single value of a piece of property. That's not to belittle the appraisal profession, because appraisers are frequently called upon to determine a given value on a given date for such purposes as estate settlement, property tax, liquidation, or other reasons--all of which carry a separate set of conditions of sale.

To determine whether you need a professional appraisal of your property, you must honestly analyze your basis for judgment. To properly measure the market, you should have well-founded information about all sales occurring within the surrounding area during the past 3 years. You need to know the price, terms, acreage, and nature of the property sold. In appraisal terms, this is called the sales comparison or market data approach. It simply compares farms which have sold in your area to property you own. You must, however, be able to objectively analyze the differences and how this would affect the price.

Assuming you have the basic understanding of value, you should then seek the counsel of one or two land brokers in whom you have confidence. Your banker may also be a good test, if he is not too conservative. When you have realistically sorted out the facts, and feel that you have a good idea of what your land is worth, add approximately 10% to that figure and you should have your asking price for the property.

Q. If I don't have enough information to make a judgment as to value, what should I look for in an appraisal?

A. First, know exactly what an appraisal should be. An appraisal is a definite, detailed, and documented opinion of value. It is usually written.

A competent appraisal of a substantial and complicated property may take several days and cost hundreds or thousands of dollars. The benefit is being relatively certain of what the property is worth. The appraisal may also serve as a tool to demonstrate to buyers and lenders the value of the property.

Q. What will an appraisal do for me?

A. A professional appraisal report will include, but not be limited to, the following basic information:

- Background of the appraisal assignment.
- Purpose and reason for the appraisal.
- Location and identification of the property.

- Accurate description of the property, including size, shape, occupancy, zoning, etc.
- A map of the area showing the location of the property.
- An aerial photo of the farm, showing all important physical features.
- Soil maps by type.
- A physical description of the property, including buildings and improvements.
- Classification by acres of each type of usable land.
- A complete discussion of the type of operation.
- The productive capacity of the property described in full.
- Discussion of the income potential from the farm.
- Income and expense statement.
- Capitalization of the net income into an estimated value of the property.
- Sales study of all comparable property sold in the recent past.
- Detailed comparison of the subject property with similar property sold so as to allow a value judgment to be made.
- Each type of land, buildings, and improvements inventoried in a summary ascribing value to each of the assets. (If all of the land is of a similar type, and there are no building improvements on the property, then the summation is less important. However, if there are separate acreages of pasture, cropland, timberland, etc., a summation of the property more easily allows you to measure the individual assets of the farm.)
- Finally, each of the views of the property will be brought together and a single estimate of value will be explained and justified, in the appraiser's opinion.

Throughout the appraisal, other elements that will affect value will be considered. For example, the consideration of "highest and best use" may involve key assumptions about the property. It is necessary to understand these underlying assumptions made by the appraiser. It is not unknown to have an owner convince an appraiser that the highest and best use of his land in the middle of nowhere is for an "automobile assembly plant," making the land value $40,000 per acre, instead of $800 per acre as dictated by the present use. On the other hand, the location of the property may be a very important factor in future development of the property. Access and general desirability will also affect the price a buyer is willing to pay.

Q. My partner wants to ask 50% more than what's reasonable. Most of the land in this area has been selling for $1,500 to $1,800 per acre. He heard that the dairy near town brought $2,500 per acre. Could we price ourselves out of the market?

A. Absolutely. And a more difficult problem is that once you start to lower the asking price, it's hard to stop. Remember: your best and most earnest buyers are frequently the first ones to look. When a new property goes on the market, those persons who have been looking for property will immediately check on the details to see if it fits into their plans. These people aren't stupid. If the property is substantially overpriced they aren't going to make a counteroffer, or even mention that they were interested. Consequently, you can scare away the most likely buyers.

Selling a small piece of ground for recreational purposes to a weekend fisherman is one thing. If he sees something he likes, he's going to buy it, and the price is not that consequential. If you are selling a substantial parcel of land for agricultural or investment purposes, you aren't going to find any suckers who will come by and overpay for the property. They just don't exist.

Assuming you have missed your best buyer, once you start to bring the asking price within reason, many people will sit by and wait for the decline to become a real bargain. If the property stays on the market an excessive length of time, it becomes shopworn and people continue to pass it by. Everyone has seen "For Sale" signs that have been tacked onto fence posts for so long that no one even notices them anymore.

If you are only fishing for offers, you can't do anything but hurt yourself by putting your property on the market. Price the property about 10% above what the consensus of opinion of value is and do what is necessary to sell the property.

Q. Our family has accumulated 1,200 acres over three generations. Now, family problems and personal reasons leave us no choice but to sell. Where can we find a buyer for this land, which is worth in excess of $1.5 million?

A. The answer to this question may involve another consideration. Have you thought of splitting the property?

At first the thought of dividing property that has been assembled by your family over many years may be objectionable. However, once you face the fact that the property is going to have to be sold, whether it remains intact is really a sentimental consideration. The new owners may decide to split it up immediately after buying anyway.

The division of a large property allows many more buyers to enter the picture. There are far more parties who can raise $100,000 cash to buy a $400,000 property than can put together $400,000 cash to buy a $1,500,000 property. This is particularly true if the property is already bounded by access roads.

Remember that over half of the buyers of land are existing operators, usually located in the general vicinity of the farm. You may have six neighbors in the vicinity who would each like to increase their operations by 200 acres and will pay dearly for the opportunity. A single buyer of 1,200 acres might have to pay only 80% as much for the property because of its size.

The proper approach to your problem may be to determine a reasonable split of the property and then price it in more than one manner. In other words, price the property as one parcel, and as four-300 acre parcels, or whatever seems reasonable. That way the buyers have a choice. Only in the event of some disproportionate value of a property could this be a bad decision. If, for example, a substantial portion of the property is low value pastureland, you would certainly want to assure that a high enough price is placed on the tillable land so you would not be left with an unsalable parcel of pastureland.

Splitting the property into smaller tracts may not always be the answer, however. For example, certain large tracts may be attractive to well-financed buyers such as investor groups. Instead of having to assemble a large-sized land parcel from smaller holdings, these buyers may look more favorably on the purchase of a tract of this type. Much depends on the nature of the property itself, and the type of buyers it can be exposed to.

Q. What about selling off farm buildings? My wife and I are getting ready to move into town. We would like to keep the land-320 acres-for income, but we know the buildings will deteriorate if they are left vacant.

A. The American people are an interesting phenomenon. Here you have lived on the farm for many years, and are now ready to retire and move into town. You are probably looking forward to the many conveniences which you or your wife may feel you have missed over the years because of living in the country. This could include a more active social life, or the convenience of shopping, or other personal reasons. Conversely, there are many people who live in our towns and communities today who want the benefits of rural life, perhaps as a place to raise their

children, or to have a horse, or simply to get away from traffic and people. In any event, if you are near a reasonably sized town--which might
be 2 miles from a town of 1,000 population, or 10 miles from a town of
10,000 population--buyers for your property will be happy to commute
to their occupation in town.

You might need to include 5 to 20 acres with the buildings, depending
on how extensive they are. A further consideration is that when you
decide to sell the remaining land, chances are that the absence of buildings will not affect the value of the land one cent. In fact, there may be
more buyers for the property who are operators who wish to expand.
They would rather not contend with the buildings by tearing them down
or finding someone to live in them.

Q. What can I do to make our farm more attractive to a buyer?

A. You've owned your land for a long time. There may be a lot of things
that you look right by and take for granted--things like old machinery
sitting around, or buildings that should be torn down, repainted, or
repaired. Roadways and fencelines should be mowed. It wouldn't hurt
to mow the pastures and do some pickup around the buildings and yard.

Remember, the first impression people get is very important. The
buyer likes to walk onto the property and sense the feeling of prosperity
and pride in something he's going to buy.

I have been amazed over the years at how many otherwise sophisticated buyers will pass up a property that is run down and in need of
repair. This holds true whether it is a $50,000 property or $500,000
property. Buyers are still affected by cosmetic appeal.

*Q. Would a brochure containing all the details--perhaps even with pictures--
be helpful in selling my ranch?*

A. Brochures can help sell certain types of property if they are
employed in a distribution plan or direct mail campaign that ensures
their placement in the hands of potential buyers.

If a property has many appealing or complicated characteristics, a
sales brochure can help. Pictures may be the only medium to convey the
unique buildings of a major livestock operation. Mountain landscapes
and vistas are often best portrayed in color.

Some real estate firms prepare elaborate brochures listing all the
details of the land, buildings, and the community. They are used in extensive mail campaigns to other brokers, and to persons who respond to

classified newspaper and magazine advertisements. The cost of preparing and mailing extensive brochures can become substantial, however.

For most properties, a data sheet or short brochure may be adequate to properly furnish interested parties with the minimum information. Examples of a data sheet and a short, 1-page brochure for farm and ranch properties are shown on the following pages.

Doane Agricultural Service, Inc. / 8900 Manchester Road / Saint Louis, Missouri 63144 / (314) 968-1000

JOHNSTON RANCH

Size & Location:	580 acres located 8 miles south of Ranchville, Mississippi.
Legal Description:	In office files. Available upon request.
Acreage Data:	All cleared; improved pasture of fescue and Dallisgrass.
Topography:	Level to gently rolling land with excellent surface drainage.
Improvements:	4,800 square foot, two-story main residence converted from old barn. There are 5 bedrooms, 4 baths, built-in kitchen, and gameroom; 576 square foot detached garage. Sale barn with a 60' x 50' sale area, 2 offices, balcony area with carpeted lounge and wet bar. Working pens, constructed in 1979, adjoin sale barn. 2,400 square foot feedlot with automatic feeding system. Two Harvestores -- 20' x 70' and 25' x 90'; feed mill with 40T capacity; 8,000 bushel grain bin; and 20T capacity hopper bin.
Equipment:	Silage chopper, 3 silage wagons, and silage blower.
Fencing:	Approximately 12 miles of perimeter and cross fencing.
Water:	Two-inch water lines serve the farm with automatic waterers in each pasture.
Taxes:	$704.80 in 1978.
Price & Terms:	$1,220,000 (includes equipment). 29% down with owner financing on the balance for 30 years.
Comments:	This ranch is developed for registered cattle production. Silage produced for cattle population; hay cut from pastures in 1978-79.

For appointment to see, contact:

C. T. Lowry, Jr.
Doane Agricultural Service, Inc.
4230 Elvis Presley Boulevard
Memphis, Tennessee 38116
(901) 398-1354

(All listings subject to change, error or omission.)

View of farmstead

Upland crop ground

Pasture sown to Trefoil Legume & Orchardgrass

Hillside pasture

685 Acre
Smith Farm

Location: Approximately 12 miles south of Ottumwa in Davis County, Iowa.

Legal Description: In office files, available upon request.

Topography: All rolling, except 75 acres of bottom ground.

Improvements: 7-room house, 20' x 50' silo, good 35' x 50' barn, 35' x 60' steel machine shed, grain bin, range barn, 3 ponds.

Taxes: Approximately $1,895/year.

Possession: January 1, 1980.

Price & Terms: $732,000. Cash on either tract with contract on other.

Comments: This farm is in two tracts—460 and 225 acres, ½ mile apart. They can be bought separately or together. The farm would make a nice grain/livestock unit, with good fences and beautiful pasture for a cow/calf operation.

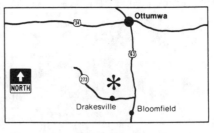

For appointment to see, contact:

Glen R. Smith / Real Estate Sales / Investments
Doane Agricultural Service, Inc.
213 North Ankeny Blvd. / Ankeny, Iowa 50021
(515) 964-5064
or
Russ Landers or Tom Irvine
Real Estate Sales / Investments
Doane Agricultural Service, Inc.
3120½ Kimball Avenue / Suite B / Waterloo, Iowa 50702
(319) 233-1147

(Information herein is not warranted and is subject to change without notice. We assume no liability for errors.)

Listing No. 462-4

Q. Auction sales have become more popular in my area in recent years. I have an unimproved (without buildings) all tillable quarter section in which several neighbors have expressed an interest. Should I try an auction?

A. You should certainly consider it. A good auctioneer who properly exposes your property can frequently get a higher price.

Auctions can be strange. Occasionally emotion enters the bidding and a property sells for more than could be obtained in negotiations. Conversely, neighbors sometimes don't want to bid against each other, and will stay out of the bidding. To avoid selling too cheaply, you can specify an "upset" or minimum price below which a sale will not be honored. You may also reserve the right to reject all bids, though this must be announced in advance and may deter some bidders.

Q. We're only an hour's drive from a city. Should I advertise in the paper?

A. Investor buyers may be less resistant to higher prices. If they come from a city, they are accustomed to seeing land prices at $5,000 per acre--maybe far more. Your local buyers may have too long a memory. Your land might be worth $3,000 per acre, but they remember that you only paid $500 per acre for it 10 years ago.

Remember that investor buyers must be treated differently. Let's assume you have a doctor with an active medical practice interested in your land. Almost always he is going to be interested in tax shelter. Unless a farm is used for raising breeding stock, or can be used for some exotic purpose, it may be overlooked as a tax benefit. On the contrary, let's see what an ordinary farm of 320 acres producing both livestock and grain might look like:

Item	Size	Age	New Cost	Present Value
House	2,000 sq. ft.	20 yrs.	$40,000	$18,000
Barn	3,200 sq. ft.	20 yrs.	15,000	8,000
Silo	14' x 40'	10 yrs.	20,000	12,000
Machine shed	2,000 sq. ft.	10 yrs.	8,000	4,000
Garage	600 sq. ft.	5 yrs.	3,000	2,000
Wells	-	-	-	2,000
Fences	6 miles	-	-	4,000
Underground pipe	-	-	-	2,000
Corrals	-	-	-	2,000
Miscellaneous	-	-	-	3,000
Value for depreciation				$57,000

If an average remaining useful life of 10 years can be justified, straight line depreciation will shelter $5,700 of income. Bonus depreciation or investment credit on other items may increase this amount.

A major benefit of this type investment is that interest and taxes are deductible against ordinary income for the investor, but when he sells it for appreciated dollars in the future, his profit will be taxed at the lower capital gains rates.

In addition to pointing out tax benefits to investor buyers, seek out their other interests and motivations. He may want to build a second home for weekend use on the land. Point out logical sites. History, antiques, folklore--these are all of interest to the city buyer.

I speak from personal experience. Even though I spent my entire childhood on a working farm in Nebraska, when I was in business in St. Louis and bought a farm 90 miles away for weekend use, I really wasn't interested in how many bushels of corn I got to the acre. I was more interested in taking my daughters down to the creek to look for arrowheads, or riding a trail bike through the woods. While the investor may be motivated by profit, he will probably make his decisions on a weekend farm by emotion; by restoration of some old log buildings; by a Civil War gravesite.

Q. I'm forced to sell my farm but I'll probably reinvest a portion of the proceeds in other income property. Would a "tax-free exchange" make sense?

A. Under Section 1031 of the Internal Revenue Code, real estate held for investment may be exchanged for other investment property, provided the properties are of like kind. This qualification avoids the necessity of paying the capital gains tax. The term "like kind" means of similar nature. You could exchange land for buildings. You could not exchange land for personal property.

In the event the exchange does not come out equally, one party may receive cash or other property, called "boot." This gain may be taxable. The tax basis and mortgage status of the properties greatly affect the tax savings involved in exchanges, and must be examined carefully by a tax expert.

A three-way exchange is possible. Such an arrangement may work by permitting one party to receive cash, and satisfying the two other parties' property requirements. The process is critical, however, and to make certain that the arrangement achieves the goals of all parties, expert tax counsel should be sought.

Q. *I want $300,000 for my land. I told the broker I wouldn't consider any-thing less, but he insists on bothering me with lower offers. Any comment?*

A. First, don't blame the broker. By law, he is required to convey to you every offer he receives. He does not have the right to be discretionary about what he tells you. More important, don't be insulted by low offers. Look at all offers as a sign of interest. Understand that bargaining for a property takes many forms. Certain buyers will be terribly concerned about leaving money on the table. Consequently, a serious buyer may make a ridiculously low opening offer. Simply come back with your ask-ing price as a counter-offer so he'll know you're serious.

Some buyers will decide what the property is worth to them and make one offer only. So treat all offers courteously. Anyone interested enough to make a commitment at any price may turn out to be your buyer.

Q. *Are buyers generally more interested in the price or the terms?*

A. Contrary to popular belief, the terms of the sale are usually more im-portant than the price, (assuming the price is somewhere near value). Most buyers will be directly concerned with the cash required to close. After that, other factors come into play. The ability of the typical buyer to handle the purchase of a farm will be dictated, in order of their im-portance, by the following terms:

1. Size of the down payment.
2. Annual principal payment required.
3. Amount of annual interest.

Against these terms, the prospect must weigh:

1. His available cash.
2. His borrowing ability.
3. Net income expected to be produced from the property.
4. His income from sources outside the property.

The sellers' willingness to "carry" a purchase money mortgage, or deed of trust, may greatly affect the price and the availability of a buyer.

Take, for example, the investor who doesn't have a large amount of cash available, but does have a high annual income from other sources. A doctor fits into this category. He may be willing to pay 20% more for the property that only requires a 10% downpayment rather than 25%.

Q. If a buyer only makes a small downpayment, does the seller need to look for assurances through other special provisions?

A. Probably. Assuming the buyer is giving a note or other debt instrument to the seller for the balance, the exposure of the seller in a low downpayment transaction depends on three factors:

1. *The type of property.* If the property could suffer extensively from lack of attention, thereby depreciating in value, a low downpayment could be unwise. If the buyer has little at stake, it may be easier for him to walk away from the deal. The cash received by the seller may not be enough to restore the property to the previous condition. Examples could be a dairy operation, which included a fine purebred herd, or a citrus grove that requires close attention to maintain its production and, therefore, value.

2. *The seller's circumstances.* If the seller has reached retirement age, he may require substantial cash to satisfy his retirement needs. If the buyer defaulted after one or two years, the seller may no longer be physically capable of going back to his land and putting it back in condition to sell, or the seller may need the principal and interest income to sustain his standard of living. In these circumstances, a downpayment of much less than 30% is not appropriate.

3. *The type of buyer, his circumstances and reliability.* If the buyer is a professional man who is not going to operate the property, but has demonstrated his stability in the community, and his ability to earn a substantial income, his note will probably be sound. That is, unless he suffers a business or health reversal. You may wish to require a life insurance policy from a buyer. You will certainly wish to see his financial statement and check his references. Banks and other institutional lenders have no hesitancy in requiring that a borrower assign a life insurance policy in the face amount of the loan, even if the amount is small. There is no reason a seller, who becomes the mortgagee of his own property, should require less.

If the buyer is a young tenant farmer who wants to get started on his own, despite your desire to help him, you should make a purely business decision, based upon his ability to pay. Perhaps he has a father with substantial assets who is willing to co-sign the note, and thus provide additional security.

Q. What is meant by an installment sale?

A. To be perfectly technical, an installment sale could be any transaction where the buyer makes payments over a set period of time, as opposed to paying cash. For example, if you bought a car and took an installment loan from a bank, you might make 24 monthly installments to pay for the car.

In the jargon of land sales, however, an installment sale has come to mean a low-equity land transfer between a seller and buyer where the purchase price is paid over a period of years to the seller who acts as the lender as well.

In the minds of many buyers and sellers, an installment sale also means 29% or less downpayment in the year of sale. Why 29%? Partly mistake. Actually, the magic number is 30% or less, and the importance comes from a provision for the installment method of reporting capital gains in the Internal Revenue Code. This installment method applies to sales of real property if no more than 30% of the purchase price is received in the year of sale. The use of 29% or less has become common because the law is exacting as to not more than 30%, and it is best to allow at least a small margin for error in calculating closing costs.

The installment sale will be discussed in more detail in later chapters, but the importance of this type of sale is immense. Historically, nearly 50% of the money required to buy farms has been provided by the sellers. The advantage to the buyer is that he is able to purchase land with a lower capital investment. The seller benefits because the income tax laws allow him to spread his capital gain over a period of years, if the transaction qualifies as an installment sale. Easier terms may also allow the seller to realize a higher sale price.

Q. I need more cash out of the sale. How can I make it easy for the buyer, keep the price up, and still free up some cash?

A. Probably the best way to make more cash available is to place as large an institutional loan as possible, and then carry a smaller second mortgage. Let's look at three situations, one of which will work:

Facts
1. You, seller, have a $200,000 farm for sale.
2. The only real buyer you've found has $50,000 cash available.
3. You want a minimum of $150,000 cash.
4. The existing mortgage on the farm is $35,000.

Situation 1

Buyer offers you $50,000 down, assumes the $35,000 mortgage, and you have to carry a second mortgage for $115,000. Works for buyer, but not for you.

Situation 2

You want $150,000 cash, buyer to assume $35,000 mortgage, you offer to carry a $15,000 second mortgage. Works for you, not for buyer.

Situation 3

Seller applies for a 50% loan with an insurance company (getting $100,000 in loan proceeds), and lets buyer assume loan. Buyer puts in his $50,000 cash, bringing seller's cash to $150,000, and seller conveys a $50,000 second mortgage. Works for seller; works for buyer. (Obviously a buyer could also apply for a new mortgage but seller's credit position may be better).

A note of caution: If seller's tax basis is low, the above method could prevent the use of an installment sale. See your tax advisor.

CHAPTER 5

Using a Broker (Or Not)

Professional land buyers and sellers prefer to work through brokers. They know that the expert broker spends all of his time finding land and knows the pulse of the market. The professional land broker knows his territory, and the personalities he deals with. Ownership of land includes emotional attachments that must be dealt with.

Many brokers have clients who will engage the broker to represent them in the acquisition of property, even though they have selected the site, and perhaps know the owner. These buyers have done two things: they have recognized the value of an expert middleman to buffer and guide the negotiations, and they have sought out a broker in whom they have complete faith and confidence.

On the other hand, some buyers and sellers will almost refuse to employ a broker, and, in fact, will not hesitate to "go around" a broker and prevent him from earning a commission.

Since a sale only occurs when buyers and sellers can be brought together, the broker must act as a focal point in bringing the deal together. The typical land market suffers from the lack of published and reliable data on which decisions can be based; the skills needed are highly specialized, and the market is thin. The broker must act as the clearing house, matching buyers and sellers.

Dealing in land requires a knowledge of :

Crops	Financing
Soils	Leasing
Livestock	Managing
Production Methods	Appraising
Terminology	Counseling
Buyer Sources	Zoning
Seller Sources	Comparable Sales
Economic Conditions	Availability Of Utilities
Tax Saving Techniques	Contracts

As important as knowledge, is an awareness of your lack of knowledge in certain areas. Specialists may be needed to fill in these knowledge gaps.

Attorneys: Competent legal counsel is required in every transaction. Those attorneys that specialize in real estate should be sought out for any complicated transactions.

Accountants: Certain properties require an operating analysis.

Appraisers: Documented value estimates will assist in making intelligent decisions.

Managers: The availability of qualified managers may make the difference. A knowledgeable operating consultant will provide invaluable feasibility reports.

Banker/Mortgage Brokers: Innovative financing will often be the key to a deal.

Engineers: Pitfalls may be avoided by preliminary engineering tests.

Tax Specialists: Some attorneys and accountants specialize in the structure of transactions and bring about enormous tax savings.

Yet, after all the other players have given their input, the competent broker will have a broader grasp of all of the implications than any of the others, and thus bring about a meeting of the minds.

Q. How do I go about finding the best qualified broker to help me sell my property?

A. Most farm communities have at least one good real estate brokerage firm capable of properly representing an owner in the sale of his land. Unfortunately, this is not always true. Some firms specialize only in the sale of residential property and have not developed the experience and talent for dealing with land as a specialty. In recent years, several national firms have emerged which specialize in farm real estate.

Nearly every state now has educational requirements associated with licensing which have upgraded the real estate industry considerably. This helps insure that your broker will have the basic competence in dealing with real estate generally.

Q. What traits should I look for in selecting a broker?

A. Look for these characteristics in the broker you choose to represent you:

1. The man should have a solid, honest reputation in his community.
2. His firm should have continuity of advertising.
3. He is located nearby and has good local knowledge of the area.
4. He is cooperative with a network of other professional brokers in the state, perhaps nationally.
5. He is well-known to the buying community.
6. He knows land, and looks at it closely.
7. He asks the right questions, and gets answers.
8. He is a member of professional real estate organizations.

Q. One broker said he wanted an "exclusive" listing. Exactly what did he mean?

A. When you list your property with a broker, you have technically employed him. There are two general methods of hiring--open listing and exclusive listing.

An open listing generally applies where more than one brokerage firm is authorized to sell the property. Whichever firm sells is entitled to the commission, or the owner may sell to a customer of his own procurement without becoming obligated to pay a sales commission.

An "exclusive agency" listing gives one firm exclusive right to find a buyer, although other firms may work through the exclusive agent. The owner may procure a buyer himself and not be obligated to pay a commission.

An "exclusive right-to-sell" entitles the agent to a commission, whoever procures the buyer, including the seller.

Q. Giving an exclusive listing to my broker may be the professional way to get my land sold, but this property represents most of my net worth. What approach should my broker use in promoting and advertising my farm, and how do I know he'll actively pursue this sale?

A. As to whether your broker will perform, include standards of performance in the listing contract, like:

1. How much, when, and where is he going to advertise?
2. Does he have a mailing list?
3. Is he going to put up signs?
4. Does he cooperate with a wide-area multiple listing service?
5. Does he have a regular clientele looking for property?
6. What kind of brochure or data sheet does he use?

Advertising and promotion methods are generally designed to expose the property to the most potentially qualified buyers. It is important to recognize, however, that many sellers do not wish to have their property "shopped". This is particularly true in predominantly agricultural areas. Many owners will object to having a sign placed on their property, or having advertisements placed in their local paper. If this is the case, the seller's wishes must obviously be respected.

Q. If I don't use a broker, what methods can be employed to attract buyers?

A. If wide exposure is desired for properties which should be exposed beyond a local market, consider the following methods:

1. Preparation of a brochure for mailing.
2. Classified or display ads to be placed in major metropolitan newspapers. The Wall Street Journal has a special real estate section in their Friday edition for national or regional placement.
3. Name lists purchased by zip code, income, profession, etc.
4. Rosters of various groups may be acquired, such as:
   a. Realtor groups
   b. Doctors/dentists
   c. Builders/developers
   d. Purebred livestock breeders
5. Magazine ads may be directed to appropriate audiences.

Q. Is there a difference between a broker and an agent?

A. A real estate broker is acting as an "agent" for the principal who hires him. Usually the broker is employed by the owner to procure a buyer. However, a broker may be hired by the buyer. In either case, the broker must be able to show that he was employed to act as an agent for whichever party he claims a commission from.

Q. What is meant by the term "Realtor"?®

A. A Realtor®is a person who is affiliated as a member at the local, state, and the national level of the National Association of Realtors.® He is governed by a strict code of ethics, and is generally among those persons most active in the professional sale of real estate. This does not mean that persons who are not Realtors® are not qualified to handle the sale of real property.

Q. Do certain Realtors® specialize in the sale of land?

A. Those Realtors® who are members of the Farm and Land Institute of the National Association of Realtors® specialize in the sale of all types of agricultural and urban land. This institute grants the designation "Accredited Farm and Land Member" (AFLM) to those members who have met rigid educational standards, and have demonstrated maximum proficiency and expertise with land through examination and training.

Q. "My land is choice and this is a seller's market. Why can't I sell the land myself and save a brokerage commission?"

A. No one said you couldn't sell it. Actually, there is a chance you could be quite successful at getting the property sold. However, you had better be the rare exception, or very lucky. Here are the pitfalls:

1. You may not know what the property is worth. What point is there in selling the property to save a 5% commission if you undersell the property by 20%? Most owners are too close to their land to know what it is worth.
2. Do you have the time and patience to work with the buyer, if you find one? In other words, is this the best use of your time?
3. Most prospects are reluctant to tell an owner their true feelings. They do not want to insult him, and consequently you may never learn what doubts or fears a good prospect actually has. With a broker, the prospect is free to be critical and express himself in a way that should lead an experienced broker to determine what assurances will turn this prospect into a buyer.
4. Do you know where to find the buyers? If you waste money on advertising, brochures, or mailings directed to the wrong areas, you may find that you haven't saved any money after all. Remember that most good properties that are well priced and properly exposed will sell promptly. A property that lingers on the market month after month becomes shopworn and suspect. Even good potential buyers assume that there must be something wrong with a property that languishes on the market.

In short, even an owner who is well-informed and skilled in selling may not be saving money by acting as his own broker. Remember, you could also be your own dentist; write your own will; fix your own TV set. The question is whether you are qualified to handle your own property in the professional manner that will bring about the best results. There are usually only a few good prospects for each property, and you can't afford to lose any of them.

Q. Why should anyone grant an "exclusive right-to-sell listing"?

A. As a general rule, the most professional real estate agency will work only with exclusive right-to-sell listing contracts. The reason is that these firms take their employment very seriously. When they list a property, they bring all of their resources into play in order to see that it is sold. This may mean extensive research of market data, professional preparation of detailed sales brochures, distribution of sales literature, erection of signs, and literally hundreds of hours of professional manpower devoted to the sale of this property.

Despite the agent's best efforts, not every property that he works with will sell. This means that those properties that do must pay for the time and expense devoted to all properties. This time and expense will no doubt exceed many thousands of dollars in the sale of a major property.

Q. I understand the advantages of motivating a broker by giving him an exclusive listing. However, I have two very good local brokers I want to have work on the sale of my land. What would you recommend?

A. Often, a good alternative is to give "cooperative exclusive" listings to two or more brokers working cooperatively. This way you have combined the talents of both firms. Usually, they are satisfied to work under this arrangement, and frequently work out an agreement whereby they will each share in a sales commission, regardless of who sells the property. They might do this under a method whereby the broker who actually procures the buyer would get 60% to 75% of the commission and the other firm would receive 25% to 40% of the commission. In this way, they are assured that they will receive something for their efforts, even if they are not successful in acting as the procuring cause.

Q. I've decided to sell my half-section of farmland. I told all the brokers in town that I would consider selling at $1,000 per acre "net" to me. Won't this get action for me?

A. Probably not. Whatever action does take place may be bad. First, no-one had an exclusive listing. Thus, no single agency is working on your property with reasonable assurance that they are going to get paid for their efforts. Next time you have a load of livestock for sale, try telling your local sale barn what you want "net" for your animals, and see how quickly they tell you to put 'em back in your truck.

Q. But won't I save commission using a net price?

A. A bigger problem with "net" deals is that your property may have as many prices as there are agents. For example, Broker "A" decides he'll just tack on a 3% commission and hope somebody stumbles in the door so that it doesn't require much work. So, he's asking $1,030 per acre. Broker "B" had a set policy of 6%, so his price is $1,060 per acre. Broker "C" decides he may want to refer this to a broker in another city, thus requiring a split of commission, so he ups the price 10%, making it $1,100 per acre. Thus, there is no single asking price. If you want to turn off a good prospect, just let him hear of three different prices on the same property.

Q. I told my broker that I would take $100,000 net for my land. However, now he has a buyer who is willing to pay $150,000, and because I have given him my net listing he expects to keep $50,000. Is this fair?

A. First, let's hope that you learned that a net listing is not such a good idea. It puts undue restrictions on the broker. Secondly, net listings are conducive to fraud, and should generally be avoided. A number of states prohibit the use of net listings. Other states may rule that a broker may not receive more than a customary commission as a fair return for his services, holding that a broker may not collect an unconscionable amount.

Q. I am willing to sign a listing contract and the broker wants the contract to run for 12 months. Is this reasonable?

A. Twelve months is probably too long. Unless this is such a unique property that you could honestly expect it to take a year or two to find the right buyer, most property should be sold within 6 months.

If the property doesn't sell within 6 months, then it is either over-priced, underexposed, or you are simply in a very bad market situation. Anything less than a 6-month period is probably too short. Rest assured that the broker, too, wants the property to sell quickly. However, by the time an advertising program is developed, and all of the information is properly gathered and distributed, 6 months goes by quickly.

Q. Who sets the price, the broker or me?

A. Actually, this should be a consensus of opinion. Both the broker and you should be aware of, and unbiased toward, all comparable sales that have occurred on similar property. A good rule of thumb is to set the price at 10% more than what the property should sell for to a willing and able buyer from a willing and able seller. There is no single price for a piece of property. Five different buyers can look at the same piece of property and have five substantially different opinions as to what they would pay. Thus, make reasonably certain that you, as an owner, don't leave any money on the table, but also provide assurance that buyers won't ignore the property because it is priced out of reason.

Q. What is the normal rate of commission for selling farm property?

A. There is no "normal" commission rate. Organized real estate trade associations are prohibited by law from suggesting uniform commission rates. Commission rates will range from 3% to 10% of the gross proceeds of the sale. A 10% rate will apply to smaller properties, such as those $150,000 and under in price, or to properties that are particularly difficult to sell. In my opinion, 10% is too high for large farm or land properties. If the broker receives a 6% commission for selling a $500,000 property, or $30,000, he has been adequately compensated.

There is no law that says the commission must be a single percentage rate. The owner could make an arrangement that, in the event the broker was the only agent involved in the sale, he would receive a 4% commission. In the event two brokers were involved in the sale, the owner would agree to pay a 6% commission. In the event the owner sold the property himself, he may still agree to pay the broker a token commission--for example--2% .

Q. My implement dealer referred to me the person who turned out to be the buyer for my land. Now he has implied that he expects a fee for finding me a buyer. What is the proper way to handle this?

A. First of all, assuming that your implement dealer does not hold a real estate license, it would be illegal for you to pay him a fee, and technically illegal for him to ask for, or receive a fee. This obviously eliminates any obligation that he may think you have. If he does hold a real estate license, unless you had employed him to sell your property, you still would not be obligated to pay him a commission.

Q. What real estate services require a license?

A. This varies by state law. However, a license is generally required for all or most of the following real estate activities:

- Sale
- Exchange
- Purchase
- Rental
- Leasing
- Lending
- Appraising

Some states require separate licenses for the handling of mortgages, and for the sale of personal property, such as selling a business.

Q. Two months ago I saw my friend, Mr. Broker, at the bank and I told him that if he found a buyer for my property at a price of $200,000, I'd pay him a 5% commission. It kind of slipped my mind, but today he brought me an offer from a buyer for the full price, and it is payable in cash. I have changed my mind about selling. Do I have to sell, and if I refuse to accept the offer, is Mr. Broker still due a commission?

A. If you live in a state where an oral listing is valid (and it is in most states), then you do indeed owe Mr. Broker a commission. When the broker obtains a qualified buyer upon your terms, he is entitled to the agreed commission. This is true even though you may have changed your mind about selling and refuse to sign a sales contract. You have no obligation to actually sell the property to the buyer.

Q. Even though I am giving my broker an oral listing, he wants it in writing. This seems unnecessary; what do you think?

A. First, your state law may require that the listing be in writing to be valid. In any event, a written listing limits misunderstandings and thus is beneficial to both parties. The listing should contain a description of the property, terms of the sale that the owner will accept, commission to be paid, and length of listing. Both parties should sign the listing agreement. A letter from one party, with the receiving party acknowledging receipt of the letter and its terms, is satisfactory in most cases.

An exclusive right-to-sell agreement is shown on the following page.

DOANE

LISTING AGREEMENT

Doane Agricultural Service, Inc. / 8900 Manchester Road / St. Louis, Missouri 63144   _____ , 19____

    In consideration of the agreement of DOANE AGRICULTURAL SERVICE, INC. hereinafter referred to as DOANE, to endeavor to procure a purchaser therefor, I for myself and my heirs and assigns hereby appoint DOANE, sole and exclusive agent for a period of_____months, ending_____19____, to sell property described as:

_____

_____

_____

_____

consisting of_____acres more or less, for a total price of_____

($_____) or for any other price to which I shall consent.

    If during the term of this listing, DOANE shall produce a purchaser ready, willing and able to purchase for the above price, or if said property shall be contracted by me to be sold to or exchanged with any person procured either by DOANE or by me, or by any other person, or if within an additional term of_____months, the property is contracted to be sold to or exchanged with anyone contacted by DOANE within the first period, I will pay said DOANE a_____% commission on the total selling or exchange price. This commission shall be a lien on the property and on earnest money until paid.

GENERAL CONDITIONS:

    1. Owners agree to furnish title insurance or a complete abstract showing merchantable title and will convey said property if and when sold by a good and sufficient Warranty Deed.

    2. Owners agree to pay owners' share of attorney's fees for preparation of Contract, Warranty Deed, and other necessary legal papers required of seller in a sale transaction.

    3. The owners to pay in full all State and County taxes and assessments, general and special, which are a lien on said property except taxes for this calendar year which shall be prorated as of the date of delivery of the deed, or in the alternative, the owners agree to pay the taxes until _____ . If the amount of taxes cannot be ascertained, proration shall be computed on the amount of general taxes for the preceding calendar year.

    4. DOANE is hereby authorized by the owners to accept a deposit to be applied on the purchase price and to place said deposit in DOANE'S escrow account until the transaction is consummated or terminated.

    5. Owners hereby authorize DOANE to co-broker the sale of this property or to list property in multiple listing services and further authorize DOANE or its representatives to place "For Sale" signs on the property and to remove all other signs, and to advertise said property in any manner deemed wise by DOANE.

    The owners acknowledge that the efforts and endeavors of DOANE to procure a purchaser through advertising, co-brokers or otherwise, shall constitute good and sufficient consideration for this agreement.

    It is understood and agreed that the properties listed below are not to be considered as a part of the property and their value is not included in the listed price of the property.

Portable Buildings _____ ____   Other Property_____

_____   _____

Crops _____   _____

_____   _____

LISTING ACCEPTED   _____
                                                    OWNER/AGENT/OFFICER*
DOANE Agricultural Service, Inc. Broker   _____
                                                                ADDRESS
By_____   _____
                          TITLE   OWNER/AGENT/OFFICER*
                                                    _____
                                                                ADDRESS

    * As an agent or corporate officer I warrant that I am authorized by appropriate corporate resolution or agency appointment (or power of attorney) to list the above described property for sale under the conditions set forth in this agreement and further agree to furnish such authorization upon request.

FORM 27A REV. 11-73

Q. My son-in-law spoke to the real estate agency about selling my property. Now, one of the salesmen has a buyer for it, and claims that if I am not willing to sell he will sue me for a commission. This doesn't seem right.

A. The reason it doesn't seem right is because it isn't. The agent failed to do his homework as to who actually owned the property. The broker will probably find that his lawsuit for commission is futile, unless he can prove that your son-in-law actually had authority to offer the property for sale. If he wishes, he might try suing your son-in-law for misrepresentation, but his chances of collecting may not be too good.

Q. I told my broker the basis on which I would sell my property, and he has indeed found a buyer. Even though I promised to pay him a commission, I didn't realize that the buyer was going to be my next-door neighbor. I know him much better than the broker does, and I see no reason why I should have to pay the broker a commission for bringing me a buyer who would have bought the property anyway.

A. When you hired the broker, you didn't exclude your next-door neighbor from being a purchaser. The broker has a commission due. Be happy that the property sold.

Q. My broker's exclusive listing on my farm runs out in about 2 weeks. He had shown it to my neighbor, who later came by to see me. My neighbor is interested in buying the property, but he suggested that we wait until the listing expires and split the amount I save by not paying a commission. I would like to save the money but this doesn't seem right. What do you think?

A. That is fraud, my friend. The broker is entitled to a commission because he placed a buyer in touch with your property during the term of the listing. That's called "procuring cause". Chances are that if you waited long enough after the listing expired, you might get by with it. But it's still illegal and unethical. Is it worth it?

Q. This broker contends that he referred a prospect to my property and wants a commission. In fact, he has threatened to put a lis pendens - a lien - on the property. I never employed this broker, but I don't want my land tied up in litigation. Should I settle?

A. Talk to your attorney. In many states, a real estate broker is specifically prohibited from filing a lien for commission. Even if the broker was hired, and had earned a commission, normally the only course open to him would be to file suit and obtain a judgment. The broker is usually prohibited from blocking the sale to anyone.

Q. I was convinced by my broker to sell at a price lower than I considered fair. Now I find that the buyer and broker are partners in the ownership of my land. Do I have recourse for my complaint?

A. Absolutely. Full disclosure is an absolute necessity for a broker of property. He has a fiduciary responsibility (in most states) when it comes to dealing with his client. Most modern brokers like to think of themselves as professionals, and the courts agree that brokers must be ethical and competent. Among the things that a broker can't do are:

1. Buy for his own account without the knowledge and consent of the seller.
2. Be disloyal to his principal (usually the seller).
3. Fail to transmit all offers to his client.
4. Misrepresent the property to the buyer.
5. Engage in the unauthorized practice of law.
6. Mix client accounts with personal accounts.

CHAPTER **6**

Those Final Negotiations

A good negotiator has an advantage when buying and selling land. Business schools have recognized the importance of negotiating skills. Courses and seminars are offered regularly on "The Art of Negotiating." It may be an art form. More likely it's a style or technique used to persuade.

The Statute of Frauds, which requires that enforceable real estate agreements must be in writing, evolved because of the need for a buyer and seller to reach firm agreement regarding price and terms. The real estate contract is a culmination of a "meeting of the minds", which is always preceded by *final negotiations*.

A successful negotiator does not follow a rigid style. He is not necessarily glib, articulate, tough, soft spoken, harsh, demanding, agreeable, unyielding, patient, pushy or smooth. Yet, during a long negotiation, he may be any or all of these things, at the appropriate time.

In any negotiation, there is no substitute for knowledge. A buyer or seller must know the parameters of when a deal ceases to be a good one for his purposes. I've had partners and clients who don't understand why I won't even consider certain parcels of land--yet in other cases I'm willing to pay the full asking price and terms.

With knowledge, an equally important talent is the ability to read and understand people. People are a product of their environment, education, and experience. There is generally no problem dealing with a person who knows as much or more than you about land deals. It's in dealing with someone who knows less that problems occur.

Know when to stop negotiating. Certain people will always negotiate "past the close". Here are a few personality types that can be found in the real estate arena:

- *The Never Enough Type* - Every time he's satisfied with one concession, he finds another reason to delay. He'll reword a paragraph; want to close ten days later. He never can commit himself. To deal with Mr. Never Enough, be tough. Set the deal, give him 24 hours to commit. He'll be back, so keep one concession open that doesn't affect the deal. Offer it at the right time, and he may take it.

- *The Bargain Type* - Would rather pay 50% too much for a property where he can get 20% reduced from the asking price than pay the asking price on a property offered at 20% below market value. Don't try to deal with him on the basis of knowledge.

- *The Chop-Chop Type* - Wants to make sure he's not leaving any profit in the deal, or money on the table. He's afraid the next buyer--or last seller--will make a profit. Concentrate on pointing out the benefits to him. He's greedy, so capitalize on his avarice.

- *The Bashful Type* - You can never tell what stage he's in, or if he's interested at all. Can't pull the trigger. Give him time to make up his mind. Be patient and helpful. Keep making suggestions to him.

- *The Nervous Type* - Can't stay with a deal. Needs constant reassurance--provided by someone else. Never does his own investigation. You just have to catch him on the right day. Be casual. Review all of the positive sides of the deal.

- *The Strong Silent Type* - He's usually listening; knows that the last word is the best word. He's generally dealing from a position of strength. Speak softly and firmly. He respects strength. Deal in facts. Get him to agree to something.

- *The Erratic Type* - Makes his deal as he goes along; unpredictable. Make it a point to list all of the areas of agreement, and repeat them from time to time.

- *The Lawyer Type* - Finds some reason not to agree. His client or partner is always his 'out'. Let him deal with your lawyer.

- *The Greedy Type* - Wants concessions on every point. Stay with him--he'll usually outsmart himself.

- *The Mousetrap Type* - With superior knowledge, lets you think you won. Be well informed. Let him suggest the price. Get a commitment of some kind, and build from that.

- **The Sneaky Type** - Doesn't help make deal; lets you do it; then takes advantage of any weaknesses you've opened up. Don't make the first concession.

- **The Arrogant Type** - Related to the lawyer type, his opinions are beyond question. Impossible to convince him with reason because his mind's already made up. May be the most difficult to deal with, but the least dangerous adversary, because he not only tells all he knows, but more. Eager to impress. Play to his ego. Exchange concessions, and protect yourself by improving your position every time you agree with one of his demands.

A Negotiation Checklist

The most pleasant and rewarding negotiations are where parties involved follow most of these articles:

-Negotiate from knowledge, not just from instinct.
-Negotiate from reason, not from emotion.
-Negotiate from trust, not from suspicion.
-Negotiate with subtleties, not with bravado.
-Negotiate from strength, not bluff.
-Negotiate with consistency, not erratically.

GETTING DEALS STARTED

Q. The prospect has offered to buy a piece of property. He has signed a purchase contract, put up earnest money, and the contract has been mailed to the owner. Now, he is having second thoughts. Is it too late for the buyer to call the deal off?

A. No. An offer can be withdrawn by the buyer at any time prior to acceptance. To properly withdraw his offer, he must immediately notify the seller. Even if the seller had signed the contract and accepted the offer, if his acceptance had not been communicated to the buyer prior to his withdrawal of the offer, buyer should be entitled to a refund of his deposit and be relieved of any further obligations of the transaction.

Many printed contracts--and some narrative contracts--will specify that the seller has a certain period of time in which to accept the offer. The language may explicitly say:

"Buyer agrees that this offer is irrevocable until May____, 19__."

Not true. The buyer is simply not obligated to keep his offer open until the designated date.

This type of situation may frequently result in a dispute concerning the earnest money. If a broker is holding the money, he will find himself in the middle of diametrically opposite viewpoints. If the broker is wise, he will pay the money into court, or follow the rules and regulations established by the real estate licensing agency of his state.

Q. What is the proper way for a buyer to submit the first offer . . .orally, or in writing?

A. Because the personalities and motives of the principals involved will always be entirely different, there is no single correct way to submit an offer. Assume you are the buyer, and you are relatively indifferent about the property. That is, it's only one of several properties you are considering, and you would move on this one only if the price was too good to pass up. In this case your thought process might go like this:

> "The property is 100 acres--a little big for me. He wants $1,200 per acre--I like the land a mile south better at $1,100 per acre. But, this is a good buy at $1,000. I think he wants to sell badly, so I'll offer $800 per acre, with him carrying a second mortgage. On that basis I can't lose. I could always resell it for a quick profit."

Since this is a frivolous offer--one you don't think he'll accept--it may not call for a formal offer. Here is where a broker can pass along the information in a helpful manner, and get an informal reaction from the owner without offending anyone.

A *letter of intent* may be the right method by which to approach a particular seller. This recital of proposed agreement demonstrates a serious intent about the property, without entering into a formal contract or offer to purchase. For example, I may represent a buyer by submitting a letter of intent, shown on the following page.

LETTER OF INTENT

December___, 198_

Mr. Ralph A. Nonnamuss
2433 Downtha Street
Southov, Florida

Dear Mr. Nonnamuss:

The Soicoren Corporation has asked us to convey their interest
in acquiring your 320 acre property in Section 12, T125, R49E.

Subject to your expression of approval, it is their intent to
enter into a formal offer to purchase on the following terms
and conditions:

  1. Price: $1,500 per acre, or $480,000.00.

  2. Terms:

       a. 5%, or $24,000 at contract.

       b. 20% or $96,000 additional at closing.

       c. Balance of $360,000 payable at the rate of
           $20,000 principal, plus interest, annually
           for nine years from date of closing.

       d. The balance of $180,000 due and payable in
           the tenth year.

       e. Interest at the annual rate of 9%, payable
           semi-annually.

  3. A thirty-day contingent period from contract, during
      which time buyer may conduct soil tests, drill for
      irrigation water feasibility, and conduct other
      analytical tests. At the end of thirty days, buyer
      may request the refund of the earnest money, and
      the contract is null and void; or proceed with the
      contract as drawn.

  4. Customary closing conditions to be part of the
      formal contract.

Please advise us of your reaction to their offer.

Sincerely,

Dwight W. Jundt
Registered Real Estate Broker

There are sellers whose attention you cannot get without a formal contract or offer to purchase, accompanied by a check. This technique of submitting a formal contract at the outset may also be useful if you wish to make one firm offer, and one only. A show of preparation may convince a seller of the buyer's credibility and conclude a deal where none was possible under other conditions. Occasionally, sellers have been hassled by lookers and talkers and are ready to do business only with the serious customer who has done his homework.

Q. *What are the advantages and disadvantages of an option?*

A. In an option, the advantages nearly all lie with the buyer. An agreement of sale constitutes agreement and obligation of both parties (usually). In an option, the optionor (seller) gives certain rights to the optionee (buyer). The optionee now is free to use those rights, or leave them alone, in which case an option becomes null and void on its expiration date.

An option in real estate is simply a contract by which an owner gives another person the right to buy at a fixed price under specified terms within a given time. The buyer may agree to pay the seller a certain amount of money, called the "option consideration", for these rights.

Normally, the purpose of an option is to allow the interested potential buyer to satisfy certain doubts or secure certain information during the option period. For example, a buyer of a dryland farm may wish the right to make well borings to determine the availability of irrigation water. Financing may be the key to a purchase and will require time gained through an option in order to submit a loan application.

A developer will normally require time to accomplish all of the following:

1. Soil borings and other engineering studies
2. Financing
3. Zoning, platting, and other solutions to government regulations
4. Market and other feasibility studies to determine the economic propriety of the development.

The advantage to the buyer, of course, is a period of time to investigate. A speculative buyer may also take an option and attempt to resell or "flip" the property within the option period, thus realizing a good profit on a low-risk, low capital investment.

The advantage to the seller may be two-fold:

1. The option consideration may be substantial enough to be meaningful in the event the buyer forfeits the payment and does not exercise his option. This is not likely, however. Most buyers are not willing to pay more than a nominal option consideration. The longer the period of the option, the higher the payment should be.

2. Granting an option may be the only way to convince a buyer that he should purchase the property. For example, a developer would prefer to ignore a piece of property rather than enter into a firm contract to purchase something upon which he does not have full information. With unanswered questions, a property, apparently ripe for development, may only bring $5,000 per acre. With the answers in place, a developer may pay $10,000 per acre.

Q. What is a customary "option consideration?"

A. There are no firm guidelines regarding the amount of payment to be made in return for granting an option. While the option requires a consideration to make it valid, the consideration may be as nominal as $10. In fact, if the option recites a consideration of $1, that is sufficient, even though it has not actually been paid.

Normally, the option amount reflects a certain element of logic. For example, if the buyer wants to take the property off the market during the peak or most logical selling time, he should expect to be required to make a more valuable consideration. On the other hand, if there was little likelihood of a sale during the option period, then the minimum consideration might be in order. For example, if I owned a country estate worth $100,000, and it was autumn when many potential buyers want to look at property, I would probably want an option consideration of at least $5,000 to take the property off the market for 90 days. My reasoning would be that if I were going to remove the property from the market for the period of October 1 to December 31, I would actually be losing at least 6 months good selling time because there would not be many of these buyers out looking again until April 1. On the other hand, if the buyer wanted to have a 30-day option during February, I might give him an option for $500.

Sometimes the consideration for granting an option will be the requirement that the buyer conduct certain tests or studies on the property which have a value to buyer or seller. For example, let's say a developer wants to run extensive engineering tests on your property. He may spend $25,000 investigating soil conditions, drainage, costs to fill the property, costs to put in sewers and water, etc. The consideration for your granting him the option may be the right to receive all of this information at the end of the option period in the event that he does not exercise his option.

The seller must be cautious. A buyer may state that he intends to run extensive tests and spend exhaustive amounts of money during his investigation, when, in fact, all he wants to do is to take the property off the market while he can find a buyer who will pay a higher price and turn a quick profit on his deal. To guard against this, a seller may wish to specify that the buyer must spend at least "X" amount of dollars in his investigatory work or forfeit an agreed-upon option consideration. The option may also be made non-assignable. Notes and mortgages may be structured without assignability.

An optionee may want a series of options. It is reasonable that one set of investigations will lead to another set of investigations if, in fact, everything is found to be satisfactory. In that case, there may be an option consideration paid at time of execution; an additional amount to extend the option 30 days, an additional amount to extend the option for another 30 days, and on ad infinitum.

Q. How can I, as the seller, be certain that a proper sale contract will be entered into if the optionee does exercise the option?

A. At the time the option is entered into, the complete agreement of sale upon which the transaction is based should either be embodied in the option agreement, or attached to the option agreement, and made a part thereof. Too often, a seller and buyer will enter into a simple option agreement which does not contain all of the necessary terms and conditions of a normal sale contract. This may cause an otherwise satisfactory agreement to fail. Be certain that the contract, by reference or otherwise, encompasses all of the details of the agreement in a manner that is satisfactory if and when the option is exercised.

Q. I need time to arrange my financing, but options seem to be a "dirty word" in this area. How else can I buy some time?

A. Try a contingent contract. For some reason many sellers simply will not grant an option. Probably, this is because it would appear that the buyer was getting something for nothing. Perhaps the idea of a unilateral contract simply does not appeal to most people. Human nature is such that people don't mind giving as long as they receive something.

Contingent contracts are more acceptable to sellers. By this I mean that you enter into a standard agreement of sale, reciting all of the customary provisions. However, in the body of the contract you cite contingent conditions of closing. A typical clause would be as follows:

"This contract is contingent upon the ability of the buyer to secure satisfactory financing within 30 days of the execution. In the event that said financing is not available, the earnest money previously referred to will be returned to the purchaser and this contract will be considered null and void."

The above is obviously an open-end clause which allows the buyer total flexibility and does not require him to put up an option consideration. Since this is essentially a free option, the contingent contract is not only more favorable to the purchaser than an option, but is also much more readily acceptable than the option. The clause above could be tightened to specify the amount of the financing, and the terms of the interest rate, repayment, and other ingredients of the loan.

The well-informed seller will want the right to satisfy certain of the buyer's contingencies himself. In other words, to insure that the buyer is not getting a free period of time to take the property off the market, the seller may want the right to obtain or otherwise provide financing for the buyer, perhaps even through his own mortgage, in order to facilitate the sale.

Financing is only one of the contingencies that a buyer may desire. All of the reasons that may cause a buyer to want an option are also valid for the contingent contract. The contract may also be contingent upon something required of the seller, such as rezoning. In this event, the buyer may wish to insure that he has the right to waive the satisfaction of the contingency. This is for his protection in the event that the seller does not want to go through with the contract and is looking for a reason to void the contract. The following words would be in order:

"In the event this condition is not satisfied by the required date, the purchaser has the right to waive this contingency and accept the property as is."

Q. Does every seller expect to negotiate his asking price?

A. Not necessarily. Some sellers go to great length to establish what they consider to be the proper price of the property, and that's what they expect to get for it. They may be offended by someone who insists on making what they would consider to be an insulting offer. As in most fields of endeavor, if you're going to be successful in the real estate business you must understand the motivations and unique traits of people. Otherwise you are going to end up treating people in a manner that might alienate them from your objectives. Unless you, as a buyer, are particularly adept at negotiating, you are well advised to be represented by a professional negotiator in the form of a highly qualified broker or other individual.

There is that class of buyer, too, who arbitrarily insists that unless he is able to get the seller to reduce his asking price, he is not going to buy the property. Typically, it is this kind of buyer who is unable to recognize a true value when he sees it. The bargain hunter may be happier paying 50% too much for a property that he's gotten reduced in price as compared to getting an exceptional bargain at the original asking price. It's the same old story: the bulls make money; the bears make money; and the pigs go broke.

This doesn't mean that a buyer shouldn't attempt to negotiate a sale price. It is true that many sellers will add 10% to 20% or more to what they expect to accept on the basis that most buyers do want to negotiate a price reduction before they will be happy. The important point is to recognize your adversary's nature and be able to respond to it effectively.

Q. I don't completely like the first offer for my land; should I make a counteroffer, or let the buyer continue on the offensive?

A. First, recognize that if you have a bona fide offer for your property, you have the right to accept it by signing the offer, and you have a binding transaction. In the event that you make a counteroffer, you have voided the original offer and cannot go back to it in the event your counteroffer is not accepted.

Once you make a counteroffer, the purchaser is no longer obligated to honor his original offer. Let's say that you've been offered $90,000. You've been asking $110,000 and really want to get $100,000. Now you have a decision to make.

Should you reduce your asking price to $105,000 and hope that you'll end up with $100,000, or is it possible that you'll scare your buyer away and you would be better off to go directly to $100,000 on the counteroffer? This is a judgment you're going to have to make. An alternative is to make a counteroffer for $105,000, but offer an additional concession such as lowering your purchase money mortgage interest rate one percentage point. Perhaps you can include some personal property with the sale. In other words, it all comes down to how anxious you are to make the deal; how long the property has been on the market; and your ability to gauge the interest of your buyer.

Recognize that human nature is strange. I recall one of the first farms I bought. It was 365 acres and owned by an elderly couple. They were asking $165 an acre. The property was in a rundown condition, but I thought there was potential to do some renovation and repairs and have a valuable piece of merchandise. I was a little embarrassed to offer $100 per acre, but I considered that we would conclude negotiations at approximately $130 an acre and everyone would be happy. Much to my surprise, the offer of $100 per acre was accepted immediately. How did I feel? Instead of jubilation at buying the property for much less than I expected, my first reaction was that maybe I offered too much and left some money on the table. And I'm in the business! I should know better than to be greedy in making a deal. But that's human nature!

WAYS TO GET A DEAL OFF DEAD CENTER

Q. We're close to concluding a deal, but seem to have reached an impasse. How can I get negotiations underway again and get the property bought?

A. If you both have gone as far as you can on the price, then move away from the price and start negotiating on some terms. My philosophy has always been, "If I can't buy at my price, then I want to buy on my terms." In other words, I'm willing to pay a much higher price for most properties, if I can get the terms that I want. Or, I'm willing to pay cash if I can get the price that I want.

But let's talk about terms, because you have more options to work with. You can be more flexible without affecting the end result. For example, assume that you're the buyer. So far you've agreed to:

1. A 29% downpayment.
2. Assumption of an existing mortgage for another 51%.
3. Giving the seller a second mortgage of 20% of the purchase price.

It may very well be worth paying the price if the seller will agree to accept a 25% downpayment, and carry a mortgage equal to 24% of the sale price. You might try increasing the interest rate by 1% per annum. Maybe you can make it worth your while to decrease the period of principal payments from 15 years to a period of 10 years. Try buying some of the personal property at a price that will make the sale of the farm more attractive to the seller. The important thing is that you are close to a deal and you're down to those final negotiations. If you really want the property, don't let a minor consideration stand in your way. If you don't want the property, then simply pass and go about your business of finding one that you're satisfied you can agree upon.

Q. How can several prospective buyers for the same property be handled in a fair manner, yet yield the highest price and most favorable terms?

A. Irony is a part of land dealing. Many times a property languishes on the market for no apparent reason. It's priced right, has good exposure, has been advertised, is desirable. Yet, not a serious prospect has appeared. Suddenly, four qualified buyers show up in 2 weeks time!

So what is so bad about having four buyers?

The seller is an ethical man with longstanding tenure in his community; he is known as a man of his word. The deal was well along with Buyer A before B, C, and D came along. In fact, he had told Buyer A to have the contract drawn up.

Let's say, however, that the asking price was $300,000. Buyer A would go no higher than $250,000, which the seller had about decided to take since no other offers had been forthcoming.

Along comes Buyer B. The broker tells him that a contract is being drawn. Until it is executed by both parties, however, the broker is obligated to submit all offers. Buyer B says he'll pay $275,000.

The seller wants to be fair, but can't afford to turn down a $25,000 higher offer. Buyer A says he'll match the offer.

Along comes Buyer C. He wants to pay $275,000, and will increase the downpayment from 20% to 29%.

Along comes Buyer D. He'll pay $280,000--all cash.

Now the seller really feels like a bad guy. (He also feels good!) The broker is concerned that he's going to end up with three people angry with him, and a reputation of turning negotiations into an auction. Both the seller and the broker realize that unless negotiations are handled delicately, some of the buyers may walk away from the deal.

The buyers all insist that their latest offer is their final offer . . . but want the opportunity to renegotiate. They all want to make the last offer. None of them want to get into the auction.

Here are several choices for the seller:

1. Simply decide on one of the offers on the basis of friendship or another less technical reason.
2. Actually hold an auction, opening the bidding to all parties. Many buyers, particularly those who want to buy on a specific set of terms, may pass, preferring private treaty negotiations.
3. Sealed bids, on one or more specific sets of terms, may be the answer, although this method is seldom used. If there are four buyers, one buyer could be eliminated on the first opening; another on a second opening; and let it go to the remaining two interested parties for final disposition. This method allows for greater flexibility, and should result in the most money to the seller.

Q. The deal is too big for me. How can I buy part of it?

A. Resell part of the property before you buy it. Say you're farming a half section, and the adjoining quarter is coming up for sale. You need and want it, but can't quite handle it financially.

Go to a neighbor, or an investor, and split it with him. An investor is probably better, because he'll rent it to you while you keep the benefits of farming it. If you go to your neighbor, though, you may avoid a bidding war. Just remember: part is better than none.

Most sellers will be accommodating enough to take a property off the market for a few days if the buyer has shown sincere interest. This allows time to firm up the possible split, or resale.

Q. The seller needs an edge. What else can I offer him?

A. Offer to let the seller participate in a resale profit.

I recently had an institutional owner (a bank) express interest in selling a tract of raw land, which had some development future in the next 3 to 5 years. To hold a piece of ground for this period, an investor must look for three features: a fair price, reasonable terms, and a chance of the property doubling in value in 3 years.

We weren't far apart on the price. We were willing to pay $1,200,000. They wanted $1,300,000. As to down payment, we wanted to hold it to 15%; they wanted 20%.

Since the prime interest rate was at 10.25%, they wanted 12%. This was completely out of line, eating up too much profit, and costing too much to hold.

At an impasse, my suggestion was for the seller to receive 20% of the profit on resale to a developer, and accept the following:

Price:	*$1,200,000, including a $50,000 commission*
Down Payment:	*15% ($180,000) at time of closing, then interest only payable semi-annually, with a balloon note to the seller coming due in 4 years.*
Interest Rate:	$7^3/4\%$
Profit Participation:	*Seller participate in 20% net profit on resale.*

This solution should allow the seller to obtain an overall yield in excess of the 12% interest they were seeking, and still allow our investment group to acquire a property with a manageable cost of carry.

Q. The farmer wants to sell but doesn't want to pay taxes. What can I do?

A. Very often as the city moves out into the country, the farmer has good news and bad news. The bad news is:

a. His neighbors and old friends are moving farther out.
b. Hired help is hard to get because of the supply of better paying jobs with shorter hours in the city.
c. Moving his machinery and livestock on the road has become extremely hazardous because of heavy local traffic.
d. He needs to expand but land prices are 300% of agricultural value.

The good news is:

a. His land is now worth enough to purchase a farm three times as big 50 miles out.
b. A developer wants to buy the land, and Mr. Brown would sell, except that his Capital Gains Tax would be so high as to be ridiculous.

The answer: make a trade. The developer may have to be the catalyst to find Mr. Brown substitute property. The substitute property can be exchanged for the land the developer wants.

Q. I have good income, but I'm short on equity, and don't want to borrow on other land because interest rates are too high. How can I sweeten the deal for the seller?

A. Two ways, at least. Since you own other land, offer to put up a portion of it for security on this new purchase. The seller should feel more comfortable about the lower downpayment because of your increased incentive to make future payments.

Secondly, you may need to make the price more attractive. If you can negotiate a reasonable interest rate with the seller, increasing the price by 5% will probably make the deal fly.

Q. I'm a developer. The best buy around is a farm, not now zoned for development, but the owner won't give me an option. How can I convince him I'm serious, but must have time to rezone it?

A. Work out a schedule of events which you must follow to keep your option alive. Say it's January 1. Agree that by March 1 you wil have surveyed the property and made submission for rezoning. The next trigger date might be April 1 for first reading before the Planning & Zoning Board; May 1 for second reading; and June 1 for final approval. If you miss any of the dates, your option expires.

Secondly, plug in periodic option payments which will be retained by the seller in the event you require extensions. Be sure, however, to give yourself enough time.

Q. I've negotiated the best deal I can to buy this farm on an installment basis, but I'm concerned that my cash is stretched too thin in case of a bad year. If I miss a payment, forfeiture will occur. How can I get relief?

A. Not uncommon is a "relief provision". Let's say you have a 20-year contract with the seller. See if he will agree to a provision allowing you to defer payment once or twice during the life of the contract. Most farmer-sellers appreciate the risks of poor prices or crop failures, and may be willing to allow such a clause.

Q. My cousin owns 160 acres I really want. He's ready to retire, but really isn't ready to sell. How can I improve my opportunity to buy it?

A. Lease the land from him for cash rent. Pay him a premium--more than he could expect from someone else. For this favor, get a right-of-first-refusal. In other words, your cousin still owns it--can sell when he wants--he's not locked into a price, but you will get notified when it's for sale. As the tenant, you will be the first to know, anyway. Very important thing about a right-of-first-refusal. It discourages anyone else from getting serious, because a prospect knows that whatever he does, he may still not end up with the property.

CHAPTER 7

Agreement of Purchase and Sale

The agreement of purchase and sale, commonly referred to as the sale contract, is the controlling document in a transaction. Since it is the single most important consideration, careful input is required before signing the document. In many respects, this agreement is more important than the deed.

Many times friends have called me to say, "I signed a contract to purchase a piece of property. Would you look at it to see if I've done the right thing?"

At that point, it's usually too late to look at the contract, or the property. What's done is done. A contract binds the parties to the bargain they have made. The seller cannot renege, or sell to someone who offers more money, without facing the penalties provided for in the contract. The buyer is bound to go through with the deal on the terms agreed to in the contract.

The contract may itself take on value. It becomes personal property which may be bought and sold. Anyone dealing in real estate must, of necessity, have a working knowledge of contracts.

A sale contract that is carelessly drawn frequently leads to misunderstanding and disagreement. Expensive litigation may follow and results in monetary losses to all parties concerned.

Essential Elements of a Sale Contract

1. A contract must be in *legal form* and, in the case of an agreement for the sale of real estate, it must be in writing and signed by the respective parties. More than 300 years ago the British adopted an act called the Statute of Frauds. Most U.S. law has its roots in the English common law, and real estate is covered by this Statute of Frauds, which requires a written memorandum to be enforceable. Rare exceptions to this requirement involve such matters as fraud, inducement, partial performance, and substantial improvements based on an oral contract.

2. *Offer and acceptance,* or mutual assent is a necessary element. This means a meeting of the minds between one party making an offer and the other party accepting the offer.

3. *The competent parties* provision requires that the persons involved must be legally competent. Voidable contracts could include persons who are minors (not of legal age), insane, drunkards, convicted felons, spendthrifts and aged with guardians, or corporations not properly empowered.

4. *Legality of object* means that contracts without a legal purpose are not enforceable. The purpose must not be prohibited by law or contrary to public policy.

5. *Consideration* is that exchange of promise or money that binds the contract. The promise of the seller to convey property in return for the buyer's agreement to pay money is a satisfactory consideration. The earnest money deposit is not the consideration and is not required at time of signing to constitute a valid and enforceable contract.

Q. Must the sale contract be prepared by an attorney, or may my broker handle it?

A. Let's make this two questions:
   1. May a broker legally prepare a sale contract, or must I use an attorney?
   2. Is my broker capable in terms of competence to prepare a sale contract, or should I use an attorney?

Legality: Legal requirements differ by state. The practice of real estate brokerage and the practice of law often tend to infringe upon each other in the area of real estate contracts. Attorneys want as many clients as possible to be required to use their services. Brokers, and often customers, may not want to bring in an attorney because of the time, expense, and inconvenience of another meeting.

Because of this question of jurisdiction, the courts have often had to rule on whether real estate brokers have the right to prepare certain legal documents relating to and affecting real estate, such as contracts, options, notes, mortgages, deeds, leases, etc. Most states, as a minimum, allow a broker to fill in the blanks of a previously approved form contract.

Colorado, for example, has ruled that the preparation of these documents does "constitute the practice of law," but that to require that all transactions be handled by attorneys would not be in the public interest and that the public should be permitted to choose between their broker and attorney in the preparation of documents.

Illinois has ruled that a real estate broker is authorized to fill in the blanks of a printed form commonly in use, may supply factual information for the contract, but may not prepare or complete any subsequent documents necessary to implement the terms of the sale contract.

Competence: Most brokers and salesmen have the necessary training and experience to fill in a sale contract on a single family house, or an uncomplicated cash transaction without contingencies.

Very seldom are land transactions simple. A sale contract should be clear on all matters of notes, mortgages, releases, representations of conditions, etc. Growing crops, livestock, and other personal property may involve substantial dollars and the contract must be specific as to their treatment.

While the conferral of a law degree does not necessarily make an attorney competent to write a good contract, you can rely upon a certain uniformity of training to protect your best interests. It is generally appropriate for the buyer and seller to each be represented by counsel in anything other than a simple cash land transaction. Even then, examination of title by an attorney will normally be required.

A word about the use of attorneys in a real estate transaction. Unless they are also your business advisors, remember that they are involved in the negotiations to help you make the deal, albeit with proper protection. They are not there to be difficult, arrogant, effect road blocks, or impress their clients with their investment knowledge. Many competent attorneys have just enough information on real estate values to be misinformed. Don't hesitate to remind your attorney that he is present to provide legal advice, not business advice. Remember that any deal is seldom risk free. The question usually evolves into what is acceptable business risk and what is not.

Q. Is there a standard form sale contract used for land, farm, and ranch transactions?

A. There is not a standard form because laws and customs vary from area to area on such matters as abstracts versus title insurance, mortgages versus deeds of trust, and customary closing proratins.

The following is a discussion by checklist of the various provisions that may be found in an agreement of sale. It should also serve as a reminder of points to be agreed on during negotiations.

Date: There will normally be a date at the beginning of the contract which indicates when it was prepared. However, there may also be a date at the end of the contract near the signatures of the persons offering and accepting. The date when the contract is truly effective or when the last signature is placed on the contract should be the controlling date. The significance is that if there are contingencies to be eliminated or time periods during which certain functions must be performed, the date that the contract was effective should be the controlling date.

Names of Buyer-Seller: The name of the seller should appear as the same name in which title to the property is held. If the seller is a divorced person, it may now be important to have him provide evidence that he owns the property individually and that he will not have to go back to his previous spouse and obtain the right to sell the property. Normally, this is done after the abstract is examined, but if you have reason to suspect trouble clearing up a title because of this problem, address it now.

If one party is a partnership or corporation, ascertain who has the authority to contract and if that body or individual has actually been properly represented as the principal. Normally, a corporation would be represented by a Board of Directors, but they may have authorized an officer or a committee to buy or sell the property. It is not unreasonable to ask for a true copy of the minutes of the meeting or an appropriate copy of whatever action took place. Similarly, it is important to know whether a partnership is a general partnership or a limited partnership and, as in the case of a corporation, who has the authority to sell and if that authority has been granted.

If the buyer is going to assign the contract or take title in some other name, then his name should appear as follows:

"JOHN DOE, OR ASSIGNS."

Otherwise, a seller may later contend that the contract is not assignable. Many contracts also contain a clause as follows:

"Contract assignable by purchaser, but not without consent of
seller if purchase money mortgage forms a consideration."

Deposit of Earnest Money: In this forepart of the contract, normally only the amount of the earnest money is shown and is tied into the purchase price as follows:

"Received from John T. Smith and Mary A. Smith, his wife, as joint tenants, hereinafter called purchaser, the sum of Four Thousand Dollars ($4,000) as earnest deposit and as part of the cash consideration for the purchase of the following described property situated in.........."

When described in the manner above, this contract also becomes a receipt for earnest money. The disposition of the earnest money is normally handled in a later paragraph of the contract and is tied into various events that could occur in terms of default or failure to provide good title, etc.

The amount of the earnest money deposit is simply a matter of agreement between what the buyer thinks is reasonable to tie up and what the seller thinks is reasonable to have as security for the contract. Unless unusual conditions exist, a deposit is seldom more than 5% of the purchase price. Sometimes the timing of a sale may be critical to the value of a property, in which case a seller might require a much higher deposit, the forfeiture of which would offset real damages due him in the event the buyer failed to close at the appropriate time. In any event, earnest money deposits may be much more or much less than 5%. It is also common to provide for an additional earnest money deposit partway toward closing. This may be tied to the occurrence of an event such as examination of abstract or satisfaction of some contingency, such as rezoning or financing.

The earnest money deposit is normally held by the broker in the transaction in his trust account, an attorney in his trust account, or a title company in its trust account. In a transaction which involves a substantial amount of earnest money several months prior to closing, the parties may agree that the earnest money deposit be paid into an interest-bearing account. It is possible to enter into an escrow agreement with a bank or savings and loan association, appointing the institution as the escrow agent and specifically instructing them on what to do with the earnest money.

Buyers and sellers are entitled to ask that the money be deposited in an interest-bearing account to accrue to the benefit of one or the other, or both. Attorneys and brokers are prone to object to placing the money in an interest-bearing account. Their individual trust accounts—which almost all brokers and attorneys maintain to prevent the co-mingling of client funds with their own funds, usually as prescribed by law—are not allowed to bear interest to the attorney's or broker's benefit.

I have often heard attorneys say that they simply cannot deposit the money in an interest-bearing account because it is "not allowed." It is possible that some states prohibit this by law, but I am not aware of them. Most escrow holders simply do not want to do it because of additional accounting work, possible confusion by the Internal Revenue Service, or pure laziness. In that event, the principals should simply direct that the money be placed in a financial institution or with a title company with the understanding that it be placed into an interest-bearing account.

The earnest money frequently becomes a point of contention as to who will hold the deposit. This is exaggerated. Brokers and attorneys must treat earnest money with the greatest care in order to prevent losing their licenses and, therefore, their livelihood. If there is a dispute over the refund of the earnest money, a well-advised holder of the money will not return the money to either party until the dispute is clearly settled, but will instead apply to a court of law for a ruling on disposition of the funds.

In the event of a default or failure of a buyer to fulfill the sale contract, disposition of the earnest deposit will be governed by agreement contained in the listing contract or the sale contract. A typical arrangement provides for the sharing of the earnest deposit between the seller and the broker, but not to exceed the normal commission to the broker.

Description: While an abbreviated description may be adequate to sufficiently describe the property under scrutiny, it is preferable to include a complete legal description from a previous deed, abstract, or survey. The description given in a land transaction will normally include the size of the property in terms of number of acres. The words, "more or less" are typical and may or may not modify the requirement that a certain amount of land be conveyed. If there is a question about the size of the property, it would be wise to include a statement such as:

"In the event that the property is more or less than 300 acres, the price will be adjusted accordingly at the rate of One Thousand Dollars ($1,000) per acre (sales price). The exact size of the property is to be determined by survey, the cost of which will be borne by buyer (seller)."

In addition to the legal description of the land, there may be a description of the improvements. Normally, the improvements (buildings) are included in the conveyance of the land. Fixtures and portable items may be construed to be personal property or real property. To avoid disputes, list everything that is to be included in the sale price.

While personal property is also frequently described within the body of the sale contract, it is preferable to prepare a separate agreement for the purchase and sale of personal property and evidence the sale of that property by a Bill of Sale.

It is not uncommon, however, to find a statement such as the following included in the contract:

"Together with the improvements thereof and appurtenances, fixtures and equipment thereto belonging, including all lighting, heating, cooling, and plumbing equipment and fixtures and all articles now provided for tenant use, including irrigation pipe, growing crops, and livestock described as follows.........."

Offer Subject to Approval Period: The contract may provide that the offer to purchase is subject to the approval of the seller by a certain date and in the event the seller does not approve by that date, that the earnest money deposit shall be returned to the purchaser. This is to provide some outside date for the acceptance of the contract. It implies, however, that the offer to purchase is an open offer until the date stated. This is not true. The buyer may revoke his offer at any time until such time as the seller has accepted the offer and such acceptance has been communicated to the buyer.

Purchase Price Allocation: A distribution of the purchase price is normally made as follows:

1. Earnest money paid with contract execution.

2. Additional earnest money to be paid by purchaser on some future date.

3. Cash to be paid on closing date of sale.

4. Existing mortgages or deeds of trust of record, subject to which title shall be transferred. Whether the buyer is purchasing the property subject to these debts or assuming them, the total current amount outstanding should be shown and the terms of these instruments should also be described.

5. Mortgages or deeds of trust to be accepted by seller as part purchase money. If the seller is going to "carry" a portion of the purchase price, the amount; terms, including type of loan; interest rate; method of payment; term of years; prepayment privilege, if any; commission, if any; and any special provisions

should be clearly described. For example: "Buyer agrees to give and seller agrees to accept as part of the purchase price a promissory note secured by a first mortgage for the unpaid balance at closing; payable $4,000 principal per year for 12 years, $2,000 principal in the thirteenth year, plus seven percent (7%) interest annually on the unpaid balance, with the first payment being due one year from date of note, with subsequent payments being due on the anniversary date of note until paid. Buyer has the right to prepay principal without penalty at any time."

6. If the agreement of sale is subject to the buyer acquiring financing, the loan should be spelled out in precise terms as to the amount, type, interest rate, repayment schedule, commitment date, and other factors. It is imperative that this not be left open, since it could provide the purchaser with an escape route should he wish to void the contract and get his money back. The seller who wishes to guard against a lost sale as a result of a purchaser's lack of effort to obtain financing may wish to include a clause such as:

"In the event purchaser has been unable to acquire financing as specified by (date), the seller has an additional thirty (30) days to attempt to acquire financing of similar terms and conditions for the buyer or may, as an alternative, agree to carry back financing of a similar nature in the form of a purchase money mortgage."

Payment of Ad Valorem Taxes and Special Assessments: Taxes may be handled in several ways according to the agreement of the parties. Annual taxes are not prorated in most farm and ranch sales. The usual practice is to specify that whoever receives the crops for the calendar year will also pay the taxes. However, taxes may be prorated as of the date of sale, with the seller paying his portion of the taxes for his period of ownership and the buyer paying his portion for the period that he will own the property. In the event the taxes are not known, it is customary to use the previous year's taxes as a base for proration. It is normal to state in the contract that all previous years' taxes have been paid by the seller. Failure to have done so will, of course, show up on the abstract or title insurance policy and be a cloud on the title.

Leases: On properties which are occupied or operated by a tenant, it is important to include a paragraph regarding the disposition of the leases. The terms and duration of the lease should be enumerated or a copy of the current lease attached and made a part of the agreement of sale. Provisions should be made for the leases to be assigned to the buyer at closing, notification of lessee, and if the seller has the obligation to terminate said lease, provisions for this should be made. A clear understanding of these items can save costly time and confusion.

For a farm or ranch property, the lease income will normally be the property of the person paying the taxes. Obviously, a number of special arrangements may be made, such as reimbursement for expenses already paid by the seller for fertilizer, seed, etc. The contract should also specify the retention or distribution of government payments, if any, for the production period.

Title Evidence - Abstract of Title or Title Insurance: According to the custom for title procedures found in the area where you live, the seller will agree to furnish the buyer with marketable title. Marketable title, sometimes referred to as "merchantable title," will be one which is free from liens, encumbrances, or clouds and would be ruled acceptable by a court. A merchantable title is not necessarily a perfect title.

If the customary method by which to handle title is through an abstract, the contract should provide for the seller to deliver the abstract of title to the buyer, his agent, or to an abstract company within a certain period of time to be brought up to date or certified to date by the abstractor. After the abstract has been certified, provision will be made for delivery to the buyer or his attorney. A time period will be specified, perhaps 15 to 30 days, for the buyer to examine the certified abstract. In the event title is defective, the buyer (or his attorney) must specify the objections in writing and deliver same objections to the seller within a certain period of time (perhaps 10 days). The seller will then be allowed a period in which to have the defects corrected (perhaps 60 days).

Provisions may also be made for substitution of a title insurance policy issued by a qualified title insurance company in lieu of an abstract or in lieu of strictly merchantable title.

In abstract areas, it is customary for the seller to pay to have the abstract brought up to date, the buyer to have it examined. If the seller provides an abstract which is acceptable and the buyer also wants a title insurance policy, then it is customary for the buyer to pay for the title insurance policy.

════════ TITLE INSURANCE FORM ════════
Real Estate Sale Contract
(For Missouri)

THIS CONTRACT, made this_____day of_____

19____, by and between _____

_____seller,

and _____buyer,

WITNESSETH: Seller hereby sells to buyer the following described real estate, together with all improvements thereon, including, if any, gas heaters, ventilating, central air conditioning, attached T.V. antennas, lighting, heating and plumbing equipment and fixtures, attached mirrors and linoleum, window and porch shades, venetian blinds, storm windows and doors, screens, curtain and drapery rods, awnings and _____

_____

in_____County, State of Missouri, to wit:

Subject, however, to any recorded restrictions, easements, party wall agreements and community contracts. Subject, also, to any existing leases, tenancies and zoning laws.

The purchase price is _____DOLLARS $_____

which buyer agrees to pay as follows: _____DOLLARS $_____ at the signing of this contract, the receipt whereof is hereby acknowledged by seller and which is deposited with _____

_____

as part of the consideration of the sale; the balance to be paid in the following manner:

_____DOLLARS $_____ cash on delivery of deed as herein provided to Kansas City Title, a Division of Chicago Title Insurance Company, a Missouri Corporation of Kansas City, Missouri, hereinafter called the Title Company, and

All deferred payments not already secured by deed(s) of trust shall be evidenced by note(s), signed by buyer, secured by deed(s) of trust, at option of seller, on the above described property, containing usual provisions, drawing interest from date of delivery of deed, on the terms specified above.

Seller shall make any payments required on existing deed(s) of trust until date of delivery of deed; and, if it is provided herein that such property is being sold subject to any existing deed(s) of trust, buyer shall, on such date, reimburse seller for any principal reductions not already considered in computing payment of purchase price and for any deposits held by the holder of any deed(s) of trust.

The rental from said property, and the interest on any existing deed(s) of trust to which this sale is made subject, shall be pro-rated between seller and buyer as of the date of delivery of the deed.

Seller shall pay all taxes, general and special, and all assessments, which are a lien on said property and can be paid at the date of this contract, except that all general state, county, school and municipal taxes (exclusive of rebates, penalties or interest) payable during the calendar year in which the deed is delivered shall be pro-rated between the seller and the buyer on the basis of the said calendar year, as of the date of delivery of the deed. If the amount of any such tax to be pro-rated canot then be ascertained, pro-ration shall be computed on the amount thereof for the preceding year, except _____

Seller shall within ten days, unless defect in title shall appear upon examination, and in that event within thirty days, from date hereof, deliver to buyer or buyer's duly authorized agent, a report on the title to said real estate and a commitment from the Title Company, in which said Title Company shall agree, subject to the conditions of said commitment which shall not be inconsistent with the obligations of seller hereunder, to issue to buyer forthwith, after seller's general warranty deed shall be placed of record, its owner's title insurance policy in the form now used by said Title Company, in the county and state where said property is located, in an amount not less than the purchase price above specified.

Upon delivery of said Title Company's title report and commitment as above provided, seller shall forthwith deliver to said Title Company for its approval and recording General Warranty Deed from seller to buyer, properly executed and conveying said property in fee simple to buyer, free and clear of all liens and encumbrances whatsoever except as herein provided; buyer shall then and there pay to said Title Company, for the account of seller the balance, if any, of said cash payment and deliver to said Title Company, as agent for seller, the note(s) and deed(s) of trust, if any, hereinbefore provided for, and furnish insurance policies for the account and necessary for the protection of the holder(s) of any deed(s) of trust containing loss clause(s) payable to the holder(s) of such deed(s) of trust as interest(s) may appear.

When said Title Company shall be ready to deliver its said title insurance policy to buyer this agreement shall be deemed to be consummated and seller shall at such time be entitled to receive all monies and mortgage papers held by said Title Company for delivery to seller; buyer shall at such time be entitled to receive, without cost to buyer for same, said Title Company's title insurance policy. Said warranty deed shall be delivered to buyer as soon as it has been recorded and is obtainable from the recorder of deeds.

In the event said Title Company shall decline to issue its said title insurance policy within said thirty day period, and in the manner aforesaid, then at the expiration of said period this contract shall be null and void and the money deposited aforesaid shall be returned to buyer.

If before recording of the deed any of the improvements on said property are destroyed or substantially damaged by fire, lightning or any cause that could be covered by what is known as extended coverage insurance, buyer shall have the option of enforcing this contract or cancelling by written notice within ten days thereafter. If cancelled this contract shall be null and void and the money deposited aforesaid shall be returned to buyer.

If there has been performance of this contract on the part of seller, and buyer fails to comply herewith, within five days thereafter, then this contract may or may not be operative thereafter, at the option of seller, and, in the event seller shall declare the contract inoperative, the money deposited aforesaid shall be paid to seller as liquidated damages. Time is of the essence of this contract.

IN WITNESS WHEREOF, said parties hereunto subscribe their names. Executed in quadruplicate.

_____   _____
              (Seller)   (Buyer)

_____   _____

If the seller cannot provide an up-to-date abstract and wishes to provide a title insurance policy instead, then the policy is customarily the seller's expense.

A merchantable title will still have certain exceptions, such as deed restrictions, easements, rights of way, zoning regulations, and other title exceptions which are not of a major concern. The same is true of a title insurance policy. It should be examined by your attorney to ascertain that the exceptions are not so broad as to affect use of the property.

In the event the seller is not able to correct the defects in a title within a certain period of time, the contract may provide that the transaction be null and void and that the monies deposited be returned to the buyer and abstracts returned to the seller. The buyer may wish to make a provision in the contract that in the event seller is unable to provide strictly merchantable title, the buyer has the option of accepting title as is.

An alternative to accepting title as is or simply voiding the transaction may be to escrow a certain portion of the purchase price while a detailed clearing of title is undertaken. Or, a reduction in price may be agreed upon.

Time of Essence: If the date or time of closing is critical to either party, a provision that "time is of the essence" should be made in the contract. This means that there is a strict time obligation on both parties to close on the date stated in the contract.

If there is no time of the essence agreement, both parties have a reasonable period of time after the date specified in which to close. Even where time has been made of the essence, both parties may agree, preferably in writing, to extend the time of closing.

Maintaining Condition of Property During Contract Period: If the property under contract has buildings or other improvements, it is important to assure that these improvements be covered with insurance during the contract period. Further, every possible situation should be anticipated and provisions should be made for what happens in the event the improvements are damaged or destroyed. A typical clause might be as follows:

"If, after contract is executed, the premises be destroyed or damaged by fire, windstorm or otherwise, seller shall restore same within 30 days, if possible, and sale closing date shall be extended accordingly. But purchaser shall have option of cancelling or enforcing contract; if enforced, purchaser shall be entitled to insurance; if cancelled, earnest deposit shall be returned to purchaser and the contract shall be null and void. Seller shall assume risk of such destruction or damage and shall have the obligation to obtain consent of insurance companies to sale contract.

Other Conditions Precedent to Closing: This section covers whatever provisions of the discussions between buyer and seller that should be put in writing. Do not rely upon verbal transmissions. Possible conditions are as follows:

A. Contract subject to the property being rezoned to a certain status.
B. Certain tests on the property to satisfy buyer as to the condition soil, water, or other elements.
C. The negotiation of a lease on the property.
D. A contingency upon the seller obtaining an easement across another piece of property.
D. A contingency upon the seller obtaining an easement across another piece of property.
E. A provision that a certain number of livestock be present on the property at closing date.

Form of Note and Mortgage: Provisions of the note and mortgage to be included at closing should be spelled out in the sale contract. For example, in giving the mortgage, the buyer may wish to specify that the seller can "look to the land only" in the event of a default. This is called an exculpatory or non-recourse provision. It means that the seller can recover the land, but cannot sue for specific performance or damages or hold the buyer personally liable in the event the note and mortgage are not paid off and released.

Closing Costs: A paragraph in the contract should enumerate the responsibility for various closing fees including, but not limited to, title insurance, mortgage costs, appraisal costs, escrow costs, transfer taxes, recording fees, and revenue stamps.

Broker's Clause: There should be a paragraph relating to the commission agreement between the broker and the seller or buyer, as the case may be. The broker should specify that he is acting as agent only in bringing buyer and seller together and is not liable to either party for the performance of the terms and conditions of agreement. The basis of the commission, in terms of amount and date payable, may either be spelled out in the sale contract or included in a separate agreement.

Other: The final paragraph is often one relating to closing date and location. Reference may be made to the date of possession.

LAND CONTRACTS

The land contract is a document that embodies the provisions of both a sale contract and a mortgage. It is also known as an installment land contract or a contract for deed. In any event, it is an agreement to transfer ownership of land. The seller retains legal title and the buyer has possession.

Land contracts have a dual personality. They resemble a sale contract, but include the terms of a mortgage. Inasmuch as the seller retains title and the buyer has possession, they also resemble a lease.

Note: As this book goes to press, Congress is considering a major revision liberalizing the tax treatment of installment sales. Seek competent advice before entering into an installment land contract.

Q. Is the land contract a financing tool, or a sale contract?

A. The land contract is subject to the same general legal and economic standards as any other contract of sale. It is quite different, however, in purpose and effect from the frequently used earnest money contract. The land contract usually remains in effect until the property is fully paid for, or at least until a substantial part of the purchase price is paid. The normal sale contract, on the other hand, describes the details of the purchase and dictates the terms under which title is to be conveyed. While certain terms of the normal sale contract may survive the closing, other documents, such as notes, mortgages, and deeds of trust, are executed at closing. The land contract thus includes and combines the features of a sale contract, note, and mortgage or deed of trust.

The effect of postponing passage of legal title is to create a security interest for the seller. This security interest may be enforced directly against the land in a summary, non-judicial procedure. It is the availability of this summary remedy, commonly called a forfeiture provision, that sets the installment land contract apart from other security arrangements involving land.

Q. Where is the land contract used most frequently?

A. Land contracts are of primary importance in the Midwest and Corn Belt states. The unavailability of extensive land credit from other sources and the requirement of high equity generally associated with mortgage lending have made the land contract the principal security device for purchasing land with a small down payment. The land contract as a device for facilitating low-equity transfers has become important for the following reasons:

- Buyers of farmland often use credit to finance the transactions because of high land prices.
- Buyers borrow a major portion of the purchase price, thus making low downpayments.
- Sellers finance more than half of farm sales.
- Sellers require lower downpayments than other lenders, using their land as a security.
- Land contracts are used by sellers with the same frequency as mortgages.
- Land contracts historically require lower downpayments than mortgages. Downpayments of 20% to 25% are typical under land contracts; institutional mortgages typically require from 30% to 50% equity.

Q. What are the contrasts between a regular sale contract and a land contract?

A. The previous discussion in this chapter relative to sale contracts largely applies to provisions that are also necessary in a land contract. The primary differences in sale contracts and land contracts are as follows:

Title: The seller retains legal title as security for the payment of the remaining installments. The buyer becomes a "beneficial" owner upon making the downpayment. This divided ownership has caused some states to hold that the buyer, although not yet entitled to a deed, is the true owner. This involves the "doctrine of equitable conversion." Behind this doctrine lies the ancient, equitable maxim that "Equity regards as done those things which in good conscience ought to be done."

Low equity transfers can also be made through "buyer-acquired legal title." That is, some variation of any of the conventional mortgage instruments, such as the purchase money mortgage or the deed of trust. The deed of trust as the basic security device with installment notes evidencing the debt is the most common type used. This type of instrument is used extensively in certain states, such as Missouri, in preference to the installment land contract. The deed of trust actually involves the transfer of legal title by warranty deed to the buyer and then the re-transfer of a limited power of sale by the buyer to a trustee by use of a deed of trust.

Possession: Normally, possession follows legal title. Thus, the land contract must provide expressly for a provision delivering possession to the buyer. Certain states place a limit upon the buyer's possessory rights for the protection of the creditor.

Risk of Loss and Insurance: Since this is a long term contract, the need to assign the risk of loss and the requirements of insurance is important. The typical insurance clause may require coverage with a reputable insurance company payable to both parties, the deposit of the policies with an escrow agent, and may provide for the seller to pay the insurance premium in the event the purchaser fails to do so.

Buyer's Duty to Prevent Waste: The contract may contain a general provision relating to crop rotations, conservation practices, cutting of trees, removal of buildings, etc. The law places a duty on the buyer not to allow the property to be wasted.

Taxes: Payment of taxes is a duty that passes to the buyer in possession. It is common practice that if the buyer fails to pay the property taxes, the seller may do so and add the amount spent to the amount due under the contract.

Oil, Gas, and Mineral Rights: The right to remove any deposits must be clearly defined.

Rights of Creditors: The seller may wish to insert a provision requiring the buyer to obtain the seller's written consent before anything is done on the premises from which a lien might arise, such as construction.

Right of Assignment: Sellers may require a provision prohibiting assignment by the buyer without the prior consent of the seller. This is particularly important under a very low downpayment sale.

Default and Forfeiture: The special provisions available under these clauses are unique to the land contract. Normally, when a contract is breached, the remedy is one of the following:

- Liquidated damages
- Specific performance
- Actual damages
- Recission
- Foreclosure.

Under the land contract, the foreclosure provisions may be much more rigid and forfeiture may entail serious consequences for the buyer. A seller may foreclose a defaulting buyer's interest under an installment land contract as though it were a mortgage relationship. Normally, these would be under a strict foreclosure or foreclosure by judicial sale.

A forfeiture is effected without court action, while strict foreclosure requires court action. In a strict foreclosure action, the court simply terminates the buyer's equity in the land under the contract and places the seller in the same legal position as if the contract had never been made. This means that once the seller has obtained the land back through strict foreclosure, that is the end of the matter.

Foreclosure of installment land contracts by judicial sale is recognized in nearly all states and is the only method of foreclosure recognized in some of them. To foreclose by judicial sale, the land contract is treated as a mortgage and the procedure is governed by the law with respect to mortgages.

The primary advantage of using the land contract as the security device instead of some type of mortgage is the availability of the remedy of forfeiture, if the proper provisions are included. Forfeiture avoids court action or the sale of the property. Forfeiture or cancellation is controlled by statutes in many states. The contract must contain a forfeiture clause under the law of the state. Some courts have held that forfeitures are not favored since they result in giving the seller an unfair advantage. Some state courts have used various means of easing the harshness of the forfeiture provision when the buyer has paid a substantial part of the purchase price or when other conditions make it inequitable to enforce the strict terms of the forfeiture. Some states may set aside a forfeiture unless there has been a "willful default," subject to interruption. Because of the harsh implications of forfeiture, courts have at times required the seller to show that he did not defraud and act in bad faith, that proper notice was given, that the period of time to correct the fault was extended, or other waivers.

While many states still enforce forfeiture provisions if they are strictly complied with, the tendency of many courts is to provide an "equitable test." Most courts will not enforce a forfeiture provision resulting in a "gross inequity." They may require a foreclosure sale, with the proceeds first used to settle the claims of the original seller, with any excess over this amount belonging to the buyer.

Recording: Many installment land contracts are recorded, although it is not legally necessary to do so. Recording is designed to put all parties on notice of the instrument recorded. The only valid reason for not recording is that, in some states, if a land contract is recorded and subsequently the buyer does not complete the contract and obtain a deed to the property, the existence of the land contract on record is a cloud on the title and must be settled through a quiet title suit or a quit claim deed from the buyer. Since quit claim deeds are difficult to obtain from the buyer after default, it may be appropriate to obtain the executed quit claim deed from the buyer at time of signing the land contract. The quit claim deed should then be held in escrow, pending final satisfaction of the land contract.

The following sample contract form appeared in the University of Illinois Publication, Installment Land Contracts for Farm Land, Circular 823. It is not meant to be an exact model of a contract and all parties should consult legal counsel prior to entering into such a contract. However, it does illustrate what a land contract should contain.

INSTALLMENT LAND CONTRACT

This agreement is made this _____ day of _____, 19
between the seller, _____, and the buyer, _____.

1. Description of premises. The seller agrees to sell and the buyer to buy the following described real estate with all improvements thereon: (the full legal description would be inserted here).

2. Price and terms. The total purchase price is $_____ to be paid as follows:

$_____ paid concurrently with the execution of this contract, the receipt of which the seller hereby acknowledges.

_____ annual installments of $_____ each, which, together with accrued interest, shall be paid on the _____ day of _____ of each year,[1] commencing on _____, 19____, and ending _____, 19____.[2]

Whenever $_____ of the principal sum has been paid, the warranty deed shall be released in exchange for a note and mortgage. The balance of the purchase price, $_____, is to be paid in accordance with the terms of a note and mortgage agreement executed concurrently with the execution of this contract.[3]

Interest on principal shall be computed at the rate of _____ percent per annum on the unpaid balance. All payments called for under this contract are to be paid at the _____ Bank in _____, Illinois, to be deposited to the account of the seller.

(See footnote 4 for optional payment provisions.)

3. Possession of the premises. The buyer is entitled to exclusive possession of the above-described premises during the life of the contract. The buyer's right to possession shall terminate in the event of his default in any of the terms of this contract sufficient to entitle the seller to consider the contract terminated and to retake possession of the premises.

The seller shall deliver possession of the said premises to the buyer on or before _____, 19____.

4. Escrow provisions. The _____ Bank of _____ is appointed escrow agent for the buyer and the seller, and the original signed copy of the contract shall be deposited with said escrow agent. Concurrently with the execution of this contract, the seller shall deliver to the said escrow agent a good and sufficient warranty deed of the premises, to be delivered to the buyer upon the payment of all installments of principal and interest and all other debts and charges provided for under this contract.

The seller shall furnish an abstract of title, brought down to date, on or before _____, 19____, showing title in seller, and shall allow the buyer a reasonable time to have the abstract examined and to notify the seller of any objections. If title is found defective, the seller shall have a reasonable time to put same in merchantable condition.[5] The seller shall then deliver to the escrow agent, the abstract of title of said premises (or a title insurance policy in the amount of the contract price), showing merchantable title in fee simple in the seller.

The buyer shall deliver to the escrow agent a mortgage of the premises to secure a note in the amount of $_____ as the balance of the purchase price, said note and mortgage to be delivered to the seller upon completion of payment of installments as provided in section 2 above.[6]

Escrow charges shall be paid by _____, 19____.

5. *Right to prepayment.* At the regular time set for annual payment of installments and interest after the first year, the buyer shall be entitled to pay future annual installments of principal not to exceed two such future installments in any year.

At the time of payment of a future installment, interest on such installment shall also be paid at _____ percent.[7]

The buyer shall not be deemed to have defaulted in any payments of installments as long as the total of all such payments, including prepayments, made at the time a default is alleged is equal to the number of payments that have fallen due up through the time of the alleged default.

6. *Grace periods.* If the buyer is in default as to any portion of an installment due and payable, or any portion of the accrued interest due and payable, he shall be allowed a grace period to make payment starting with the first day after such default, according to the following schedule:

If the buyer has paid less than 20 percent of the purchase price plus accrued interest, there shall be 60 days' grace.

If the buyer has paid 20 to 40 percent of the purchase price plus accrued interest, there shall be 90 days' grace.

If the buyer has paid over 40 percent of the purchase price plus accrued interest, there shall be 120 days' grace.

Overdue installments of principal and accrued interest shall bear interest at the rate of 7 percent per annum. To prevent default, it shall be necessary to pay within the applicable grace period the accrued interest and overdue installments of principal and regular accrued interest.

Immediately upon the expiration of the applicable grace period, if the buyer has not made full and complete payment of all installments of principal and interest then owing, the buyer shall, at the option of the seller, forfeit all his right and interest in the premises and the seller shall have the immediate right to re-enter and take possession of said premises.

7. *Right to assign and to mortgage.* In the event the buyer wishes to sell or assign his interest during the life of this contract, the seller shall have the first option to repurchase the above-described premises from the buyer at the contract price plus the appraised market value of improvements made with the consent of the seller.[8]

Furthermore, during the life of this contract, the buyer shall, before mortgaging his interest, secure the written consent of the seller.[9]

8. *Taxes and assessments.* Real property taxes for the year 19____ shall be paid by the _____. All other taxes and assessments levied on the premises subsequent to the date of execution of the contract, and any unpaid installments of special taxes or assessments not yet due for improvements completed at the date of this contract, shall be paid by the buyer.

9. *Insurance.* The buyer agrees to pay to the seller the unearned portion of prepaid premiums on insurance now in force on improvements on said premises with possession date.

It shall be the duty of the buyer to keep all improvements insured by reputable companies during the life of this contract, and such insurance shall be kept sufficient to cover the full insurance value of the improvements. The insurance shall be made payable to both the seller and buyer, and the policy shall contain an endorsement to this effect.[10]

A copy of each policy shall be placed in escrow with the escrow agent or submitted to the seller for his inspection.

10. *Farm management.* The buyer agrees to farm said premises in accordance with sound farming practices and to keep the premises in good repair at the buyer's expense.

The buyer agrees that the seller and his authorized representatives and agents shall have access to said premises at all reasonable times for the purpose of examining the condition of said premises.

The buyer agrees not to do any substantial remodeling work or new construction on said premises without the seller's prior written approval.[11]

11. Mineral deposits. If income is realized as a result of leasing for or development of oil, gas, or any valuable mineral deposit while this contract is in force, the net return, after deduction of necessary and ordinary expenses, shall be paid in equal shares to the seller and the buyer for a period of _____ years, or for the length of the production period, whichever time is shorter.[12]

12. Advancements. If the buyer fails to insure improvements or to pay taxes or other charges or assessments as provided above, then the seller, may, but is not obligated to, procure such insurance, pay such taxes, discharge or purchase any tax lien accruing by virtue thereof, or any title or mechanic's lien affecting such real estate that accrued by virtue of acts done or permitted to be done by the buyer or by any party claiming or holding under the buyer. The buyer shall repay all money so paid immediately upon demand together with interest thereon at the rate of 7 percent per annum from the time of such payment.

13. Arbitration. If any dispute, difference, or question shall at any time hereafter arise between the parties under this contract, or their respective representatives, heirs, administrators, executors, or assigns, concerning anything contained herein or as to the rights, liabilities, or duties of the said parties hereunder, the same shall be referred to three arbitrators chosen as follows:

One person is to be chosen by the seller and another chosen by the buyer. These two persons shall select a third person, and the three shall pass on the issue at hand.

The arbitrators shall submit a report in writing to the seller and the buyer. The report shall be given within 30 days from the time the arbitrators are chosen, and the report shall be binding on both the seller and buyer and on their heirs, executors, administrators, and assigns.

The expense of arbitration shall be borne equally by the parties.

14. Default and forfeiture. If the buyer fails to make payment of all moneys specified to be paid by him under this contract and within the time for payment allowed under the contract, or to keep the improvements on said premises in good repair, this agreement shall, at the option of the seller, be forfeited and determined. The buyer shall forfeit all payments made by him under this agreement, and such payments shall be retained by the seller in full satisfaction and in liquidation of all damages sustained by the seller, and the seller shall have the right to re-enter and take possession of said premises.[13]

It is mutually agreed that all agreements herein contained in this contract shall extend to and be binding upon the heirs, executors, administrators, and assigns of the respective parties.

In witness whereof, this land contract has been executed and delivered this day of _____, 19____.

(seal)

_____ Seller

(seal)

_____ Seller

(seal)

_____ Buyer

(seal)

_____ Buyer

Footnotes:

[1]Contracts frequently provide that annual installments be broken down into two or more payments during the year.

[2]If it is desired to keep payments at the same level throughout the contract, the parties may provide for lower principal payments at the beginning, the payments gradually increasing as interest becomes less. Attorneys can provide schedules that show how much of each payment is credited to principal and how much to interest, and will draft the appropriate provision in lieu of the one shown here.

[3]This paragraph to be used when the buyer anticipates paying off the balance of the purchase price by a mortgage to the seller.

[4]For long-term contracts, the parties may wish to provide for one or more of the following optional provisions:

Revisable payment plan. The total price for the premises, not to exceed a total of $_____, shall vary as the average price per acre of farm real estate in Illinois changes, in accordance with the following rules: (herein will be inserted detailed provisions for adjusting the amount of payments in accordance with the fluctuation in land values).

Product payment plan. $_____ of the yearly payments shall be in cash. The remainder of each and every payment may consist of _____ bushels of (corn, soybeans, wheat, etc., or a combination) or the cash equivalent of the amount of the product due. Any payment wherein the above specified option to pay in products or their cash equivalent is exercised, shall have the same force and effect as if the cash-installment payment called for in section 2 of the contract had been paid.

Revisable interest rate. The interest rate shall remain as specified in section 2 of this contract, except for such changes as may be made effective because of subsequent changes in the average interest rate on first mortgages of farmland in Illinois, to be determined as follows: (herein will be inserted provisions designed to effectuate the goals of the parties in using this option).

[5]In some cases a title insurance policy will be used in lieu of an abstract.

[6]This paragraph to be inserted in the contract only when the balance of the purchase price is paid in accordance with the terms of note and mortgage.

[7]Optional paragraph. Prepayments may increase the income tax of the seller and he may have some expense in reinvesting such proceeds. Therefore, it seems fair that the buyer pay some interest on prepayments, although it may be smaller than the regular interest rate.

[8]This clause is frequently desired in family transactions when the parents want protection against the son or daughter, or their heirs, transferring the farm out of the family.

[9]If no option to repurchase is used, written consent to sell or assign is usually required.

[10]The parties can provide that insurance proceeds for loss of improvements may, at the option of the buyer, be applied to the purchase price. Consider carefully, however, the effect of such a clause on federal income taxes payable by the seller. If the loss occurred during the year of sale and the proceeds are applied to the purchase price, the 30-percent maximum may be exceeded.

[11]The purpose of this provision is to give the seller some protection against liens for the value of improvements.

[12]This section may be desired in family transactions.

[13]The parties could provide that there be some reimbursement for improvements made by the buyer with consent of the seller. In most cases, however, it would be better to amend this contract or enter into a separate contract for reimbursement at the time the improvement is planned.

CHAPTER 8

Sources for Financing Your Land Purchase

Nearly every buyer of real estate must supplement cash with a loan to finance his purchase. The use of land as security for the borrowing of money has a history centuries old. Not until millions of acres of land were repossessed during the depression years of the 1920s and 1930s, however, did financing reach the sophistication now known.

History

The tenure of agricultural land has progressed through four distinct periods: prior to 1820; from 1820 to 1920; from 1921 to 1941; and the period since World War II.

Prior to 1820. The acquisition of land for farming operations began with the extension of credit in colonial days. Though land was cheap, organized land-credit institutions did not exist and following the revolution, the federal government enacted legislation facilitating the purchase of public land.

The Land Ordinance of 1785 was intended to raise revenues. Three steps for the settlement of an area were structured: clearance of the Indian title; survey of the land; and offering for public sale.

Townships were disposed of in alternate fashion—one for sale in its entirety, the next auctioned by sections of 640 acres each. All parcels sold at $1 per acre. Even so, takers were disappointingly few in the beginning. Prices were high, sales were held at places far removed from the land being offered, and the blocks were too large for individual settlement. Purchasers, often settlers with limited means to pay, frequently did not keep up payments. About 1.1 billion acres of the national land estate were transferred to individuals, states, and corporations.

The second key ordinance, the Northwest Ordinance of 1787, proved to be a cornerstone of the Republic. New states were created from the territory northwest of the Ohio River, and this promise of Statehood assured those moving to the frontier that they would not sacrifice political rights and privileges by doing so.

By 1803, when President Thomas Jefferson gambled with the purchase of the Louisiana Territory from Napoleon, the Nation's westward movement had been established. While Jefferson was criticized for paying $15,000,000, which amounted to a few cents per acre, his vision proved to be a major step in American development. Under his direction the Lewis and Clark expedition was undertaken. Their contribution to scientific knowledge, westward expansion, and even international relations is now legend. As development and settlement increased, it became apparent to Congress that an agency was required for administering and disposing of public lands. This responsibility was given to the Commissioner of the General Land Office under the Treasury Department in 1812.

From 1820 to 1920. In 1820, the government slowed credit sales and public land was sold for cash. By this time settlement was spreading in all directions. Alabama, Mississippi, and parts of Louisiana and Arkansas were settled, largely through land sales following Eli Whitney's invention of the cotton gin in 1793. By 1820 no less than 30 organized expeditions had probed the new West. Some came back with the word that the West was unfit for human habitation, thus giving birth to the "Great American Desert" myth. While this myth persisted for decades, there was no restraining the land hunger of the American people.

The term "doing a land-office business" soon came into the American jargon, signifying the swift and lucrative transactions that took place over the next several years between the United States government and buyers of public land.

Public land sales began to boom after 1820, when the price was set at $1.25 per acre and tracts as small as 80 acres could be purchased.

A Virginia editor commented in 1829 on the flow of migrants passing his community moving toward Indiana, Illinois, and Michigan. "They were principally from the lower part of Virginia and South Carolina. They jog on, careless of the varying climate, and apparently without regret for friends and the country they leave behind, seeking forests to fell and a new country to settle."

By 1845 settlers were pulling into Oregon and California. Although few stopped short of these promised lands on the Pacific, the mountains and plateaus which intervene were no longer an unknown wilderness. Maps had grown in number and accuracy. Public land surveys had been completed in Ohio (which was the first), Alabama, Arkansas, Illinois, Indiana, and Missouri by the middle of the 1850s. Iowa surveys were then three-quarters finished, as were those in Michigan and Mississippi. The mapping in Florida, Louisiana, and Wisconsin was somewhere near the half-way mark. Those in Minnesota, California, Kansas, Nebraska, New Mexico, Oregon, Washington, and Utah were only just beginning.

While Abraham Lincoln was best known for freeing the slaves, he also called for free soil. His homesteading law provided "free land" to anyone who wanted to settle in the public domain. The year 1861 was a landmark with the passing of the Homestead Act. It opened the door of western opportunity to thousands of Americans who could ill afford to purchase public lands. Under this legislation, adult citizens of the United States as well as aliens seeking citizenship status were eligible to apply for homesteads. It provided that, having "resided upon or culti-vated" the acreage for 5 years, and if by then a citizen, the settler could receive a patent. The law provided that his homestead could not be seized by a creditor to satisfy earlier debts. Eventually some 270 million acres of public domain lands became a million and a half farms.

Two other acts passed under Lincoln's administration became very important to agriculture. The Morrill Act of 1862 provided grants of lands to the States for colleges. These land-grant colleges led to the scientific research and development in agriculture that we know today. The Department of Agriculture was also created in 1862, giving early recognition to the importance of food production to the young country.

By 1900, much of the choice farmland had been acquired throughout the eastern Corn Belt, and land prices began to move higher. Credit was not readily available, and in 1916 the federal government created the 12 Federal Land Banks under the Federal Loan Act.

World War I brought an increase in product prices and a correspond-ing boom in land prices. The average price of farms increased nearly 400% from 1900 to 1920. Like many land booms, this one would be followed with a bust.

From 1921 to 1941. During this period land prices were erratic, financing was chaotic, and farming went through one of the most traumatic times in our history.

My father, born in Nebraska in 1895, was selling land as a young man in the early 1920s, and recalls his experiences:

"Through World War I, land prices had continued to increase at an unbelievable rate. The prices of corn, hogs, and cattle were higher than any of us could remember. In eastern Nebraska and South Dakota, big land buyers were moving in from Ohio, Illinois, and Iowa, looking for cheaper land . . . and they found it. The land looked similar to what they had seen selling at much higher prices in Illinois and Iowa. At that time we didn't know that the rainfall was significantly lower in the western Corn Belt, or that the soils were not as productive. Anyway, the speculators came and bought. They would arrive in Creighton on the morning train, and Count Von Roden, a colorful owner of the local hotel, would pick them up in his horsedrawn coach, in uniform, and seated next to his matched Dalmation coach dogs. After lunch at the hotel, we would take the buyers by horse and buggy to see the properties. It was not unusual to sell a section before dark. And not just the strangers in town bought. I bought the 80 acres where you and Bruce and Dale were born for $190 per acre in 1919. Twenty years later I bought the 80 acres next to it for $40 per acre. It wasn't until the 1970s that the land I bought 50 years earlier got back to its original price."

Author's Note: Unlike many buyers of the 1920s, my father didn't lose his land. He'd saved his money, invested a high percentage of equity, and managed it wisely. I vaguely remember a night our family gathered around a pot-bellied coal stove in our living room, and ceremoniously burned a piece of paper, something called a mortgage. My mother and father seemed to think it was an important day . . . and today I know that it was.

In the early 1920s land prices took a sharp drop, as did commodity prices. Foreclosures of land numbered in the thousands as farmers could not repay the debt on properties bought at much higher prices. It was not unusual to owe a mortgage of $150 per acre on land worth but $50 per acre. Life insurance companies and Federal Land Banks were making few loans during this period, and the number of farm foreclosures remained high.

The Great Depression was the catalyst for substantial government action affecting all real estate, including land. Hundreds of thousands of farm families were made homeless and destitute by the economic crisis triggered in 1929 by the stock market crash. Banks closed and the depression was followed by the dust bowl years of the 1930s. Banks, insurance companies, and finance companies were forced to repossess land from farmers who could not pay, wiping out their equity and savings, sometimes allowing them to remain on the farms as tenants. Since the national economic picture was also strained, the customary lenders retreated from land financing, making money almost non-existent.

In 1933, the Farm Credit Administration was formed. The immediate purpose was to provide a measure of emergency assistance to distressed farmers, through the Emergency Farm Mortgage Act of 1933, and the Resettlement Administration (now called the Farmers Home Administration) of 1935. While of small comfort to those owners foreclosed, the government actions did bring a degree of order to the financial chaos of farm ownership, and encouraged other institutions to re-enter the field.

Post World War II. Banks, insurance companies, and individuals again became active lenders as rising farm product prices made land ownership profitable in the years following 1941. Since current land prices have pushed to record highs, enormous amounts of capital are now required to purchase economically viable farm and ranch properties. A combination of credit sources may be required to finance the sale of these commercial farming ventures.

Q. Where should I look for farm financing?

A. The major sources of farm financing are:

1. Sellers
2. Insurance Companies
3. Commercial Banks
4. Farm credit System
    a) Federal Land Banks
    b) Production Credit Associations
5. Farmers Home Administration
6. Small Business Administration
7. Savings and Loan Associations

SELLER FINANCING

Since sellers are the largest individual source of farm financing, they will be discussed first. Historically, sellers have supplied nearly one-half of all money loaned for farmland purchases.

Q. What advantages does the seller gain by offering financing?

A. Advantages to the seller are several:

1. Seller financing, either as a first or second mortgage, will result in the highest possible price to the owner. The number of buyers willing and able to buy at terms affording a low downpayment increases geometrically as compared to those who are able to come up with a major portion of the purchase price. Frequently, large amounts of capital are not available to a buyer. Therefore, a buyer is simply willing to pay more for property when the terms make it easier for him to meet the payments.
2. The seller retains an interest (investment) in a familiar business with which he is comfortable.
3. The installment payments may mesh very nicely with the seller's need for retirement income.
4. The tax advantages of spreading the capital gain over a period of years may be significant, constituting a substantial saving to the seller.

Q. Are there also advantages to the buyer?

A. Advantages to the buyer include:

1. This may be the only available source of money.
2. The amount of the downpayment and the repayment terms may be more flexible and tailored more closely to the buyer's ability to pay than with any other method of financing. Such flexibility can resolve some of the most pressing concerns of the buyer in formulating his purchase decision.
3. The buyer's leverage interacts with inflation to yield him the full benefit of land appreciation.
4. The ability to negotiate the trade-off between interest rate and purchase price may result in tax savings for both buyer and seller.

Whether the instrument used in seller financing is a mortgage, deed of trust, or land contract will depend upon the state where the property is located. The laws governing these instruments differ substantially. Sound legal and accounting counsel, however, may enable buyers and sellers to use the installment method of purchasing to their significant advantage.

INSURANCE COMPANIES

Insurance companies have played an important role in financing farmland for many years. Until the mid 1960s insurance companies typically provided more than 25% of loan funds for farm purchases. Since that time they have reduced their holdings in farmland investments. Current estimates are that less than 3% of the life insurance industry's total investment portfolio is in farm loans.

Q. Why have insurance companies cut back their farm lending?

A. While the reduced interest of insurance companies in farm lending is a concern to those interested in agriculture, the companies reluctance is understandable. Every agricultural property is substantially different from every other property. The degree of knowledge and attention required in farm lending is thus greater than for most other classes of property, or investments in corporate bonds, for example. Insurance companies prefer real estate loans such as shopping centers, office buildings, and other "low risk," predictable income property. More predictable guidelines can be established for income and expense of such properties. Buildings occupied by tenants with AAA credit status are more easily analyzed than a farm operated by an owner facing the various unknowns of weather and other hazards. Consequently, the amount of insurance company funds coming into agriculture will vary from year to year and depend upon the current state of the economy and other investment alternatives available to the insurance company.

The important thing to remember is that some insurance companies are often in the market and the availability of their funds may vary. Consequently, the purchaser should not be reluctant to contact insurance company representatives.

Q. How do I find insurance company representatives?

A. Most insurance companies place their loans through loan agents who are employees of the companies and also through independent correspondents. They operate through branch offices or field representatives and draw most of their loans through contacts with real estate brokers, bankers, accountants, lawyers, and others who deal regularly with farmers. The more serious farm mortgage lenders have historically operated with a field force of full-time, salaried representatives whose territories may vary in size from a few counties to several states. Occasionally banks, real estate agents, or other local institutions will act as representatives for the insurance companies.

Q. What is the length of loan available?

A. Insurance company loans normally run 20 years, although they can range from 5 to 25 years. Most are long term, first mortgage loans. They tend to be larger than the average long term real estate loan because the insurance companies intentionally search for places to invest for long periods of time, thus reducing overhead.

Q. Is the size of loan limited?

A. Percentage of loan-to-value varies with individual companies and sometimes by state. Many firms will loan up to 75% of the appraised value; others only loan up to 60%. There is normally no dollar maximum on the size of an insurance company loan.

Q. Are interest rates and loan terms standard?

A. Interest rates charged will obviously vary with what the money market dictates. The prime rate will have a substantial influence over the interest rates charged. For a loan to be made, the return produced by the interest rate must compete favorably with other alternatives. In the past, during periods of tight money with corresponding high interest rates, rather substantial shifts away from farm loans have occurred because other types of properties could bear a higher interest rate. Typically, the insurance companies maintain a constant interest rate for the life of the loan. Occasionally balloon type loans are allowed. Most companies allow the buyer to place a second mortgage behind the first mortgage. This does allow the seller to participate in the financing through the use of a second mortgage, thereby decreasing the amount of equity required by the buyer.

Q. Do certain types of properties have preferential treatment?

A. Most companies have bias as to the type of property eligible for security. As could be predicted, all companies would prefer to loan on land that is all tillable and located within the prime Corn Belt region. Some companies shy away from loans on ranchland. Not many companies will offer a large ratio of loan-to-value on properties that are highly improved with buildings. Land used for specialty crops such as vegetable, citrus, cotton, or rice is not generally looked upon favorably. Land being held for urban development is not a favorite of most insurance companies.

In a survey completed for this text, insurance companies were asked to rate their preferences as to property types preferred for lending and their consensus was as follows:

1st: All tillable land within the Corn Belt.
2nd: Combination grain and livestock operations.
3rd: All tillable land outside the Corn Belt.
4th: Ranchland.
5th: Land highly improved with buildings.
6th: Specialty lands such as cotton, rice, vegetable, or citrus.
7th: Land being held for urban development.

COMMERCIAL BANKS

Long term real estate loans are not generally compatible with commercial bank operations. When banks do decide to lend on farm real estate, it is normally because they have other financial interests with the client and a long history of previous dealings.

Since most bank deposits are short term, they prefer short-term loans. Their funds are not adaptable to long-term financing. Most bankers will admit, however, that they will make short-term renewable farm ownership loans to good customers; meaning individuals who have several relationships with the bank and whose business they value. Even in these cases they would prefer to limit their loans to 1 to 5 years and tie in financing with other traditional long term lenders such as insurance companies or Farm Credit Administration lenders.

FARM CREDIT SYSTEM

The farm credit system consists of three components:

1) Federal Land Banks and Federal Land Bank Associations.
2) Federal Intermediate Credit Banks and Production Credit Associations (PCA's).
3) Banks For Cooperatives.

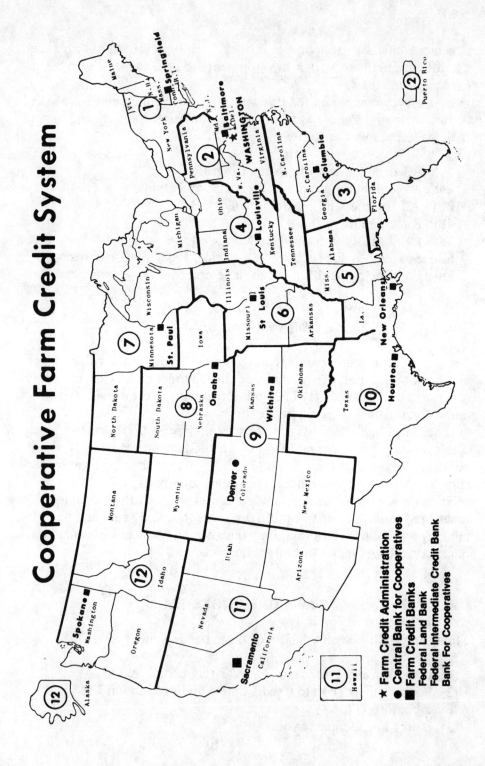

Cooperative Farm Credit System

★ Farm Credit Administration
● Central Bank for Cooperatives
■ Farm Credit Banks
  Federal Land Bank
  Federal Intermediate Credit Bank
  Bank For Cooperatives

How Farmers Share in Control of Cooperative Farm Credit System

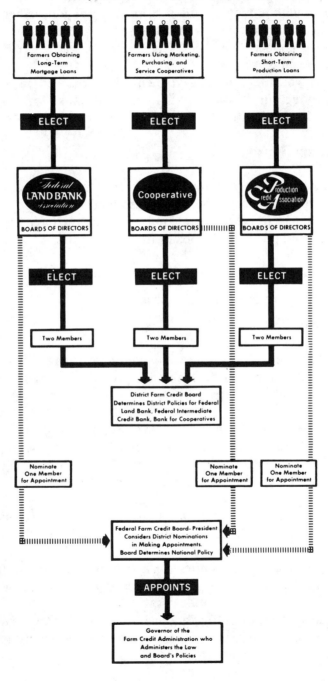

This system is managed by the Farm Credit Administration, which is an independent agency of the federal government. All three branches were created with money provided by the federal government, but have since repaid the government's investment and are now completely borrower-owned cooperatives operating under the Farm Credit Administration in Washington.

The units which lend directly to farmers are the Federal Land Banks and the Production Credit Associations. The Banks for Cooperatives, makes loans to agricultural cooperatives, but not to farmers directly.

Federal Land Banks

There are twelve Federal Land Banks in the United States, one in each of the twelve farm credit districts. These banks make long-term loans secured by first liens on real estate in rural areas through more than 500 local Federal Land Bank Associations.

Q. What are the principle features of Federal Land Bank Loans?

A. The key features of FLB financing are:

Terms. Five to forty years.

Eligibility. Farmers and ranchers, corporations engaged in the production of agricultural products, businesses providing farmers with on-the-farm services, and non-farm rural homeowners are eligible.

Loan Use. Use for any agricultural purpose, including the purchase of farms, farmland, equipment, and livestock; refinancing existing mortgages and paying other debts; construction and repairing buildings; and financing other farm, farmhome, or family needs.

Amount of Credit. The amount of credit extended is based on the credit worthiness of the applicant and cannot exceed 85% of the collateral.

Procedure. An individual applies for a Federal Land Bank loan at the local Federal Land Bank Association serving the county in which the property is located.

When the application is filed at the association, the applicant gives information regarding his financial status, the purpose for which the loan will be used, and other pertinent data.

A representative of the association or bank then appraises the property and checks the credit worthiness of the applicant.

When the loan application is approved and accepted by the applicant, the title to the property is examined and, if it is acceptable, the loan is closed.

Legal Entities. Legal entities are partnerships, corporations, trusts, or other types of organizations legally authorized to conduct a business. A legal entity must meet the qualifications of being a farmer, grower, or rancher.

Repayment Plans on most loans specify a fixed number of annual, semi-annual, quarter-annual, or monthly installments. They include accrued interest on the unpaid balance and sufficient principal payments to retire the loan in the number of years for which it was made. Borrowers may repay any part or all of their loans at any time without penalty. Other variations of these terms may be allowed.

Interest Payment Plans. Federal Land Banks have variable interest rate plans in effect. They provide a means by which interest rates may be lowered or raised, depending on the cost of money to the bank. This type of plan allows the banks to adjust quickly to changes in the money markets and makes funds available at the lowest possible cost to all borrowers.

Stock Ownership. Each borrower may be required to purchase stock in the Federal Land Bank Association equal to at least $5 for each $100 borrowed. The Association in turn buys an equal amount of stock in the Land Bank of the District, thus making the farmer-borrowers the owners of the Federal Land Banks in their respective districts. Money to buy the stock is normally included in the loan proceeds.

Production Credit Associations

Production Credit Associations (PCAs) are short and intermediate term agricultural lending institutions. Their loan terms are limited to a maximum of 7 years, with only very limited exceptions. While they may take real estate mortgages as collateral, their primary business is financing farm operating and capital needs—not financing the purchase of farmland.

Q. Who is eligible for a PCA Loan?

A. Eligible borrowers are:

1. Farmers and ranchers who own agricultural land or are engaged in the production of products.
2. Legal entities may include partnerships, corporations, estates, trusts, or individuals.
3. Producers or harvesters of aquatic products.
4. Rural residents who either own or occupy property located in a rural area or soon intend to. Homes must be in open areas primarily devoted to agriculture and in towns or villages where the population does not exceed 2,500 persons.
5. Businesses which furnish custom type services performed on the farm and directly related to farm operating needs.
6. Combined operations wherein applicant's operations include a combination of farming, producing or harvesting aquatic products, or a farm related business.

Q. Is stock purchase required for PCA loans?

A. As with Federal Land Banks, when you borrow from a PCA you must "invest" an amount equal to at least $5 for each $100 you borrow. More than 400 Production Credit Associations serve more than one county - often with a branch office in each county served.

THE FARMERS HOME ADMINISTRATION

The Farmers Home Administration is not a branch of the Farm Credit Administration. Rather, it is a rural credit agency of the U.S. Department of Agriculture.

The Farmers Home Administration(FmHA) makes and guarantees farm ownership loans and provides technical management assistance to eligible applicants who will operate family-size farms. These farms can be operated by individuals, partnerships, cooperatives, or corporations.

All loan funds are supplied from private sources. Insured loans are made directly from an FmHA revolving fund to the borrower. Guaranteed loans are made and serviced by usual commercial sources, such as Federal Land Banks, local banks, insurance companies, and savings and loan associations. In these cases, FmHA provides the lender with a guarantee against losses on the loan.

FmHA also makes farm ownership loans in participation with other lenders and sellers of farms who supply a part of the needed loan funds. In these cases, FmHA loans may be secured by a junior lien on the property.

Each farm ownership loan is tailored to the borrower's needs. The lender or the FmHA county supervisor helps the borrower analyze the situation, determine available resources, and plan how these resources, plus the funds obtained by the loan, may be best used. Technical assistance helps the borrower solve problems that arise in making major adjustments in the operation and in adopting improved practices. Special emphasis is given to meeting the credit needs of limited resource borrowers and beginning farmers.

Loans may be used to finance structures for farming enterprises that are consistent with local antipollution or environmental quality standards and regulations.

All who apply get equal consideration without regard to sex, race, color, religion, national origin, marital status, or age.

Q. How may FmHA loan funds be used?

A. Farm ownership loans may be used to buy, improve, or enlarge farms. Funds can be used to construct, improve, or repair farm homes and farm service buildings, to drill wells and otherwise improve on-farm water supplies, to install pollution control measures, to develop energy conservation measures, and to refinance debts. In addition, these loans may be used to develop and improve farm forests, provide drainage systems, carry out basic land treatment practices, and to make other improvements.

Loan funds also may be used to provide facilities for producing fish under controlled conditions and to finance nonfarm enterprises to help farmers supplement income. To assist in these enterprises, loans can be used to develop land, construct buildings and other facilities, purchase equipment, and make other real estate improvements.

Nonfarm enterprises which may be financed on family farms include camping and swimming facilities, tennis courts, riding stables, vacation rental cottages, lakes and ponds for boating and fishing docks, nature trails, picnic grounds, repair shops, roadside markets, souvenir shops, craft and wood or metal working facilities, and small grocery stores or service station facilities.

Q. What are the terms and interest rates?

A. Repayment terms and interest rates vary according to the type of loan made. Repayment is scheduled according to the borrower's ability to repay. The maximum repayment term is 40 years. The interest rate is set periodically, based on the cost of borrowing by the Government.

A lower interest rate is available for borrowers with limited resources. Loans to limited resource borrowers will be reviewed after 3 years, and the interest rate increased if the borrower has sufficient repayment ability. These loans then will be reviewed every 2 years thereafter. However, if at any time the borrower has sufficient income and repayment ability to pay the then current rate being charged, the borrower's interest rate will be increased to that rate.

For loans made by other lenders and guaranteed by FmHA, the interest rate and repayment terms will be agreed upon by the borrower and the lender. Interest rates on these loans may not exceed any maximum set by the Secretary of Agriculture. Each borrower who received an insured loan is expected to refinance the unpaid balance of the loan when it is financially feasible for him to rely on commercial credit sources.

Q. Who is eligible for an FmHA loan?

A. Individuals, partnerships, cooperatives, and corporations primarily and directly engaged in farming and ranching on family-size operations may apply.
To be eligible, an individual must:

1. Have farm experience or training and possess the character, industry and ability needed to succeed in farming.
2. Be a citizen of the United States, which includes Puerto Rico, the Virgin Islands, Guam, American Samoa, and the Commonwealth of the Northern Mariana Islands.
3. Possess the legal capacity to incur the obligations of a loan.
4. Be unable to obtain sufficient credit elsewhere at reasonable rates and terms to finance actual needs.
5. Be the owner-operator of not larger than a family farm after the loan is closed.
6. Need to rely on farm and other income to provide a level of living comparable to that considered reasonably adequate for the area in which the farm is located.

In the case of corporations, cooperatives, or partnerships, the stockholders, members, or partners holding a majority interest must meet these same eligibility requirements and the entity must be authorized to own and operate a farm or ranch in the state where the land is located. If the individuals holding a majority interest in the entity are related by blood or marriage, at least one stockholder member or partner must operate the family farm. If not related by blood or marriage, all stockholders, members, or partners in the entity must own and operate the farm.

Corporations, cooperatives, and partnerships which consist of one or more members, stockholders, or partners who already have an FmHA farm ownership, soil and water, recreation, or operating loan, either individually or as a part of another entity, are NOT eligible for an FmHA farm ownership loan.

Q. How is application made?

A. Apply at the office of a commercial lender for a guaranteed loan, and the FmHA county office serving the area where the property is located for an insured loan. If the office cannot be located in the local telephone directory under U.S. Department of Agriculture, write to the Farmers Home Administration, U.S. Department of Agriculture, Washington, D.C. 20250.

Requirements. The applicant will be assisted by the lender or FmHA county supervisor in working out a plan to make the best use of land, labor, livestock, capital, and equipment. This plan will be a guide for the borrower to use in determining the soundness of the proposed operation and to follow in operating the farm or nonfarm enterprise. Before a loan is made, it must be clear that the borrower will have enough income to meet operating and family living expenses and to repay the loan and other debts. In all cases, labor must be furnished primarily by the operator and immediate family, except during seasonal peak-load periods.

Q. Is management help available?

A. Farm ownership loans are accompanied by technical advice to help borrowers make profitable use of their land and water, labor, capital, and other resources. The borrower received advice in keeping records of expenses and income and in budgeting and otherwise making wise use of income and credit. USDA agencies including FmHA are available to help the borrower with management problems.

Q. Is security required?

A. Each loan will be adequately secured by real estate to protect the interests of the lender and the government.

Q. How large may the loan be?

A. The maximum outstanding principal balance for insured loans is $200,000 and for guaranteed loans $300,000. In addition, the loan may not exceed the market value of the farm or other security.

Q. May a farmer have other income?

A. If otherwise eligible, and nonfarm income is needed to supplement farm income in order to provide a level of living comparable with that considered reasonably adequate for the area, he may be eligible.

Q. What does it cost to apply for a loan?

A. There is no cost to apply. If a loan is processed however, the private lender of a guaranteed loan may charge a reasonable fee for service, appraisal, and other services.

Q. Are other loans made by FmHA?

A. Loans also may be made to buy livestock and equipment and pay farm and home operating expenses, to convert farms to outdoor recreational enterprises, to build and improve rural homes and essential farm service buildings, to provide rental housing, to develop water supplies and carry out soil conservation measures, to install rural water and waste disposal systems, to develop watersheds, to establish businesses and develop industry, and to meet emergency credit needs of farms.

SMALL BUSINESS ADMINISTRATION

The Small Business Administration (SBA) has only been in the farm lending business since about 1976. Consequently, it is important to get the complete information on the lending policies of these institutions from either the local offices or their regional offices.

Q. Who is eligible for an SBA loan?

A. Those eligible to borrow include small manufacturers, wholesalers, retailers, service concerns, farmers, and other businesses for the purchase or expansion of their operations or to obtain materials or other working capital.

By law, the agency may not make a loan if a business can obtain funds from a bank or other private source. Therefore, you must first seek private financing before applying to SBA. To qualify as a "small" business in agriculture, your annual receipts must not exceed $1,000,000.

Q. What are the loan limits?

A. SBA may guarantee up to 90% or $500,000, whichever is less, of a bank loan to a small firm. If the loan is not obtainable from a private lender and if an SBA graranteed loan is not available, SBA will then consider advancing funds on an immediate participation basis with the bank. The agency share of an immediate participation loan may not, under current regulations, exceed $150,000.

Interest rates on SBA's portion of immediate participations, as well as direct loans, may not exceed a rate set by a statutory formula relating to the cost of money to the government. In the late 1970s this was usually between 6% and 7½%.

Copies of bulletins explaining the key features of SBA's principle lending programs are available at local offices or from the U.S. Small Business Administration, Washington, D.C. 20416.

SAVINGS AND LOAN ASSOCIATIONS

Savings and Loan Associations, sometimes called Building and Loan Associations or Cooperative Banks, have been around since 1831. Their original purpose was to provide a place for persons to save money while earning interest and to provide money for homeownership. These are still the principle uses of savings and loan associations. While some expansion of activity has taken place with certain associations, this is primarily a local attitude and each association may react differently to lending for the purchase of farmland. Most savings and loans still concentrate on lending on one-to-four family dwellings. Traditionally, over 80% of the funds of savings and loan associations go to properties of this type. Occasionally loans are made for commercial income properties for periods not longer than 25 years. Most land loans have been for short periods of time.

The loan officer of the local savings and loan association is the only sure way to procure information on the availability of this source in a specific area.

CHAPTER 9

Going in Debt: Notes and Mortgages

Differing philosophies about owing money will always abound. Fiscal conservatives of our society espouse the cause of liquidity and the need to structure a business with a manageable debt load. Thus, most members of the conservative school can be identified as old enough to remember the Great Depression. The financial survivors of that period had strong equities and ample cash reserves. The losers were those who were highly leveraged and who had insufficient cash to cover their debt positions.

The lessons of that period have faded with over forty years of inflation. Inflation always favors the borrower because the loan is paid off in cheaper dollars. Consequently, much of the real estate mentality is geared to maximum leverage, i.e., borrow as much as possible, pay it off as slowly as possible, and use the minimum equity required to make the deal. Only the future will determine the prudence of the gambler. However, the terms of the debt instruments strongly influence the desirability of a transaction.

The previous chapter discussed lending sources and the normal need to borrow money for the purchase of real property. If money is going to be loaned, the lender will want a promise of repayment. The document representing this promise has come to be known as a "promissory note." Since lenders are generally only comfortable with more than a promise, the device used to give them more security is called a mortgage or, in some states, a deed of trust.

PROMISSORY NOTE

The note is the basic loan form. It is the promise of the borrower to repay to the lender the amount borrowed. Also referred to as the mortgage note, this document is the evidence of the debt.

INSTALLMENT NOTE
Equal Annual

February 10 19_73_

FOR VALUE RECEIVED, the undersigned (whether one or more) promises to pay to THE FEDERAL LAND BANK OF ST. LOUIS, a corporation, or order, at its office in the City of St. Louis, Missouri, the principal sum of $ _120,000_ with interest on the whole amount of said principal sum remaining from time to time unpaid at the rate of _7½_ per centum per annum or at said bank's option at such other rate applicable to this class of loan as may be subsequently adopted by said bank all in accordance with the Farm Credit Act of 1971, the regulations of the Farm Credit Administration and as hereinafter provided, from date to maturity, payable annually, and reasonable attorney's fees if this note be placed in the hands of an attorney for collection; both principal and interest being payable on an amortization plan in _24_ equal annual installments of $ _9480_ each, unless the same be more or less by reason of a different rate of interest adopted as aforesaid, beginning on the first day of _March_ , 19_74_ and maturing annually thereafter, and a final installment of the balance of principal and interest remaining unpaid, payable on the first day of _February_ , _1998_ , unless this note shall be matured prior thereto by extra payments on account of principal. In the event that the period from the date of this note to the due date of the first installment is more or less than one year, the amount of the first installment shall be increased or decreased by a sum equivalent to interest for the period in excess of, or less than, one year.

The undersigned may at any time make advance payments of principal in any amount and the same shall not affect the maturity or amount of the installments thereafter to be made except that such shall operate to discharge the loan at an earlier date by reducing the number of future payments in proportion to the number of such installments paid.

The undersigned shall pay interest on the entire unpaid principal balance, the defaulted payments of principal and interest, attorney's fees and all advances made by said bank as provided in the real estate mortgage securing this debt at rates adopted and made applicable to this loan by said bank, including interest on defaulted and advanced items which shall now and at all times accrue at a rate of ten percent per annum or at a rate of one percent per annum in excess of the loan rate in effect for this loan whichever rate is higher, and if any payment herein provided for be not paid when due the remaining payments due thereafter and the whole loan in its entirety shall, at the option of the holder thereof, become immediately due and payable without notice, and if the debt be so accelerated the same shall bear interest until paid at the default rate in effect at the time of said acceleration.

The makers, endorsers, sureties, and guarantors of this note hereby severally waive presentment, notice of nonpayment, protest and notice of protest, and diligence in enforcing payment hereof, and consent that the time of payment of any installment or other payment due hereunder may be extended and that the indebtedness evidenced hereby may be reamortized without notice and hereby waive all defenses or right of offset which they or either of them may or might have against the payee, its successors and assigns.

For value received, the undersigned hereby guarantees the payment of the within note, according to the terms thereof, both as to principal and as to interest.
Federal Land Bank Association of

_____

By _____
        Manager

Jack Jones (SEAL)
Jane Jones (SEAL)
_____ (SEAL)
_____ (SEAL)
_____ (SEAL)

Q. What are the essential elements of a note?

A. The note should contain the following provisions:

Date of Note. The date the note is signed is important since it may be necessary to calculate the due date and the amount of interest.

Total Amount of Loan. The dollar amount is normally shown in numeral form, and is also written in the note.

The Promise to Pay. While the word "Promise" need not be used, it normally is to show that it is undertaking a binding obligation. If more than one person is signing a note, the promise may read "jointly and severally," which means that either party may be sued separately for the entire amount due, or the parties may be sued together.

The Payee. This insertion of the name of the lender is important not only for identification purposes, but also to insure that the note is negotiable. Thus, if the note states a promise to "pay to the order of" it is negotiable. The note may also state that the instrument is "payable to bearer."

Interest Rate. The note states the amount of interest payable from the date of the note. It is normally stated in a percentage per annum until paid. Immediately following is the method by which principal and interest are payable, either as a lump sum or by stated installments. To be negotiable, a definite due date must be shown.

Special Provisions:

Waiver of demand or notice of maturity or other requirements.

Agreement to pay costs of collection and attorney's fees in the event the note is not paid.

Penalty for late payment, normally at a higher interest rate.

Acceleration Clause gives the note holder the right to declare the entire principal sum due and payable upon default, or possibly upon the borrower's sale of the property without the lender's consent. This may also be called "due-on-sale" or "alienation" provision.

Prepayment Provision may be stated as a privilege or a penalty. When the note states that the payment is due on a specific date, the borrower may be prohibited from paying off the note ahead of schedule unless a penalty is paid. This concept reflects the right of the lender to do no more than what was initially anticipated under the terms of the note. Naturally, a borrower will want to provide for prepayment without penalty at anytime to allow him to refinance the property, or make it easier to sell the property. Normally, the only time that a seller will want a prepayment penalty is under one of the following conditions:

1. When the interest rate he is receiving is higher than what might normally be anticipated.
2. If the note is paid off early, the seller may void what was an installment sale for him (by taking more than 30% down in the year of sale) or may increase his rate of taxation if he receives a large lump sum in one year.

Endorsements. If the lender feels that the borrower is not capable of repaying the note, he may ask for a co-signer. When a party endorses a note for the accommodation of the maker, he becomes liable to the lender for repayment in the event that the maker defaults. This may also create a contingent liability on a balance sheet of a co-signer.

Non-Recourse Provision. In a low downpayment transaction, if the property later drops in value, the amount of the note may be larger than the value of the property. To protect himself from personal liability, a buyer will frequently want to limit his obligation to the property only. This means that if a foreclosure of the note and mortgage would be insufficient to satisfy the mortgage amount, the lender would have no further recourse against the borrower. The following is an example of a non-recourse provision of a note:

"The maker of this promissory note assumes no personal liability for payment of said note and the holder of this note is limited in his recovery to the property which is described in the mortgage executed simultaneously with this instrument."

This provision, which is very important in the purchase of land, may also be called an exculpability clause or a waiver of right to deficiency judgment. In any event, it means that the note holder can "look to the land only" for repayment of the debt.

Exoneration Clause. In the event the property is held by a person other than the owner, such as a trustee, the trustee may require a provision exonerating it from any personal liability under a mortgage.

Termination of the Note. When the entire debt has been paid, the note is terminated. When paid, the borrower should obtain a release, sometimes called a discharge. This release should describe the mortgage or deed of trust and where it is recorded, certify that it has been paid and that the lender is willing to have it removed from the record. This release should then be recorded so that the title to the property is clear from the note.

MORTGAGES

Q. Must a mortgage always accompany a note?

A. No, a note may be unsecured. In its simplest language, the mortgage secures the note. In other words, the mortgage is a security instrument which pledges real estate as collateral for the repayment of money. Some states use a deed of trust in lieu of a mortgage instrument, and while they have the same function, they are considerably different in form.

A mortgage involves two (2) parties, the borrower (mortgagor) and the lender (mortgagee). The mortgagor gives a mortgage to the mortgagee. This gives the mortgagee the right to foreclose on the property which is covered by the mortgage in case of a default on the promissory note. As long as the maker of the note makes the required payments on time, the mortgage does not come into play.

Individual state laws vary substantially as to how a mortgage is written and affects the property. In some states a mortgage actually becomes a transfer of title of the real estate subject to conditions. This is called *title theory.* In other states a mortgage is considered and treated strictly as a lien which is a claim upon property of another as security for the debt. This is called *lien theory.*

Q. What are the minimum mortgage requirements?

A. The following provisions reflect minimum mortgage requirements:

1. Mortgages should be in writing.

2. The parties to a mortgage must have the legal capacity to contract,

THE FEDERAL LAND BANK OF ST. LOUIS

Mortgage

Jack Jones and

Jane Jones, his wife

mortgagors, being justly indebted to THE FEDERAL LAND BANK OF ST. LOUIS, a federally chartered corporation, of St. Louis, Missouri, mortgagee, for money borrowed, hereby mortgage and warrant to said mortgagee the following real estate in _Home_ County, Illinois:

The South ½ of the Northwest ¼ and the Northwest ¼ of the Southwest ¼ of Section 7, Township. . .

together with all rights, interest, privileges, easements, and appurtenances thereunto appertaining, and the rents, issues, and profits thereof, and together with all improvements and fixtures now or hereafter erected thereon, including all heating, air conditioning, lighting, plumbing and water supply apparatus, storm windows and doors, window screens, screen doors, window shades, awnings, locks, fences, including gates, trees, shrubs and such other fixtures and improvements used or useful in the operation of the premises and all of the rentals, royalties, bonuses, payments and moneys which may at any time become due and payable under or by virtue of the terms of any and all oil, gas, coal and mineral leases now or hereafter covering said lands and all water, flowage, floodage, irrigation, and drainage rights pertaining to said property.

Mortgagors warrant that they have fee simple title to said premises, free of all encumbrances, and covenant and agree (1) to defend the same against all claimants whomsoever; (2) to use the proceeds of the loan secured hereby solely for the purpose specified in mortgagors' application for said loan; (3) to pay when due all taxes, liens, judgments, or assessments lawfully assessed against said property; (4) to keep said property insured to the satisfaction of and under policies deposited with mortgagee and insurance proceeds if not used in accordance with applicable Bank and Farm Credit Administration regulations for reconstruction of buildings destroyed are to be applied on the indebtedness hereby secured as mortgagee may elect; (5) that if mortgagors fail to pay taxes, liens, judgments, or assessments or to maintain insurance as hereinbefore provided, mortgagee may do so, and all amounts so paid shall bear interest as provided in the promissory note hereinafter described and be secured hereby; (6) that at any time hereafter the mortgagee may, at its option, require the mortgagor to pay mortgagee, along with each regular installment of principal and interest, an amount equal to a pro rata portion of the taxes, assessments, and insurance premiums next to become due, as estimated by the mortgagee who shall be the sole judge of the validity or legality of the taxes and assessments, but such additional amounts paid shall reduce the principal on which interest is charged until such time as the taxes, assessments, and insurance premiums are paid by the mortgagee thereupon increasing the principal balance on which interest is charged to the extent thereof, all being secured hereby; (7) that the mortgagor will not remove or permit to be removed, any buildings, improvements or fixtures hereby mortgaged, from said premises and will maintain improvements in good repair and refrain from the commission of waste and cultivate said premises in a good husbandlike manner; (8) that in the event the mortgaged premises or any part thereof are taken under the power of eminent domain or by condemnation the mortgagee shall have the right to require all or part of the proceeds of the award to be applied to the debt secured hereby; (9) that the mortgagee, its duly authorized agents or representatives, shall have the right to inspect the premises at all reasonable times; (10) that mortgagee may extend and defer the maturity of and renew and reamortize said indebtedness, release from liability any party liable thereon, and release from the lien hereof portions of the property covered hereby, without affecting the priority hereof or the liability of mortgagors or any other party for the payment to be secured hereby; (11) that if mortgagors default in the payment of said indebtedness, or with respect to any warranty, covenant, or agreement herein contained, then, at mortgagee's option, the entire indebtedness secured hereby shall forthwith become due and bear interest as provided in the promissory note hereinafter described and mortgagee shall have the right to enter upon and take possession of said premises and to foreclose this instrument; (12) to reimburse mortgagee for all costs and expenses incurred by it in any suit to foreclose this mortgage, or in any suit in which mortgagee may be obliged to defend or protect its rights or lien acquired hereunder, including all abstract fees, court costs, reasonable attorney fees and other expenses, and such sums shall be secured hereby; (13) and that in any foreclosure action or other proper proceeding the court may appoint a receiver for said premises, with the usual powers of receivers in like cases.

This mortgage secures a promissory note delivered concurrently herewith, in the principal sum of $ 40,000 , bearing interest as therein specified, payable in installments over an amortization period ending Feb.1, 1993 , and all renewals and extensions thereof, and all additional loans and advances, with interest thereon, which may hereafter be made by the mortgagee to the mortgagors or either or any of them during the life of this instrument, and any and all other present or future liabilities of the mortgagors or either or any of them to the mortgagee all subject to an interest rate variable at option of said bank as in said note provided.

Mortgagors waive, release, and relinquish all rights under and by virtue of the homestead and exemption laws of the State of Illinois.

Dated _____ Feb. 4 _____ , 19 73 .

_____(SEAL)   _Jack Jones_ (SEAL)

_____(SEAL)   _Jane Jones_ (SEAL)

ACKNOWLEDGEMENT

STATE OF ILLINOIS_____

COUNTY OF_____ None _____ } ss.

                                   I, the undersigned, a Notary Public
appointed for and residing in ___ None ___ County, Illinois, do hereby certify
that_____ Jack Jones and Jane Jones, his wife _____
personally known to me to be the person s whose name s _____ are _____
subscribed to the foregoing instrument appeared before me this day in person and
acknowledged that they signed, sealed and delivered the said instrument as
their free and voluntary act, for the uses and purposes therein set forth, including the release and waiver of the right of homestead.

Given under my hand and Notarial Seal this 4th day of February, 19 73

My commission expires_ June 1, 1974 _____ Dan Burns _____
                                                       Notary Public

such as being mentally competent and of legal age.

3. Since various kinds of interests in a property may be mortgaged, the specific interest being pledged should be specified.

4. A copy of the note is frequently made a part of the mortgage so that the full note is included for recording purposes.

5. The mortgage will contain language specifically mortgaging the property or granting the property by conveyance.

6. The mortgage must contain a legal description of the property.

7. Mortgages may contain many additional clauses varying the terms.

8. The mortgage must be executed by the mortgagor (borrower). The spouse may also be required to sign.

9. The mortgage must be acknowledged, delivered, and recorded. Like a deed, the mortgage should be recorded immediately.

DEEDS OF TRUST

Q. How does a deed of trust or trust deed differ from a mortgage?

A. A deed of trust, used in a number of states in lieu of a mortgage, actually conveys the land to a trustee (third party) to secure the payment. This conveyance carries with it a power of sale upon default, proceeds to

---

THE FEDERAL LAND BANK OF ST. LOUIS

Deed of Trust

*Jack Jones and
Jane Jones, his wife*

borrowers, being justly indebted to THE FEDERAL LAND BANK OF ST. LOUIS, a federally chartered corporation, of St. Louis, Missouri, the bank, for money borrowed, hereby grant, bargain and sell, convey and confirm unto Fred Fiduciary, Trustee, his successors in trust and assigns in fee simple, in trust, however, for the holder of the indebtedness hereby secured, and upon the trusts, terms, and conditions hereinafter set forth, the following real estate, together with the buildings and improvements thereon, in *Pleasant* County, Missouri:

be applied to payment of the debt with the remainder to the grantor. Wording describing the conveyance to a trustee is shown in the first paragraph of a deed of trust.

The major difference with a deed of trust is that a foreclosure becomes "non-judicial," as compared to mortgages. Since execution of a deed of trust actually conveys title to a trustee in the event of default, the trustee may then declare the entire obligation due and payable and set the time and place of sale where the property will be sold to the higher bidder, who is then awarded a trustee's deed. In this sale, there is no court proceeding and generally no period of redemption. The chief advantage to the lender is the short time necessary for foreclosure.

TYPES OF REAL ESTATE MORTGAGES

A first mortgage or senior mortgage means that this mortgage is the first lien on a property. The first mortgage holder has a claim on the property above all claims of other junior mortgages.

A second mortgage and later mortgages are usually called junior mortgages. This simply means that these mortgages rank lower or are subordinate to prior mortgages. Since prior mortgages have priority as to payment, the risk, and thus the interest rate, demanded for loans secured by junior mortgages is higher.

A balloon mortgage simply requires that a lump sum payment be made at the end of the term of the mortgage. Balloon mortgages may be either straight term mortgages, which have no provision for amortization of principal, or partially amortized mortgages, which require that some principal payments be made, usually for a short term, with a balloon for the balance at the end.

A balloon mortgage is frequently used to extend seller financing for a short period of time to allow the borrower (buyer) to accomplish his purpose within that period of time and then to pay the seller in full. As an example, a balloon mortgage may be used by a home builder who purchases 10 acres for the development and construction of 30 houses. The seller of the land may require that the buyer pay only 5% of the principal per year for 3 years, with the balance of the mortgage coming due at the end of the 3 year period.

A blanket mortgage is used in situations where several parcels of land are secured by one mortgage. The mortgagee is entitled to hold as security all of the parcels until payment of the mortgage is made in full.

A closed mortgage is one that cannot be paid off before maturity unless the mortgagee (lender) specifically later agrees to accept payment prior to that time.

Construction loan mortgage is, as the name implies, a construction loan made for the purpose of loaning money on a project where buildings or other improvements are under construction. The amount of the loan increases as the building progresses and is normally staged, based upon the building reaching certain points of completion; or increased monthly, based upon the percentage of the work complete at that time. For example, a construction loan may be made for the purpose of constructing a house on the following basis: 20% of the loan upon completion of the tie beam; 20% additional at the time the roof is "dried in;" 20% additional when electrical and plumbing are roughed in; 20% additional when finishing work is complete; and the final 20% when all inspections are complete.

Conventional mortgage is a classification which commonly refers to a mortgage from a lending institution not insured by the Federal Housing Administration (FHA) nor guaranteed by the Veterans' Administration (VA).

Leasehold mortgage is a mortgage of an interest in a lease.

An open-end mortgage allows a borrower to increase the amount of the original mortgage by a specified amount or by separate agreement as stipulated in the mortgage. This allows the borrower to obtain additional funds for anticipated uses. Repayment is made by increasing the amortization level.

Package mortgage is a mortgage which covers both the real property and the personal property on the premises.

Participating mortgage is a method used to "pool" a number of investors in a single group of mortgages.

Variable rate mortgages allow the mortgage rate to fluctuate with current market rates. It obviously favors the buyer when interest rates are high and the lender when interest rates are low. It does, however, tend to average out peaks to the benefit of both parties.

A wrap-around mortgage keeps the existing loan in place and the mortgagee assumes the payment of that existing mortgage and gives a new, larger mortgage at a higher interest rate. A wrap-around mortgage may also involve a seller who takes a second mortgage from the buyer for the total amount at a higher rate and uses the proceeds to pay off his original mortgage.

A stand-by mortgage, frequently used in development, is really more of a commitment than a mortgage. A major project, such as a shopping center, will require two kinds of loans from different lenders. A construction loan is required at the outset from an institution giving short-term money, such as a bank. However, before an institution will make a construction loan, it requires that a permanent loan is available when the project is complete. During periods of tight money or in situations where the developer has not yet secured the required number of leases or occupancy percentage to make a normal, permanent lender comfortable, some institutions will furnish a stand-by commitment. This commitment says that in the event the developer has been unable to find a permanent loan within a certain period of time, perhaps 2 years or at the end of construction, then they, the stand-by lender, will loan the necessary money to pay off the construction mortgage. Usually a stand-by commitment is made for a fee, perhaps two or three points (percentage), at the time the commitment is made and the interest rate may be several percentage points higher than what would normally be expected within the marketplace.

Gap mortgage financing is a technique which allows a developer to insure that he will have the necessary funds to cover his construction loan. If a permanent loan has been committed based upon certain occupancy rates and the project has not reached this point, the developer may need more dollars to complete the project and "trigger" the permanent loan which will be used to close out his construction loan. In that case, some lenders will extend a commitment for his "gap" to fill the difference between the permanent loan and the amount of the construction loan.

Again, very high rates are charged for gap financing.

Purchase money mortgage. A purchase money note and mortgage is given by the buyer to the seller as part of the purchase price. In other words, the seller carries a portion of the purchase price back as a mortgage. This may be in the form of a first, or more junior mortgages.

The land contract, also known as the installment land contract or contract for deed is a kind of credit arrangement for financing farm transfers. The principal differences between a land contract and a mortgage are:

1. No deed is immediately given to the buyer, and thus the seller retains legal ownership. A deed is given after partial or full purchase payment.
2. In case of default, state laws may not provide a period of redemption. Redemption may not be an absolute right as with a mortgage.
3. The rights of a buyer under a land contract are known as an "equitable interest" under the doctrine of equitable conversion, including possession.

A much more detailed description of a land contract is included in the chapter on Sale and Purchase Agreements. The land contract normally embodies all features of a purchase contract and a mortgage.

Mortgage Clauses & Terminology

Many of the provisions and terms found in the contract for the sale of the property continue through the note and mortgage documents. Certain of the following terms and clauses will also be discussed under those sections of this book relating to Contracts For Sale and Notes.

Q. What triggers an acceleration clause?

A. The term "acceleration clause" refers to a provision in a note or mortgage that requires immediate payment of the entire unpaid balance of principal and interest upon the occurrence of specific events. The first and most common event will be created through default of the borrower. Although the document may provide for immediate acceleration, most states have laws which allow the borrower a reasonable period of time in which to bring the debt current.

The other type of acceleration clause, also referred to as "due on sale" clause, makes the entire amount of unpaid principal interest due upon the sale, transfer, or further encumbrance of the property. The "due on sale" clause allows the lender to approve or disapprove of a buyer wishing to assume the loan, and may also allow him to demand an increase in interest rates or an assumption fee which he would not otherwise be able to do.

Q. Can a debt be transferred?

A. An assumption agreement allows one party to pay a debt incurred by another on terms contracted for by the original debtor. Strictly speaking, a mortgage is assumed when a formal assumption agreement is entered into between the lender and the new owner of the property. A property is taken "subject to" a mortgage when no agreement is made between the lender and the purchaser of the property. Under an assumption agreement, the primary responsibility for repayment of the mortgage falls upon the new owner. On the other hand, a "subject to" agreement allows the person who is the original maker of the note to remain primarily responsible for repayment. The fact that the new owner has made the payments since purchasing the property does not remove the obligation from the old owner since the new buyer had never agreed to do so in writing. The only party with whom the lender has a contract is the original borrower, unless the lender agrees to a substitution of parties.

Q. Could condemnation affect a mortgage?

A. Where mortgaged property is taken either in whole or part by eminent domain or condemnation proceedings, the award must be divided between the mortgagee and the mortgagor. Many states have a provision or a formula as to how to divide the award. However, there may be complications where there is a partial taking and in regard to interest payments. A specific clause may be desirable to direct how the proceeds should be paid, whether the first area should be to cover the cost of restoration of any buildings or whether the entire award should be used to pay off the mortgage. Directions may also be provided as to who should be allowed to negotiate with the condemning authority as to the amount of the award.

Q. *What is the technical term for "failure to pay"?*

A. Default. The default provisions will spell out the conditions that exist when a default has arisen, being the failure to make a payment called for by a note or mortgage. Default is specifically the failure to do what is required by the contract; various provisions such as grace periods, forfeiture, acceleration clauses, foreclosure, and others will relate to the state where the mortgage has been entered into.

Q. *How can I limit personal liability?*

A. Provide for waiver of deficiency judgment. When a mortgagee (lender) is entitled to the difference between the foreclosure sale price and a greater mortgage debt, this amount is called a deficiency judgment. This can be a very real personal liability in the event the property decreased in value after purchase. A frequent provision to waive a deficiency judgment is called a "no-recourse provision." Under this provision the borrower is removed from personal liability. It instructs the mortgagee to "look to the land only."

   A no-recourse clause may read as follows: "The maker of this promissory note assumes no personal liability for payment of the debt and the holder or payee of this note is limited in his recovery to the property which is described in the mortgage executed simultaneously with this instrument."

Q. *When can foreclosure begin?*

A. A lender is entitled to begin foreclosure proceedings when the borrower has defaulted in any of the mortgage terms. State laws vary; some allow a foreclosure suit which limits the right of redemption to a certain period. This may be known as "strict foreclosure."

   A foreclosure may be by public sale at which the property is sold, usually by the sheriff, to the highest bidder. This "foreclosure by sale" is probably the most common method of foreclosure in America today and allows the borrower to recapture a portion of his equity in the event the sale brings a price in excess of the remaining debt.

Q. *What is meant by forfeiture?*

A. Forfeiture means the right to terminate the contract (mortgage) and extinguish the buyer's interest in the land by a non-judicial procedure. Forfeiture is permitted only in a few states and usually only in conjunction with a "land contract" in which a specific forfeiture provision is part of the contract. Forfeiture is a harsh means of foreclosure since it forfeits the right of the borrower to recapture any of his equity. The doctrine of equitable conversion has led most states to allow forfeiture only in rare cases.

Q. *Would a raw land purchase require interim financing?*

A. Not normally. Interim financing refers to a temporary loan such as a construction loan that would be used from the time the project begins until the time the permanent loan is closed.

Q. *What kinds of closing fees are involved?*

A. Mortgage companies and lending institutions may charge a front-end or origination fee, which is an amount for processing of the mortgage application. A placement fee may be an additional charge of one or two percentage points of the total amount of the loan, thus allowing the lender to effectively receive a higher rate of interest on his loan.

Q. *Should the buyer insist on a prepayment provision?*

A. Yes. The privilege of prepayment without penalty is of benefit to the buyer because it allows him to reduce the overall amount of his interest charges or may permit him to refinance the property in a more favorable manner or may assist him in a resale. The prepayment provision will specify whether it is with or without penalty and what the penalty is. A seller may object to a prepayment clause because of the increase in tax liability if he receives large payments in a year. This will normally only apply where the sale was an installment sale. The seller may also want to keep his money invested and earning interest at a higher rate than he could otherwise realize.

Q. *What about redemption in event of foreclosure?*

A. Most states give a buyer a right of redemption if he has been foreclosed. The period of redemption will vary. Some states allow one year after the foreclosure sale and if during this time he can obtain enough money to meet his obligation, the property will be returned to him. Other states do not allow redemption and the original buyer's rights are cut off completely at the foreclosure sale.

Q. Can I own part of my land free and clear, leaving the mortgage in place?

A. Many mortgages will contain a release clause to allow the borrower to release certain portions of the property from the mortgage and own them free and clear. A release may be required if the buyer intends to construct a house or other buildings on a certain portion of the property and wishes to obtain a separate mortgage loan or construction loan on that improvement. A buyer of land for the purpose of building houses will insist that the mortgage contain specific release provisions, probably by lot. In this instance, a builder, having sold recently constructed houses, might use the proceeds to gain the release of a new group of lots on which he intends to build.

The provision may specify that upon the payment of a certain sum, a calculated portion of the property will be released. Some releases are known as "dollar-for-dollar releases," meaning that whatever percentage of the property is released will require an equal percentage of principal payment on the mortgage. Other release provisions may require a disproportionate payment. For example, if the amount of the mortgage is $1,000 per acre and the buyer wishes to have 5 acres released from the mortgage, the seller may specify in the mortgage that there is a "120%" release provision, meaning that the release price is increased by 20%, or $1,200 per acre. A specific release pattern must be specified in the mortgage.

Q. What is subordination?

A. Subordination is important to the buyer who plans to refinance an existing first mortgage in order to raise funds for improvements or for other purposes. If the seller is taking back a purchase-money mortgage, he will have to subordinate his claim to the refinanced mortgage if the refinancing is to be allowed. The seller may not object to this because his security supposedly will be increased by whatever improvement the buyer is planning to make.

If a seller has taken back a second mortgage, the purchaser will want him to be willing to subordinate to an increased first mortgage to avoid having to pay off the second mortgage. Obviously, the mortgage holder must evaluate how much equity remains in the property or whether his mortgage amount is jeopardized. While subordination is very important to the buyer because it reduces his required equity, it obviously must be carefully scrutinized by the seller because it reduces the amount of equity that he has guarding his loan, and thus increases his risk.

Q. What is the legal rate of interest?

A. Most states have laws limiting the rate of interest that may be charged. Rates may differ for the amount charged for an individual versus the amount charged for a corporation. Charging a rate of interest in excess of that permitted by law of the individual states is called "usury." When interest rates climb, the usury limits imposed by states frequently limit the amount of loans that a lender may extend because the cost of lending is higher than the interest rate that he may charge. As interest rates have climbed, many states have increased the usury limit, or have done away with it completely.

CHAPTER 10

From Contract Through Closing

The sale contract has been signed, containing the conditions for closing the transaction. The time lag before closing could be as little as 30 days, more likely 90 days, but possibly over a year. Preparations, however, are under way for that time when the transfer of title will occur, called "the closing".

Most buyers and sellers have some concern about their preparedness as the closing date approaches. Has everything been done? Is the closing statement ready, and correct? What about the closing papers--deed, note, mortgage, releases? How do I want to take title? While the attorneys, brokers, and title companies are involved in closings with some degree of frequency, the principals to a transaction are less familiar with the detailed procedures.

PRIOR TO DAY OF CLOSING

A *checklist of items* to be considered will help you, as a buyer or seller, to prevent last minute delays.

(1) Check Seller's Title

The sale contract normally requires the seller to provide an *abstract* or other evidence of title within a certain period of time. If he fails to do so, and the contract provides a "time is of the essence" provision, the buyer could claim the seller in default.

A puzzle occasionally arises, called "Who Has The Abstract?" Depending on the instructions, if any, which were given at the time of the last sale, the abstract could be at any one of the following places:

- At the abstract or title company office.
- In the hands of a mortgagee (the lender).

- At the lawyer's office.
- In the possession of the seller, but long forgotten. He probably should have kept it in his safe deposit box, but it could be anywhere.

While a lost abstract can be recreated through public records, it is costly and time-consuming. Abstracts should be kept with other valuable papers. Some lenders may insist upon holding information relating to title. It is not unknown for a recalcitrant borrower, foreclosed out of his property, to be less than cooperative in returning an abstract, and lenders like to protect against this possibility by holding the abstract while a note is unpaid.

Once the buyer, or his attorney, or a title insurance company, has received the abstract, an *opinion of title* will be rendered. Defects, if any, will be noted, and the seller has a stated period of time in which to convert these faults. If an attorney is handling the examination, he may then issue a *revised opinion of title,* showing clear title or any remaining problems.

Certain exceptions may be noted which do not affect *marketable title,* such as some public rights-of-way, easements, and other such restrictions. If a title insurance policy is to be issued to the buyer at closing, a pre-closing title *binder* or commitment is issued in anticipation of closing, when the final policy is issued.

(2) Decide How Title Will Be Taken

The sale contract always names a buyer, but title may be taken in another form at deeding or closing. The question of who should own the property is extremely important from the view of: family circumstances; tax aspects; the legal form of management to be operating the property; the type of property involved; and the purpose of ownership. If there are questions about how to take title, seek competent legal advice.

The following types of ownership include those most often used, although variations occur for specific purposes.

Individual Form
A. Sole Ownership by one individual
B. Tenancy in common
C. Joint tenancy
D. Tenancy by the entirety

Partnerships
A. General
B. Limited
C. Family

Corporations
A. Regular or "stand-up" corporations
B. Subchapter S corporations

Sole ownership by one individual. This type of ownership occurs when a person owns, or takes title to a property, solely in his name.

When a person owns property as the sole owner, he can determine what will be done with the property both during his lifetime and after death. Any determination of this sort is subject to limitations imposed by state law, but the sole owner has the most complete degree of control of any of the forms of property ownership. Such property will pass at death to the person named in the will or in accordance with the state laws if there is no will.

Note: In states that recognize dower (wife), curtesy (husband), or community rights, tax problems require special consideration.

Tenancy in common. If two or more persons own property as tenants in common, they each have an undivided interest in the whole property. Each person can sell or divide his share and transfer his interest in the property by will, gift, or other arrangements. No right of survivorship exists under this type of co-ownership. If one of the co-owners dies, his interest simply passes to those entitled to share or inherit his estate by virtue of his will, or to those entitled to inherit under state law if there is no will.

The obvious question is: Why should anyone ever own property in this form? Tenancy in common ownership does have its advantages under certain circumstances. Suppose, for example, two business associates decide to buy property to be used in their business operation. It may well be that, in order to be usable, the property will need to be preserved as one parcel.

Since the business associates may not be related, it does not seem practical to include a right of survivorship provision so that if one dies the other automatically takes his interest in the property. Therefore, they would very advisably use a tenancy in common arrangement, so that each would have an undivided interest in the entire property, but the property itself would not be divided. At the death of either of the business associates, his interest in the property would then pass to whomever he designates in his will, or under the rules for descent and distribution if he dies without a will.

It is also quite common for land to be owned in this form by several members of the same family. For example, suppose an older family member dies, leaving his entire farm property to all of his children in equal shares. Each child would then own an undivided interest in the entire property. While the property might well be suited to an equitable division so that each could take his separate interest, the family members might prefer to see the farm remain in one unit owned by all of them in this form of co-ownership. They would not likely want their interest to pass to the other brothers and sisters at the time of their own death, but probably would prefer that it go instead to their surviving children or spouses. The tenancy in common arrangement would be desirable under these circumstances.

Joint tenancy and tenancy by the entirety. Joint tenancy is similar to tenancy in common in that two or more parties hold an undivided interest in the property. The important difference is that the joint tenancy arrangement carries with it a *right of survivorship.* This means that at the death of one co-owner, the entire interest in the property passes automatically to the surviving co-owner or co-owners. Therefore, such interest cannot be conveyed by will and does not pass by operation of state law when there is no will.

The third type of co-ownership, tenancy by the entirety, is very similar to joint tenancy. Tenancy by the entirety also carries with it a right to survivorship. It can, however, exist only between a husband and wife. In some states there is no distinction made between joint tenancy and tenancy by the entirety. In other states a distinction is made, but basically in name only. The fact is that neither the husband nor the wife may individually, without the consent of the other, sever the tenancy, whether it is a tenancy by the entirety, or the regular joint tenancy arrangement between a husband and wife. In some states a presumption of the tenancy by the entirety exists between spouses when they hold property as co-owners. In other states a tenancy by the entirety must be specifically created between husband and wife.

There are a number of advantages normally attributed to joint tenancy and tenancy by the entirety property by virtue of the right of survivorship. The most important of these is the advantage of avoiding a probate proceeding which may delay transfer of the property upon the death of an owner and publicize the proceedings. Avoiding probate may save money.

Joint ownership is also advantageous when co-owners have property in more than one state. The right of survivorship in such a situation allows title to pass directly to the survivor and *ancillary administration* is eliminated. Ancillary administration is a probate proceeding which is required in states other than the state or residence of the deceased person. Elimination of this proceeding can result in considerable savings to the estate.

Joint ownership has its disadvantages as well. One such disadvantage of joint tenancy, or tenancy by the entirety arrangements in many families, is the fact that one loses testamentary control because of the survivorship features of the property. This can result in a person not being able to achieve the desired distribution of the property.

For example, suppose a husband and wife own all their property as tenants by the entirety. Assuming the husband dies first, the wife automatically becomes owner of the entire property. This means that she can make whatever disposition she chooses of that property during her remaining life or at her death. She could leave the property by the terms of her will to anyone she might choose. Also, she might remarry and in that way allow her second husband to share in the distribution of the property upon her death. Her deceased husband may have wished an equal distribution of the property among his children upon the death of his widow.

These are problems that can arise and should be clearly discussed and understood by all members of the family when property is held in a co-ownership arrangement. Another consideration in using joint tenancy arrangements is the possible effect on other family members, depending on the order of death of the parties.

A situation that can cause difficulty within the family is when property is held jointly with minor children. Should the parent die, the child becomes the owner of the property under the right of survivorship. This can pose special problems in many states where restrictions are placed on the ownership of property by minors.

One more problem that is often overlooked in considering joint tenancy or tenancy by the entirety arrangements arises from the tax effect of these types of arrangements at the death of one co-tenant. The federal and state tax implications of joint ownership are substantial, and require careful analysis before taking title in this manner.

General partnerships. The legal requirement for establishing a partnership is that two or more persons associate themselves for the purpose of conducting a business for profit. By tax law, a partnership may be a syndicate, joint venture, group investment, or other unincorporated entity doing business, and not a corporation, trust or estate. A true joint venture has important differences from a partnership as to the relationship established and should be closely scrutinized.

The laws under which a partnership operates are normally spelled out in the Uniform Partnership Act--the statutory law in most states. This Act provides the basic rules governing partnership operation, but also allows the partners to adopt additional rules as a part of the agreement. Thus, the partnership agreement becomes the rules of operation for the business, and should be put in writing with the help of counsel. Partners need to agree on such matters as:

Management	Taxation
Profit and loss sharing	Termination
Property ownership	Dissolution
Record keeping	

Where title to property is held in the partnership name, any of the partners may convey the title to that property by conveyance executed in the partnership name. This is true if the conveyance is carried on in the usual way and unless the partner making the conveyance has, in fact, no authority to act for the partnership in that particular matter. But if the person with whom he is dealing has no knowledge of the fact that the partner has no authority, the conveyance may be binding on the partnership even though the partner has exceeded his authority.

As an example, let us assume that a partnership has acquired certain real estate in its name. Further assume that the partnership agreement included a specific provision that no member of the partnership could convey any of the property of the partnership without the express written consent of the other partners. If one partner does, in fact, transfer the property in a normal business fashion, and the unsuspecting buyer has no knowledge whatsoever that the partner does not have this authority, then the partner's act will bind the partnership. The conveyance of the property will have to stand.

Another important aspect of partnership operation is that each partner is an agent of the partnership for the purpose of its business. The act of every partner for the apparent purpose of carrying on the usual business of the partnership binds the partnership unless the partner has, in fact, no authority to act for the partnership, and unless the person with whom he is dealing has knowledge of the fact that the partner is exceeding his authority.

Also very important in the relationship of the partners is the fact that if any partner acts in the ordinary course of business of the partnership, or with the authority of the other partners, and by his willful act of admission causes a loss or injury to any other person, the partnership is liable for the acts of the individual partner. In addition, the law provides that each partner is personally liable for all debts and obligations of the partnership. There is no way that the partnership agreement can protect a partner from this liability as to third parties.

Naturally, the agreement can contain provisions as to the division of the responsibility between the partners. These provisions are not binding on the third parties who have no interest in the partnership. Thus, partners' liability is one of the most often cited disadvantages of operating as a partnership.

Other considerations of a partnership include termination procedures. Normally partnerships dissolve upon death of a partner.

Income tax due as a result of a partnership is paid by the individual partners. A partnership tax return is filed for informational purposes only. This "pass through" provision is often viewed as an advantage of the partnership over a corporation, where profits are taxed at both the corporate and individual level--so-called "double taxation".

While complicated, partners may, by agreement, structure profit and loss distribution contrary to their interests in the partnership's assets.

Limited partnerships. A variation of the ordinary partnership is the limited partnership. This is an agreement in which one or more of the partners has only limited personal liability for the debts and obligations of business. Strict compliance with the requirements of a limited partnership is necessary for limited partners to avoid liability.

The limited partner cannot participate in management of the business, nor can his name appear in the partnership name. The partnership agreement must be in writing and specifically indicate the share of profit to be paid to the limited partner. The agreement must be recorded so that there is constructive notice to customers who may be doing business with the partnership. There are other technical requirements that should be understood before such a device is used; therefore, if this arrangement is contemplated, legal counsel should be used in drafting the agreement.

While the limited partnership is not, in itself, a tax shelter, it is frequently structured as one for many deals, including those involving real estate.

The chief advantage of this form of ownership is the combination of corporate and partnership traits. Limited partners have limited liability; profits and losses are passed through without double taxing; and the general partner provides a certain amount of control and continuity.

Family partnerships. One method of sharing income with family members is to become their partner. Many times children have little or no income, and if the partnership meets the rigid test of the tax code, the benefits derived from the tax savings are substantial.

Without going through the qualification tests, which a tax specialist should assist in, let's look at how a family partnership works: Assume you own the farm business individually. Let's say all of your expenses are paid from the business, and you have no other income. You and your wife file a joint return, taking the standard deduction. Your two children have no income of their own.

To split the income with your children (reducing the tax rate), each would receive as a gift 24% of the business. A family partnership agreement would be drafted paying you a salary; the balance could be distributed 24% to each child and 32% to yourself. The gift can be made through a trust. The total tax bill is normally substantially less.

A sample partnership agreement between a father and son is illustrated at the end of this chapter.

Regular or stand-up corporations. An increasing number of farm operations are incorporating to take advantage of the favorable characteristics of this form of business organization. Among the factors which have encouraged incorporation are estate planning, income tax minimization, continuity of management and ownership, and limiting personal liability. No one factor can be considered an advantage of the corporate form for all individuals. Careful consideration should be given to these factors, as well as other characteristics of the corporate form of business organization, to determine if incorporation will meet the needs of the owners.

A corporation is a separate "legal person" and a *tax entity* separate and apart from its shareholder owners. Because of this characteristic it can carry on a business, make contracts, hold property, sue and be sued, and has other rights and duties much like those of an actual person.

A corporation is organized according to the procedure set out in the statutes of each state. This involves a formal application and the payment of certain fees and taxes. Once approved by the proper state officials, the corporation can begin operation of the business in its own name. Since the corporation is an artificial person, the board of directors (elected by the shareholder owners) must choose the corporate officers and employees and authorize them to conduct the business.

In most family corporations the shareholders, directors, officers, and employees are the same persons. It is important that they observe the formalities and abide by the statutory rules of incorporation. They should treat the corporation as a separate legal entity and not commingle their personal business affairs with those of the corporation. Otherwise, if questions arise, a court might look through, or "pierce", the corporate form and treat the owners as partners which could greatly change their liability for corporate obligations.

One of the characteristics of a corporation is that it can be sued on contracts made in its name, or for torts (negligent acts) by its officers or agents. Since it is a separate legal entity, ordinarily these liabilities can be satisfied only from the assets of the corporation itself, and not from the personal assets of its shareholder-owners. It is because of this characteristic that some people chose the corporate form. It is a particularly favorable characteristic when the shareholder has assets that are outside the corporation.

Other of the advantages offered by the corporate form may include certain tax benefits. The regular corporation is taxed on its income to a certain level. The tax rate is less than the tax rate for individuals at high income levels. However, if dividends are distributed to shareholders, this income is taxed again as ordinary income.

Other potential tax minimization possibilities exist through the use of pension and profit-sharing plans and other fringe benefits for employees. Not only are some tax savings possible but, because the owners of the business are also employees of the corporation, retirement programs, group insurance programs, and other employee benefits are available that are not available to the partner or sole proprietor.

Subchapter S corporations. A small business corporation, assuming it meets the requirements, can elect to be taxed under Subchapter S of the Internal Revenue Code. The election is available to domestic corporations with ten or fewer shareholders having only one class of stock. All shareholders must be individuals, or estates of individuals, and no more than 20% of its gross receipts can come from royalties, rents, dividends, annuities, and sales and exchanges of stock or securities.

If the corporation meets all of these requirements, it may elect to be taxed in a manner similar to the method of taxation of a partnership. The corporation will pay no income tax itself but each shareholder reports his share of income actually received from the corporation and his pro rata share of the corporation's undistributed income.

The corporation which elects Subchapter S taxation still retains the legal attributes of a corporation, except taxation, and still shares any advantages of operation under the corporate form available to a regular corporation.

(3) Are Contingencies in the Contract Satisfied?

The sale contract may have called for certain "Conditions Precedent To Closing". The contract should have been specific as to form and method of satisfying these conditions. These requirements may have been imposed on both buyer and seller. The most typical contingencies deal with the satisfaction of requirements relating to:

1. Financing availability
2. Survey availability
3. Zoning
4. Site plan approval
5. Approval of all government agencies
6. Issuance of building permit
7. Soil tests

It is important to monitor the contract to make certain that all time schedules are met.

(4) Review the Survey

In addition to establishing the size of the property, which may govern the price, you should review the survey to gain reassurances as to other aspects of the property, such as:

1. Location of building and other improvements
2. Location of known monuments
3. Restrictions

4. Encroachments
5. Frontages
6. Streams, rivers, lakes, and other prominent physical features

(5) Conduct a Lien Search

If personal property is involved, or recent construction has occurred, you should ascertain that no bills are outstanding, and that property is free and clear of encumbrances. Lien waivers should be in order from all purveyors.

(6) Inspect the Property

There is no substitute for a detailed personal inspection of property being purchased. This attention to detail may reveal anything from a "squatter" to evidence of tenants, or recent removal of timber or other crops. Inspection may reveal unrecorded easements, or violations of zoning or building ordinances.

(7) Exchange Required Documents

The parties to the transaction should exchange copies of the actual documents several days prior to the actual closing date. Federal law requires that buyer be notified of settlement costs in advance. Not only are closings hectic, occasionally not all of the parties are available to make or agree to changes required. Documents requiring a preview include:

Deed	Survey
Mortgage	Leases
Note	Assignments
Releases	Tax bills

About deeds. Particular attention must be paid to the deed, as this is the form of conveyance used to transfer title.

The types of deeds used may vary from state to state since deeds are provided for by statute. The most common deeds are:

Bargain and Sale Deed - This deed conveys the property the seller has, but does not covenant or warrant the defense of title against future claims.

WARRANTY DEED

This Deed Witnesseth, that   Larry M. Landowner   Grantor, for and in consideration of the sum of Ten Dollars and Other Good and Valuable Consideration do by these presents, GRANT, BARGAIN AND SELL, Convey and Confirm unto   Ben Buyer and Betty Buyer, husband and wife whose mailing address is: Rt. 1 Grantees,   and their   heirs and assigns the following land situated in   White County, Missouri, to-wit:

The Northwest Quarter (NW¼) of the Southeast Quarter (SE¼) of Section Six (6), Township Five (5) North, Range Thirteen (13) West in White County, Missouri, containing Forty (40) acres more or less.

    TO HAVE AND TO HOLD The premises aforesaid with all and singular, the rights, privileges, appurtenances and immunities thereto belonging or in anywise appertaining unto said Grantees and unto   their   heirs and assigns forever; said Grantor hereby covenanting that   he is   lawfully seized of an indefeasible estate in fee of the premises herein conveyed; that   he   has good right to convey the same; that the said premises are free and clear from any incumbrance done or suffered by   him   or those under whom   he   claims, and that   he   will warrant and defend the title to said premises unto said Grantees and unto   their   heirs and assigns forever, against the lawful claims and demands of all persons whomsoever.

    WITNESS THE HAND of said Grantor this   23rd   day of   July   19

            Larry M. Landowner

In the State of   Missouri , County of   White , on this   23rd   day of   July   19 , before me, the undersigned, a Notary Public in and for said County and State, personally appeared

            Larry M. Landowner

to me known to be the person described in and who executed the foregoing instrument, and acknowledged that   he   executed the same as   his   free act and deed, and the said

            Larry M. Landowner

further declared   himself   to be unmarried.

Witness my hand and Notarial Seal subscribed and affixed in said County and State, the day and year in this certificate above written.

            (N.P. Seal)   Jane Official
                                   Notary Public

            My Term Expires   March 1, 19

Warranty Deed
(1) The general warranty deed (see illustration) is sometimes called the "full covenant and warranty deed". This deed gives the grantee the greatest guarantees possible.
(2) The special warranty deed is used in some states, and limits the grantor's guarantee to persons claiming "by, through or under" the grantor or his heirs.

Quit Claim Deed
Normally used to clear a "cloud on the title", by executing this deed, grantors simply release claims or interests, if any, that they may have in the property. No warranty or guarantee is involved.

Other deeds may include special purpose deeds:
1. Sheriff's Deed
2. Trustee's Deed
3. Referee's Deed
4. Executor's Deed

Normally, these are conveyances relating to court actions.

Essential elements of a deed include: (1) Names of grantor/grantee; (2) In writing; (3) Granting clauses; (4) Competent parties; (5) Adequate description; (6) Proper execution; (7) Delivery and acceptance.

Acknowledgment (declaration before a notary public) is necessary for a deed to be recorded. Recording does not affect title, but does protect the purchaser against subsequent conveyances by putting notice in public records. Deeds should generally be recorded as soon as possible after closing the land transaction.

(8) Arrange for Insurance

Prior to taking title, arrange for the assignment of existing insurance, or placement of new insurance, covering buildings against fire, windstorm and extended coverage, as well as general liability.

(9) Trial Closings

Trial closings are often helpful if a transaction is particularly complicated. Even if all parties are not present, many of the problems can be worked out in advance.

(10) Postponement of Closing

If buyer or seller is delayed from closing for valid reasons, the request for additional time should be made well ahead of closing date. If one of the parties is going to enforce a "time is of the essence" clause, such possible action should be known in advance.

ON DAY OF CLOSING

By the time the day of closing arrives, you should have completed a check of the items mentioned earlier. Closing will involve a final accounting of the deal, ending in an exchange of documents and money. The following items require attention.

Parties Needed At Closing

Normally, the persons sitting down in the closing room will include:

1. Buyer: husband/wife, all principals
2. Seller: husband/wife, all principals
3. Buyer's attorney
4. Seller's attorney
5. Title company representative (optional)
6. Loan officer if institutional loan is being placed
7. A closing secretary

Final Check Of Title

A final review must be made of the title records for the period between the date of the abstract or title search and the date of the closing of the sale. This will insure that only the encumbrances permitted by the contract will be in place. It is possible that liens may have been placed on the property during the interval.

Because of the time frequently required to examine the title, closings are often made in escrow as to the actual exchange of title and sales proceeds until this search is accomplished. In some locales, title companies have a title officer located in the courthouse. This allows the placement of a phone call at closing to give a timely report on the title which will allow closing at that moment.

BUYER'S STATEMENT

Date _____

NAME OF BUYER _____

NAME OF SELLER _____

NAME OF BROKER _____

ADDRESS OF PROPERTY PURCHASED _____

(1) Your loan of $_____ payable to_____
_____ in the amount
plus
of $_____ per month including interest at____%.

Your first payment will be due as of _____
_____

(1a) Your second loan of $_____ payable to
_____ in the amount
plus
of $_____ per month including interest at____%.

Your first payment will be due as of _____
_____

(2) Tax adj. Total annual estimated taxes $_____
We have given you credit for____ months____days taxes
in the amount of $_____. You are therefore to pay
your own taxes for this year when payable.

(3) Insurance. Your policy is for $_____ covering the
above property against fire and the extended coverage
provisions. The policy expires as of _____
_____.

Name of Insuring Agent_____

(4) Rent. Name of Tenant _____

Monthly rental $_____. Date rent is paid

to_____

Name of Rental Agent_____

(5) _____
_____
_____

I, we have examined the above statement and find it correct and acknowledge receipt of one copy.

_____
Buyer
_____
Buyer

	Debits or Charges to Buyer	Credits Due to Buyer
Sale Price	$	$
Earnest Money		
Deed of Trust (1)		
2nd Deed of Trust (1a)		
Interest Accrued		
Tax Adjustment (2)		
Insurance Adj. (3)		
Rent Adjustment (4)		
Miscellaneous Adj.:		
Recording (W. D.)		
" (D. of T.)		
" (Misc.)		
Attorney Fee		
Abstracting		
Credit Report		
Loan Fee		
Survey		
Insurance Reserve		
FHA Insurance Prem.		
Tax Escrow		
Title Insurance		
Notary Fees		
Appraisal		
Photographs		
Loan Guarantee Ins.		
Misc. Charges:		
Sub Total		
Balance due from you		
Total		

Sample Only

Approved by Legal Counsel for the Missouri Association of REALTORS®.
Form RE503—Printed and for sale by the Missouri Association of REALTORS®, P.O. Box 1327, Columbia, Missouri 65201—
Copyright 1969—Revised November, 1975.

(Used with permission.)

SELLER'S STATEMENT

Date _____

NAME OF SELLER _____

NAME OF BUYER _____

NAME OF BROKER _____

SALE OF YOUR PROPERTY AT _____

	Debits or Charges to Seller	Credits Due to Seller	
Sale Price	$	$	
Deed of Trust			
2nd Deed of Trust			
Interest Accrued			
Tax Adjustment			
Insurance Adjustment			
Rent Adjustment			
Misc. Adjustments			
Misc. Recording			
Attorney Fees			
Abstracting			
Survey			
Special Assessments			
Title Insurance			
Notary Fees			
Discount Points			
Sales Commission			
Misc. Direct Charges			
Sub Total	$	$	
Check herewith			
Total	$	$	

Important: Seller should preserve his copy of this statement for consideration by his income tax consultant when he files his next tax return.

I, we have examined the above statement and find it correct, and acknowledge receipt of one copy.

_____
Seller

_____
Seller

Approved by Legal Counsel for the Missouri Association of REALTORS®.
Form RE502–Printed and for sale by the Missouri Association of REALTORS®, P.O. Box 1327, Columbia, Missouri 65201–
Copyright 1969–Revised November, 1975.

(Used with permission)

Review All Documents

Don't be embarrassed to take the time necessary to read each document in its final form. Make a specific cross-check of the deed description and mortgage description. Usually this is best accomplished by reading the legal descriptions aloud to another party, making certain that they are correct on all documents. Mistakes are constantly found at the last minute, and there is no substitute for this final check to avoid having to spend additional hours and dollars clearing up mistakes.

Miscellaneous Charges

Any costs such as utility bills, insurance assignments, and other continuing matters that require proration should be calculated. These are normally part of the closing statement adjustments.

Closing Statements

The contract of sale usually stipulates that various closing costs will be paid by the buyer or seller. Local custom dictates who pays what costs in many instances. The pro rata costs are then assigned as credits and debits against the respective parties to result in a settlement of money due.

The closing statement will vary in format, and style is not as important as form. Sometimes buyer's and seller's statements will both be on the same form; or a separate buyer's statement and seller's statement may be prepared for each party. The statements should be reviewed and approved by the respective parties prior to and at the time of closing.

Seller credits may include:

- Full purchase price
- Unearned insurance premiums
- Supplies on hand
- Items paid by seller in advance

Credits to the buyer may include:
- Earnest money
- Existing mortgages
- Interest accrued and unpaid on existing mortgages

- Amount of purchase money mortgage to seller
- Unearned rents that have already been collected
- Deposits by tenants made as security for payment of rent
- Taxes
- Utilities, if not paid in advance

Exchange Of Documents And Money

Final steps at the closing are to exchange the respective documents and the consideration for the purchase price.

Documents to be obtained by the *buyer* at closing include:

1. Deed

2. Abstract or title insurance policy

3. Bill of sale of personal property

4. Closing statement

5. Survey

6. Paid notes on existing mortgages which buyer assumes

7. Releases of existing mortgages or satisfaction for mortgages if releases have not been recorded

8. Estoppel letter on existing mortgages

9. Insurance policies and assignments

10. Leases and assignments

11. Letter by seller to tenants advising them of sale

12. Letter by seller to other agents regarding sale

13. Statement by seller as to names of tenants, rents paid and unpaid, due date of rents, and assignment of rents

14. Receipt for taxes, special assessments, and utilities

Documents to be obtained by the *seller* at closing include:

1. Balance of the purchase price by cashier's check or equivalent

2. A purchase money mortgage and notes given by the buyer

3. Chattel mortgage on personal property sold

4. Mortgagee's title insurance policy

5. Insurance endorsements

AFTER CLOSING DATE

(1) Buyer should immediately record deed and any releases of mortgage obtained at closing.
(2) Evidence of title should be brought down to closing date in the event this was not done at time of closing.
(3) Seller should record any purchase money mortgages.
(4) Any remaining work on title insurance policies should be followed through.
(5) Buyer should attend to notification to utility companies, assessors, insurance companies, and other agents.

ESCROW CLOSINGS

The use of escrow closings varies substantially from one state to another. The advantages of an escrow closing are that often time simply does not allow the satisfaction of all details of the exchange of conveyance. For example, many states do not have a provision to check title immediately prior to exchanging documents between buyer and seller. Thus, a requirement must be placed on an escrow agent, normally a title insurance company, financial institution, or attorney.

The escrow agreement will dictate precisely what the escrow agent is required to do. The escrow agreement is normally in the form of instructions from the buyer and the seller to the escrow agent, and the agreement of the escrow agent to comply with instructions. In addition to the names and details of the transactions, the documents will be described. Directions will be given as to the delivery of the documents, disbursement of funds, deposits to be made, return of deposits in the event the transaction does not become final, reconveyance by buyer to seller in the event that problems cannot be cleared, payment of escrow, title and recording charges, commissions, and attorney's fees.

FATHER-SON PARTNERSHIP AGREEMENT

1. This farm partnership agreement is entered into this first day of January, 1976 by and between Irvin Improver, the father and Irvin Improver, Jr., the son.

ARTICLE I.

Name and Place of Business

1. The name of this farm partnership is Improver Farms.
2. The principal place of business shall be within the county and at such other places within or without the state as may be agreed upon by the partners.
3. Its legal address is Rural Route, Anytown, Anystate.

ARTICLE II.

Nature of Business

This partnership shall engage in general farming business, including the growing, purchasing and marketing of crops, livestock and other farm products and in such other businesses as may be agreed upon by the partners on the following described real estate:

> 500 acre grain and dairy farm located at Route 1, Anytown, Anystate and owned by Mr. and Mrs. Irvin Improver and on any other land which said parties may agree to rent or purchase for farming purposes.

ARTICLE III.

Duration

This partnership shall continue from year to year on the terms herein stated until this agreement is dissolved or until it is replaced by another written agreement. The agreement may be dissolved by either party serving notice on the other at least six months prior to the end of the year in which dissolution is desired.

ARTICLE IV.

Contributions

1. Each party shall contribute his entire labor and management to the farm business.
2. At the beginning of this agreement, the father shall sell to the son a one-half interest in his equity and all farm equipment, machinery and livestock. The son shall give to the father a personal note for the full amount of the transaction of said note, which bears interest at 7% and no due date.
3. The father shall contribute all feed and supplies now on the farm to the partnership without charge to the son with a stipulation that in the event the son leaves the partnership within the next five years the feed and supplies on hand at such time as the son may leave within that period

shall be considered the property of the father.

4. Hereafter, except for the above stipulation, all personal
   farm property raised for purchase shall be owned in equal
   shares by the father and the son and all debts against this
   personal property shall be the responsibility of the
   partnership.
5. It is agreed that the parents shall receive annual rent at
   the rate of 6% of the beginning equity in the real estate
   and that the partnership shall have use of the real estate.
   The parents will furnish all material for any capital
   improvements to the land and buildings until such time as
   other agreements shall be made between the parties.

ARTICLE V.

Profits and Losses

1. Farm Expenses. Farm expenses shall include the cash farm
   expenses and depreciation on farm improvements as indicated
   below.
2. Cash Expenses. The items include cash rent; crop expense;
   feed expense; livestock expense; livestock purchases;
   hired labor; custom work hired; farm insurance; purchase
   of new or used machinery and equipment; repairs and
   maintenance for farm machinery and equipment; repairs
   and maintenance for buildings, fences, tiling, ditches
   and water supply; property taxes; and miscellaneous farm
   expenses. Exceptions: (None)
3. Depreciation. The amount of the annual depreciation of farm
   improvements to be charged to the partnership is as follows:
   (None)
4. Farm Receipts. Farm receipts shall include income from
   all farm sources including such items as the sale of livestock and livestock products, crops, machinery and equipment, government payments, and custom work and other off-
   farm work by either party.
5. Inventory Changes. The difference between the beginning
   and ending values of "inventory" items of farm personal
   property, such as livestock, feed and grain, machinery and
   equipment, shall be considered inventory gains or losses
   annually and for the entire period of agreement.
6. Monthly Withdrawal of Earnings. Each partner may withdraw
   up to the total of the agreed upon monthly allowance.
7. Year-end Settlement. The net profits and losses of this
   partnership shall be shared as determined in this year-
   end settlement procedure:
   (a) from the total cash income for the year shall be
       subtracted the farm cash expenses to obtain the net
       cash partnership income;
   (b) from the net cash partnership income will be deducted
       the allocations for each partner's labor contribution
       and for each partner's property contribution;
   (c) the balance remaining is equally shared as returns
       for management.

ARTICLE VI.

Records and Accounts

1. Irvin Improver, Jr., shall have the responsibility and duty
   to establish and maintain the account books and records of

this farm partnership for the purpose of showing partnership income and expenses, each individual's contributions and income status, the financial condition of the business and other information necessary for the good management of the farm business. At the close of each year he shall make a full accounting. The books shall be open to inspection by the partners at any reasonable time.
2. The partnership accounts shall be on a cash basis.
3. A capital account shall be maintained showing the ownership interests of each partner. The capital account of each partner shall consist of his original contributions at the start of this partnership plus any additional contributions and minus his share of partnership losses and of capital distributions made to him.
4. An inventory of all farm real estate and farm personal property shall be taken at the beginning of this agreement and then annually, and these inventories shall become a part of this agreement.

ARTICLE VII.

Partners' Powers and Limitations

1. A partnership bank account shall be established and maintained by the Hometown Bank at Anytown, Anystate. Checks drawn on this account shall be signed by either partner.
2. Without the consent of the other partner no partner shall:
   (a) Make, execute, or deliver an assignment of partnership property for the benefit of creditors.
   (b) Contract to sell or lease any of the property of the partnership.
   (c) Submit a partnership claim or liability to arbitration.
   (d) Confess a judgement against the partnership or any of his partners.
   (e) Dispose of the good will of the business or do any other act that would make it impossible to carry on the ordinary business of the partnership.
   (f) Admit a new member to the partnership.
   (g) Act as surety, guarantor or accommodation party to any obligation in the name of the partnership.
   (h) Sell, mortgage, lease, or assign any partnership real property.
   (i) Borrow or lend money on behalf of the partnership.
   (j) Compromise any claim due the partnership.
   (k) Hire or dismiss any hand or other employee.
   (l) Contract or incur expenses or indebtedness on behalf of the partnership in any transaction involving more than $1,000.

ARTICLE VIII.

Death of Either Party

In the event of the death of either partner, this partnership shall terminate. In the event of the death of the son, the father shall have option to buy the son's share of jointly-owned farm property at the inventory value as of the previous January 1. The father shall accept or reject said option within 60 days of the death of the son, and if he accepts, shall pay at least 25% down, and the remainder within three years. If he rejects the option to buy the son's share, the jointly-owned property shall be sold at private or public sale within six months.

In the event of the death of the father, the son shall
have the option to rent the father's share of all farm property
used in the farm business at 6% of the inventory value as of
the previous January 1. The option to rent shall be on a
year-to-year basis, to be renewed by the son at his discretion
for a total period not to exceed _five_ years from date of the
father's death. At or before expiration of the _five_ year rental
period, the son may exercise an option to purchase the father's
share of all farm property at the value listed on the farm
inventory books the January 1 prior to the father's death.
If he exercises the option to buy, he must pay at least 10%
down and at least _10%_ additional each succeeding year until
the debt is paid in full.
    If the son fails to exercise his option to rent, or upon
expiration of the rental option period, if he fails to purchase,
then all jointly-owned farm property shall be sold at private
or public sale.

ARTICLE IX.

Dissolution of Partnership for Reasons Other
Than Death of a Partner

It is agreed that if the son wishes to dissolve the
partnership, he shall give the required _six_ months notice,
and he shall offer his share of all jointly-owned property to
the father at the book value as of the previous January 1.
    The father shall accept or reject this offer within 60
days, and if he accepts, shall pay the son a minimum of 25%
down and the remainder within three years.
    If he rejects the option, the jointly-owned property
shall be sold at public or private sale within the period
required for dissolution.
    If the father wishes to dissolve the partnership at any
date prior to January 1, 1979, the method and details of
dissolution shall be decided by family conference or, if
necessary, submitted to an arbitration committee. If the
father wishes to dissolve the partnership at any time after
January 1, 1979, he shall offer his share of jointly-owned
property to the son at the inventory value as of the previous
January.

1. If the son accepts the option, he must pay at least
   10% down and the remainder in equal installments over
   a period of ten years. If he rejects the option, the
   property will be sold at public or private sale within
   the required period for dissolution.

ARTICLE X.

Arbitration

If any matter pertaining to the farm business cannot be settled
by mutual agreement, that matter shall be submitted to one
disinterested person agreeable to both.

IN WITNESS WHEREOF, the parties have hereunto set in hands in
duplicate this first day of January, 1976:

Irvin Improver, Jr.   Irvin Improver

CHAPTER 11

Planning and Achieving Ownership Objectives

Successful farm and ranch ownership is achieved by planning and putting into effect a combination of resources to reach the goals established by the owner. The creation of a plan is mandatory after a property is purchased, but establishing objectives may also be the catalyst to trigger the would-be buyer into action. Establishing a set of objectives for the property will make a buyer more confident in his purchase decision.

The operating plan evolves from two factors:

1. The characteristics of resources available including land, labor, capital, and management.
2. The personal motivations of the particular owners involved.

DEVELOPING OBJECTIVES

An established owner-operator acquires additional nearby acreage to expand his existing enterprises with his objectives clearly defined. Added cropland may allow him to more fully utilize machinery and labor available. Extra pasture or forage acreage increases livestock feeding capabilities. Perhaps land that he has been leasing is now being sold to settle an estate, and to protect the size of his present operation, he is forced into a buying posture.

Not all land owners have the advantage of the years of experience of an existing operator, however. Land ownership evolves from many circumstances. For instance:

1. A daughter falls heir to land her father bought years ago.
2. A doctor buys a place to relax on weekends, but views the land as an investment, too.

3. A stockbroker seeks out land for income and as a hedge against inflation.
4. A businessman and father wants something of real value to leave to his children.

Whatever the reason, the intelligent approach is to define the goals of ownership and then adopt a plan that will lead to the realization of those objectives. A general objective of nearly all farm and ranch buyers is to achieve the maximum return on capital invested. Short and long-range goals will differ according to the circumstances of the buyer.

The farm family may consider several of the following goals:

1. Achievement of a better life style by increasing cash flow.
2. An increased sense of well-being and security from accelerating mortgage payments, thus reducing debt.
3. Provision of college education funds for the children.
4. An increase in size of the operation to provide a place for a son or son-in-law.
5. A desire to provide for adequate retirement income.
6. The satisfaction of conquering challenges by running a larger and more successful business.

An investor with substantial outside income, while interested in cash flow, may look for maximum deductions in the form of depreciation and qualified deductible expenses. Proper strategy will be to increase the property values by spending deductible dollars for several years to produce a capital gain at time of sale. This allows the conversion of ordinary income to a more favorable long term capital gain tax treatment.

The weekend user may only be interested in the most carefree operation possible if he is motivated by recreation and relaxation. Cover left for wildlife, and ponds developed for fishing and bating, may be among his priority objectives.

One Objective May Be Quick Profit

Any of the above individuals may become opportunists and capitalize upon the demand of erstwhile city dwellers seeking an expanded lifestyle by acquiring an acreage in the country. If so, an operating plan is very short term in nature.

An example: You come into possession of a 240 acre farm, 50 miles from a city of 500,000 people. The illustrations shown on the following two pages, depict the property in "before" and "after" situations. The property has rolling topography with one-third in woods, two-thirds in tillable land or pasture with a small creek running through it. Road frontage is available on two sides.

The property is in a run-down condition. As is, it's worth $550 per acre, or $132,000. With close proximity to an urban area of some size, there's a huge market for weekend places, and retirement acreages. Also, there is always demand for decent, tillable crop acreage from adjoining farmers.

For purposes of this discussion, planning and zoning requirements, platting needs, and other government regulations that must be considered will not be addressed. Beyond attention to these matters, a rural subdivider would apply the following techniques:

Buildings

1. Tear down structures not salvageable, or functional.
2. Treat the balance to cosmetic repair.
3. Remove all junk and distracting features like deteriorated fences, gates, and corrals.
4. Put up new fences around the house, dress up the farmstead, trim trees, cut weeds, seed lawns, etc.

Cropland

1. Repair badly eroded areas by seeding into grass.
2. Combine fields by removing cross fences.
3. Remove hedgerows or scattered trees from best crop area.
4. Get a good crop planted--fertilize, etc.

Pastureland

1. Repair or replace fences, gates, corrals.
2. Brush-hog all weeds, tall grass, and undesirable shrubs.
3. Reseed if necessary; clean up any areas of debris.

Woods

1. Cut some trails to the creek.
2. Brush-hog and clean up open areas in woods and along creek.

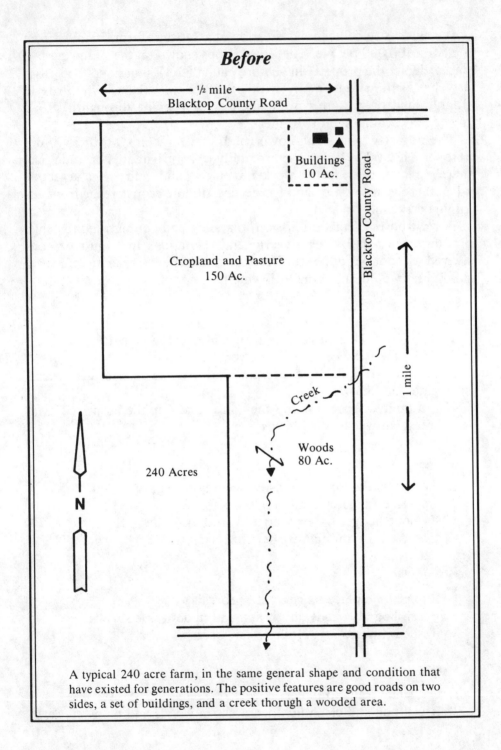

Before

½ mile

Blacktop County Road

Buildings
10 Ac.

Blacktop County Road

Cropland and Pasture
150 Ac.

1 mile

Creek

240 Acres

Woods
80 Ac.

N

A typical 240 acre farm, in the same general shape and condition that have existed for generations. The positive features are good roads on two sides, a set of buildings, and a creek thorugh a wooded area.

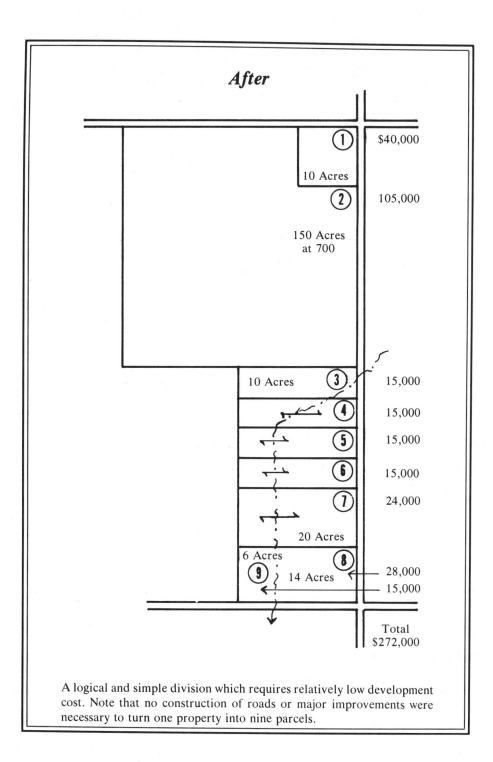

After

①	$40,000
10 Acres	
②	105,000
150 Acres at 700	
10 Acres ③	15,000
④	15,000
⑤	15,000
⑥	15,000
⑦	24,000
20 Acres	
6 Acres ⑧	
⑨ 14 Acres	28,000
	15,000
	Total $272,000

A logical and simple division which requires relatively low development cost. Note that no construction of roads or major improvements were necessary to turn one property into nine parcels.

In two years, the property could be divided and resold as shown on the "after" illustration. The results should look like this:

Sale Price		$272,000
Purchase Price	$132,000	
Renovation Cost	30,000	
Total	$162,000	162,000
Profit		$110,000

The profit is ordinary income, not capital gain, because you have subdivided the property. However, the downside risk is almost zero, assuming you know what you are doing.

This is not a sophisticated plan. No sentiment is involved. Some owners may shrink from cutting up the property, even though there are now 9 happy landowners. It's all a matter of philosophy.

ANALYSIS OF RESOURCES

Once the objective of the owner is established, the property must be examined in detail. An inventory of the physical attributes will bring into focus the process called for to achieve the objectives.

The owner's level of experience and capability will dictate the amount of assistance he should seek. Even the experienced, however, should view his latest acquisition as a stranger and take some time getting to know its disposition. The inexperienced may determine that professional farm or ranch management is needed; the employment of skilled and experienced managers who know economics, crops, soils, animal science, and management techniques.

The following outline demonstrates the process used by many experts to establish and implement a game plan for operating properties.

Establish A Permanent Record System

Insurance and Taxes. Adequacy of insurance coverage should be evaluated and a record of insurance maintained. As policies are renewed, changes in coverage occur, or new buildings are included, a proper record will reflect these changes. The assessed valuation and real estate taxes should be compared each year to insure fair and equal treatment.

Accounting Records. A farm accounting system is essential in organizing, operating, evaluating, and adjusting farming operations. Prepared accounting formats are available from most extension divisions of land-grant colleges. Staff management specialists can provide assistance.

Plats and Maps. A permanent property map and aerial photo should be part of an operating manual. The location of buildings, field boundaries, prominent physical features, drainage tile, and permanent measurements are included on this map. The various acreages of crops affected by government programs, and the ASCS (Agricultural Stabilization and Conservation Service) identification for the farm, should also be included. A current crop plat with previous years' history should be part of the records. These plats provide convenient work sheets for determining future plantings. A map showing the location of soil samples and the results of the tests should be included in the field book. Lime and phosphate maps help to plan fertilizer programs.

Machinery and equipment. An inventory of these items should include an accurate description; date of purchase and cost; total value; and depreciated value, adjusted annually.

Farm Buildings. On improved farms, a farm building sheet should include the following data for each building or structure: dimensions, including storage capacity; type of construction; type of roof and foundation; and approximate age.

The present condition of the building should also be included, and any additions after the original building inventory added as they occur.

Operating Contract. A copy of this document should always be available for reference to lease questions.

Inspect The Property And Gather Information

Off-Farm sources of information. The government offices located nearby can provide a great deal of reliable information. Information can be obtained at the county ASCS office regarding the property, including an aerial tracing of the farm property. In some cases an old aerial map of the farm may be available for your use. A new one should be ordered. Gather the government information for the farm such as base acres, average yields, tillable acres, and the acreage of the various individual fields as measured by the ASCS staff. Also report the change of owner to the ASCS office.

Check with the SCS (Soil Conservation Service) office and determine whether the soils have been mapped. If so, make a tracing of the soil types. If the property hasn't been a cooperating farm, make application for a soil report, including mapping productivity.

On-Farm Sources. If the property is leased, arrange to meet the tenant. Explain your inspection. The tenant may wish to accompany you on your field inspection, which should be encouraged. His experience with the property may be helpful in developing a plan.

A thorough field inspection, preferably by walking, will disclose invaluable information available in no other manner. A copy of the aerial photo and soil map should be in hand. Drainage and erosion problems should be noted. Type and condition of fences will be apparent. Ways to improve the efficiency of the property, such as removal of cross fences, hedge rows, and old building sites will be obvious. Observe wooded areas to be cleared or improved. Noxious weed problems and pasture conditions should be noted.

If the tenant did not accompany you on the field inspection, when you return to the farmstead you should ask questions about items you observed. Also request that an inventory of crops, livestock, machinery and equipment be completed. The inventory should include a breakdown of the tenant's machinery. Make notes regarding condition of the crops and the quality of the livestock.

The buildings should be measured and examined to determine building summary information and adequacy for the planned operation. Location of wells and water systems should be noted.

If a copy of the lease is not available from the previous owner, ask the tenant if you may borrow his copy to make a duplicate for your records. Where there is no written lease, verify the terms and promptly reduce them to writing.

Convert Data To A Plan

After the basic information has been gathered and the objectives are known, begin combining the resources to develop a program. In many cases, the type of operation is set and the task is to develop the best working program. If a decision is needed as to the type of operation, the considerations discussed below are the most basic.

Determine the crops and livestock which would be produced in an average year utilizing those practices which are feasible for the area with a high income crop combination while still maintaining the productivity of the land.

Determine the type of operation: cash rent, crop-share, direct, or other. What could be obtained for the pasture and farmstead area in relationship to the return from a livestock operation?

Consider the buildings available; do they provide adequate housing for livestock to utilize the feed produced on the farm? What capital expenditures are justified for building expansion?

ESTABLISHING A FINANCIAL PLAN

A major factor in the success of a farming operation is sound financial management. Good records are essential to determine year-end financial standing; to measure operating success, and cash flow projections for the coming year. When a bank or other lenders look at loan requests, proper financial records form a necessary part of a potential borrower's credibility.

The most useful financial statements to summarize a farm's financial position and demonstrate managerial ability are the balance sheet, income statement, and cash flow projection. To be most useful these statements should be compared over a period of time. If not available from previous years, there is no better time to start keeping these statements than now.

The statements shown are for illustration only--each is one of many varied forms available through many sources including banks and Production Credit Associations (PCA's), record associations, and state universities.

Balance Sheet

The balance sheet, also referred to as a net worth statement, is a summary of all assets and liabilities in the farming operation at a specific point in time (normally the last day of each year). The difference between total assets and total liabilities represents the owner's equity (net

Balance Sheet (Net Worth Statement)

Year_____

	Beginning	End
ASSETS		
Cash on hand		
Notes, accounts receivable		
Securities		
Feed, crop inventory		
Supply inventory		
Livestock held for sale		
Life insurance cash value		
Other current		
Total current		
Dairy, breeding stock		
Machinery, equipment		
Major household items		
Other intermediate		
Total intermediate		
Farmland		
Farm improvements		
Other long term		
Total long term		
Total assets		
LIABILITIES		
Notes, accounts payable		
Liens, past due items		
Rent, taxes, interest due		
Loan payments due this year		
Other current liabilities		
Total current		
Dairy, breeding stock debts		
Machinery, equipment debts		
Other intermediate debts		
Total intermediate		
Farm real estate debts		
Other long term debts		
Total long term		
Total liabilities		
NET WORTH		
Increase from previous year		

worth) in the business. Comparing current balance sheets with those of past years determines the rate of net worth growth or decline from year to year. The major purpose of the balance sheet, therefore, is to show the overall liquidity and solvency of the business.

Assets. Assets should be categorized, as shown in the sample statement, into current, intermediate, and fixed or long term. Current assets include all cash or assets that can be easily converted to cash or used within a 12 month period--livestock to be sold, feed, grain, supply inventories, and notes and accounts receivable.

Intermediate assets usually cannot be converted to cash within a 12 month period, but as a rule have a productive life of 1 to 10 years. These assets contribute to the productivity of the business over several years-- breeding livestock, machinery, equipment, and so forth.

Fixed (long term) assets also are needed to produce income, but they are not usually liquidated for the life of the business, or at least for a period of 10 years or longer. Fixed assets are usually land and buildings.

Liabilities. Liabilities are divided into the same categories as the assets. Current liabilities are debts payable within the year. These include personal property, real property and income taxes; interest on outstanding loans; charge accounts; operating notes due within the year; and annual payments on intermediate and long term loans.

Intermediate liabilities are usually payable in 1 to 10 years. Most commonly these liabilities represent the outstanding balances owed on loans or sales contracts for breeding livestock, equipment, farm buildings, and machinery.

Long term liabilities are those obligations that have a repayment period exceeding 10 years. Most common items within this category are outstanding amounts owed on land mortgages and contracts and on farm improvements.

Valuation of Assets. Valuation of assets is probably the most difficult step in constructing the balance sheet. The question arises as to whether book value (cost less depreciation, if any) or current market value should be shown for such assets as machinery and land. Economists may recommend using both by a double column balance sheet with cost or basis shown in one column and current market value shown in the other column.

Operating Statement (Profit and Loss)

Year_____

	Projected	Actual
INCOME		
Raised livestock sold		
Crops sold		
Other		
Purchased livestock sold		
Total current income		
Dairy, breeding stock sold		
Other capital assets sold		
Total capital asset sales		
Total cash income		
EXPENSES		
Hired labor		
Repairs-machinery		
Interest, rent		
Feed		
Seed, chemicals		
Fertilizer, lime		
Machine hire, trucking		
Farm supplies		
Livestock expenses, veterinary		
Gasoline, fuel, oil		
Taxes, insurance		
Other		
Other		
Livestock purchased for resale		
Total current expenses		
Net cash income		
Market livestock inventory change		
Feed, crop inventory change		
Supply inventory change		
Total inventory change		
Accounts receivable		
Accounts payable		
Net operating profit		
Machinery, equipment value change		
Dairy, breeding stock value change		
Buildings, improvements value change		
Total capital asset change		
Profit or loss from operation		

The same approach, they say, can be used for liabilities. Using the two values, the effects of inflation on a changing net worth can be evaluated--it also aids in evaluating potential estate tax problems.

Uses Of A Balance Sheet. There are several uses of a balance sheet other than to show equity in the business at a given point in time. For example, to show how critical a financial loss would be to the equity and leverage position of a business; or to indicate the amount of collateral (such as machinery, land, or inventory assets being held for later sale) available to support loan requests. The balance sheet also provides an annual inventory of assets and liabilities to aid in preparing an income statement and cash flow projections.

Operating Or Income Statement

While the balance sheet provides a financial picture of the business at a given point in time, the income statement reflects its profitability or success over a period of time, usually from the beginning to the end of the tax year. It is a summary of all farm receipts and financial gains during the year, minus expenses and financial losses. An income projection for the year ahead can therefore aid in planning and budgeting.

The income statement may show a good profit situation for the year, but it does not give the full financial picture. Though reasonable profits and generation of cash are indicated by this statement, the business could be in an unhealthy financial condition. Overall financial situation can be determined only through coordinated use with the other two statements discussed.

Cash Flow Projection

Unlike the balance sheet and income statement, which focus primarily on an analysis of the past or present, a cash flow projection is directed toward planning and budgeting for the coming year. Essentially, cash flow is the connecting link between the profitability of a business as shown in the income statement and its liquidity or solvency as revealed in the balance sheet.

Simply, a cash flow statement or projection is a listing of all anticipated cash inflows for the year ahead, farm and nonfarm, and all projected cash outflows, including farm operating expenses and capital outlays, along with family living expenses and tax payments. The annual

Cash Flow Projection

	Jan.	Feb.	Mar.	Apr.	May
INCOME					
Raised livestock sold					
Crops sold					
Other income					
Other income					
Other income					
Purchased livestock sold					
Current income					
Dairy, breeding stock sold					
Capital assets sold					
Asset income					
Total cash income					
EXPENSES					
Hired labor					
Repairs-machinery					
Repairs-buildings					
Seed, chemicals					
Fertilizer, lime					
Interest					
Other					
Other					
Livestock for resale					
Current expenses					
Dairy, breeding stock					
Other assets					
Asset expenses					
Total expenses					
Cash balance					
Loan payments (Principal)					
Loan payments (Principal)					
Total principal paid					
Business cash balance					
Cumulative cash balance					
Family living needs					
Life insurance payments					
Total family expense					
Net cash balance					
Net cumulative balance					

projection for each of these items is spread to appropriate months. Existing debt repayment commitments are included in the monthly breakdown. The difference between cash inflow and outflow anticipates cash shortages or excesses month by month.

A cash flow projection demonstrates to a lender when and how much credit is needed and when it can be repaid. With any loan request, repayment ability is a prime consideration. A cash flow also helps plan sales and purchases to minimize credit needs, and shows when a surplus of cash is available for capital investments and/or purchases, as well as for making repayments on outstanding loans.

Records of cash flow from previous years can provide a history of how cash moves in a business and aids in preparing year-ahead projections. Further, by comparing actual with projected cash flow during the year, one will be able to monitor actual with planned performance. It can alert an owner to problems, allowing adjustments wherever possible.

It is useful to prepare more than one cash flow projection in order to take into account variables in prices and production costs. This helps to identify the financial range within which the business can reasonably operate.

AGRICULTURAL SERVICES & TECHNOLOGY

Professional Farm Management Services

The complex nature of modern farming methods has created a need for the informed specialist who is conversant with production planning, marketing, leasing, record-keeping, and the many details of farm operations.

The membership of the American Society of Farm Managers and Rural Appraisers is comprised of trained, experienced professionals, dealing primarily with agricultural operations. A roster of their membership is available from the association office at: *P.O. Box 6857, Denver, Colorado.*

Farm management is available on a fee basis from trust departments of banks, agricultural colleges, individuals, and many private firms offering primarily management, appraisal, and consultation services. One of the oldest, largest and most diversified is Doane Agricultural Service, headquartered in St. Louis. In addition to management and consultation, their internationally operating services include real estate brokerage, investments, appraisals, publishing, and marketing research.

Professional firms are especially useful to the non-resident owner. Services performed include:

1. Operating decisions
2. Commodity marketing
3. Production planning and supervision
4. Leasing arrangements
5. Input purchasing
6. Record-keeping and reporting

Agricultural Consultation Services

Many farm owners who need management advice but do not require the full scope of professional farm management services employ agricultural consultation services. These services are structured to become a supplement to your present operation. Instead of providing continuous management of the operation, the consultant can be employed to solve a specific problem. Periodic visits will help ensure that the operation is running at peak efficiency and maximum potential.

Consultation services respond to the following kinds of questions:

1. Is an increased rate of growth a major objective?
2. Would you like to have a higher net return from investment?
3. Do you need to develop long-range goals for your operation and a plan for reaching them?
4. Do you have adequate equity capital or operating funds to carry out your planned programs?
5. Do you need help to identify "soft spots" in an operation that you haven't been able to pinpoint or correct?
6. Do you need information on costs, procedures, and profit projections for a potential new enterprise?
7. Is your present enterprise mix the most profitable, considering the basic resources of land, labor, capital, and management?

Often an outsider, trained and experienced in problem solving, can pinpoint areas in the operation that may be holding down profits. He can provide information to aid in planning a new enterprise and then help develop the goals to reach them.

Another area where a consultant can be extremely beneficial is planning a new enterprise, or planning a modification of an existing one. Here the consultant can prepare a feasibility study that will answer typical questions, such as: *Should you buy more land? . . . Should you go into the beef business? . . . Can you afford to expand? . . . Can you utilize more labor to your advantage? . . . Should you invest in irrigation equipment?*

A feasibility study takes all the pertinent elements of a proposed enterprise into consideration--items such as initial capital investment, management restrictions, production costs, labor requirements, and probable returns. The study determines if your proposed enterprise is feasible and, of course, how profitable it will be.

This type of planning puts your total project in perspective, allowing you to objectively evaluate the soundness of it. It will also be helpful in obtaining financing, if needed.

Other Assistance Available

Farmers and landowners can get information on technically sound practices from county agents, conservation technicians, state colleges and extension services, and many publications. State government agencies, such as state forestry departments, and state game and fish departments, provide technical services free-of-charge to owners. Farm equipment companies, commodity organizations, fertilizer companies, and other suppliers offer free services to customers.

Land improvement and management programs are managed through the United States Department of Agriculture and the land-grant colleges. Programs of research, education, cost sharing, credit, and technical assistance bring to the farm owner information, consultive, and facilitating services that enable him to improve the efficiency and quality of his performance.

General educational assistance is a function carried on primarily by the county agents of the state extension services working with farmers. Their information comes largely from the state agricultural experiment stations and the Agricultural Research Service.

Technical assistance in conservation of soil and water is provided mainly by technicians of the Soil Conservation Service through local soil conservation districts and watershed protection projects.

Cost-sharing and credit facilities are provided from several sources in the Department of Agriculture. Certain land use adjustments and conservation practices are available through the Agricultural Conservation

Program. Loans for soil and water conservation may be available to farmers through the credit program of the Farmer's Home Administration.

Adjusting To Future Technological Change

Every passing decade demonstrates the enormous pace of change in American agriculture. Technology constantly forces revision of plans for machinery, cropping practices, herbicides, feeding of livestock, and nearly every facet of production.

Any plans adopted require continual monitoring to ensure that the farm operation is in tune with the economic climate of change.

CHAPTER **12**

Farm and Ranch Operating Arrangements

Many landowners cannot take an active role in the operation of their property. Investors, absentee owners, or a surviving widow may need operating help. Conversely, some owners who do work their own land want control of additional property under some kind of lease arrangement.

While some type of lease is the basis for typical arrangements under which the land will be operated, the complexities of modern day agriculture and finance have generated many types of contractual arrangements. Large, all-tillable farms may lend themselves to a custom operation. Cattle feeding contracts have attracted major investors who have never been closer to a live cow than the leather in their wallet. The modern farmer may find that leasing his equipment and machinery yields distinct tax advantages. In some parts of our country, mineral rights and hunting rights are extremely important. Today's landowner must consider every potential opportunity to increase his profits.

COMMON LEASE ARRANGEMENTS

One-half of the land in the United States is under some form of lease agreement, with hundreds of variations of terms and conditions. Certain common elements which are discussed in this section should be present in all leases.

A lease is a contract between the owner of the land (the landlord or lessor) and a tenant (lessee). Under this contract the owner has transferred specified rights pertaining to the property to the tenant. In return, he receives consideration in the form of cash or a share of the returns from the property. Besides determining the legal rights and duties of the parties, the lease serves as a day-to-day basis of operation.

Q. Must a lease be in writing?

A. While farm or ranch leases can be either written or verbal, the written lease is preferable. Farmers and ranchers have traditionally relied on "handshake deals". This mental accord has major problems if the situation must be reconstructed later to settle a disagreement. Some states provide that leases for a period of more than one year must be in writing. The basis for requiring leases to be in writing is that they deal with a legal interest in land, thus falling within the Statute of Frauds.

Q. Should the lease be recorded?

A. Recording requirements, particularly for the longer term lease, are in effect in some states. This is more important for the longer term lease because the time periods may span the life of the parties and carry over into the lives of potential heirs. Be aware that recording the lease could cloud the title in the event a release would be difficult to obtain.

Oral leases that run from year-to-year usually must be cancelled by notice in advance of termination by a specific period, such as 60 or 90 days, or the lease will continue for another year. Many states have specific and detailed requirements concerning cancellation of a lease.

The advantages of a written lease could be summarized as follows:

- It protects not only the original parties, but also their heirs in case either party should die.
- It provides a point of reference in case either party is in doubt as to the terms of the original agreement.
- It provides for the more important farm practices and business procedures. Thus, in case of dispute, it will prevent common law, court decisions, or local custom from determining the application of practices that may be unadapted to the farm.
- It provides a bench mark from which to change minor provisions of the agreement, if it becomes necessary.
- It forces both parties to carefully consider all aspects of the lease, since they must officially sign the contract.
- If details of the farm operation are specified, it will serve as a record of the operation of the farm.
- It makes the term of the rental definite, and can provide a basis for continuing the term of the lease beyond one year.
- It offers an opportunity to provide for a reasonable period of notice to terminate the lease.

Q. What makes a lease legal . . . and fair?

A. There are five basic requirements for a legal lease: (1) An accurate description of the property leased; (2) a definite and agreed term over which the lease extends; (3) a definite and agreed price of rental, along with the designation of the time and place at which payment must be made; (4) the names of the lessor (landlord) and the lessee (tenant); and (5) the signatures of the parties to the contract.

Coverage of the above points normally ensures a binding lease. But, you may or may not have a *good* lease, depending on the details that were covered. A document covering only the bare bones of the points mentioned above would not be a good lease. To provide the proper basis for farm operation, a lease should anticipate as many points of potential disagreement as possible. A complete record of all items of agreement should be included in the lease and kept available for future reference.

Keep these four objectives in mind when becoming involved in a lease agreement: (1) Arrange for a fair division of the income and expense between the landlord and the tenant. (2) Make possible a profitable system of farming . . . for both parties. (3) Give as much assurance as possible to a good tenant that his lease will be continued through a period of years. (4) Give assurance to the landlord that the value of his property will be preserved.

Perhaps the acid test of a good lease lies in determining whether it provides incentive to both parties to make the farm business profitable and satisfying. It should give a satisfactory standard of living for the tenant and an adequate return on investment for the landlord. If it doesn't accomplish at least these two objectives, it won't do the job over the long term.

Q. Does a good tenant (lessee) have certain identifiable traits?

A. There is no magic formula to determine the difference between a good tenant and bad tenant until it's too late, but look for these traits: honesty; thorough knowledge of the crops and livestock enterprises to be included in the business; enough equipment and financial backing to operate the farm efficiently; a favorable attitude toward innovative practices and modern farming techniques; pride in the farm appearance; willingness to make minor repairs to buildings and other farm improvements; respect for the desires of the landlord; a willingness to enter into cooperative planning; a wife interested in farm life.

Q. What are the most common types of leases?

A. Various types of farm leases have been developed to meet the needs of farm leasing arrangements. The most common of these can be classified as:

1. The cash-lease.
2. The crop-share lease.
3. The livestock-share lease.
4. The standing-rent lease.

In addition, there may be some combination of the above leases such as one specifying part of the rent in crops, part in cash, normally referred to as a crop-share/cash lease.

The type of lease chosen will be influenced by such things as the type and condition of the farm, local custom, preferences of the owner and tenant, and financial condition of each party. Whatever type of lease you decide on, be certain it is the one best tailored to fit your personal needs.

Cash Lease

Under a cash-lease, the tenant pays a fixed, agreed upon amount for the use of the farm and improvements. He receives all of the income and usually pays all expenses except taxes, insurance, and major building repairs. The landlord has little or no management responsibility and is assured of a stable income. This type of lease is most desirable for inexperienced or absentee landowners.

One disadvantage to a cash-lease in earlier years, was the fear that tenants would "mine" the soil of fertility and otherwise exploit the property. But, under a modern farming program, the tenant will find his greatest income when he uses optimum amounts of fertilizer. If a reimbursement clause is written into the lease, guaranteeing the tenant payment for unused fertilizer applied in the last year, the tenant has ample motivation to maintain a high fertility program right up to the end of the lease.

Landlord advantages from a cash-lease:

- He receives a definite, steady income.
- His close supervision is not required.
- There is less chance for controversy since the lease is simple.

For the tenant:

- He has more independence in the operation of the farm.
- He receives full benefit of any superior management he is able to bring to bear.
- He often receives a larger percentage of the farm profits.

There are also disadvantages. The landlord could find that his land has been exploited if he doesn't give the tenant assurance of more than short-term occupancy. Also, the landlord will typically receive a smaller percentage of the profits compared to other types of leases, since he didn't assume much risk.

Tenants may find it difficult to get the landlord to make needed improvements. Also, the tenant with limited credit or capital assumes a heavy risk in years of poor crops or low prices. Rentals do not automatically adjust to changes in prices and production unless some provision is made in the lease. Often, though, the cash rent may vary, depending on a price index, or the price of the major crop or commodity produced on the property. For instance, a cash rental agreement may be for $60 per acre based on corn at $3 per bushel on a designated date. But, if corn were $3.30 on this date, the cash rent would be 110% of $60--or $66.00. This provision may allow a slightly higher rent to be charged, since some of the risk of price variation is passed on from the tenant to the owner.

Crop-Share Lease

This type of lease can be adapted to many different types of operations-- all the way from small open tracts to larger farms with a number of expensive buildings. The landlord's participation is usually limited to making decisions about land, seed, and fertilizer use, and sharing the costs of fertilizer, crop expense, and care and maintenance of improvements. Rent is typically a share of the crops produced. This typically ranges from one-third to one-half, but may be as low as 15% to 20% in some areas. In some cases there may be a supplementary cash rent for land in hay and pasture or farmstead use. Cash rent for buildings may be appropriate where the owner provides buildings for a tenant who farms considerable additional land; or in cases where the owner provides an unusual investment in buildings and equipment for livestock enterprises in which he doesn't share.

Some advantages of the share-lease for the landlord:

- He may receive a larger share of the farm profits than under a cash lease since he shares in more of the production and price risks.
- He may be more involved in the operation of the farm.
- If certain management and financial contributions are part of the lease, he may be eligible for social security.
- It may involve less risk than a livestock-share lease, particularly if the tenant is relatively inexperienced in livestock management.

And for the tenant, these advantages:

- Risk is less than with cash rent, particularly if low crop yields or low prices are likely to occur.
- Amount of capital and cash reserve required will be less.
- If the landlord will provide the necessary improvements, the tenant may be able to carry a profitable livestock operation on his own, and have greater freedom of management of the livestock portion than would be possible under a livestock-share lease.

There are disadvantages, too. Both parties may find that more adjustments in the lease are required as new practices are introduced and prices change. Also, it is difficult to develop arrangements under a crop-share lease to give the landlord an appropriate return for his investment in improvements. The tenant may find it difficult to get the landlord to furnish improvements needed for livestock production and machinery storage. In many instances the tenant may want to rent additional land and expand operations, while the landlord prefers that he devote his full attention to his farm, and try to develop a larger income per acre.

Livestock-Share Lease

The livestock-share lease most closely resembles a partnership between tenant and landlord. Under a typical livestock-share lease, the landlord owns half of the livestock, feed inventories, and special livestock equipment, and receives half of the livestock income. He pays half of all livestock expenses and feed purchases, and shares in harvesting costs. He may be involved in several decisions and financial transactions throughout the year. His net income may be higher than that of landlords in other types of leases (though not necessarily higher in relation to his inputs), but it may also vary considerably from year to year. This type of lease may not fit a landlord who cannot adequately supervise the property; who does not have the time or inclination to keep up to date on modern farming practices, who does not have adequate capital; nor one who wants a relatively predictable and stable income.

A livestock-share lease may have these advantages for the landlord:

- Over a period of years, livestock farms operated under this type of lease have been more profitable to the landlord than grain farms.
- Since the landlord makes a significant investment, he may be able to get a desirable tenant who otherwise couldn't swing a livestock operation by himself.

For the tenant:

- Risk is less, since he does not have to finance and manage all of the livestock needed to efficiently utilize his labor and machinery.
- The landlord is more directly interested in all parts of the farm business, and may be more willing to make permanent improvements.
- Particularly if relatively inexperienced, the tenant may be able to gain experience in livestock operations under the tutelage of a successful owner.

Standing Rent Lease

This is a modification of some of the types mentioned previously. It generally provides that the tenant will pay a fixed quantity of the crops or livestock as the standing rent. For example, a tenant may agree to pay a percentage of the calf crop, or a number of bales of cotton, or so many bushels of grain for the rent. It operates in much the same fashion as a cash-lease, and it has the same advantages to the landlord. It does, however, fluctuate in overall returns to the landlord in that the products' prices may vary from year to year. It offers a distinct disadvantage to the tenant in that in poor years he is still obligated to pay the same amount or same quantity of produce for rent, no matter how large or how small the crop is. Naturally, this works in his favor in good years.

OPERATIONAL LEASES AND CONTRACTS

Standard lease arrangements may be modified to fit unusual operations. Specialized production techniques and tax laws often play independent but similar roles in dictating the structure of complex contractual arrangements.

Q. Are farmsteads and pastures ever rented under separate agreement?

A. Farmsteads are generally rented with the farm at no specific rate, or are included at a cash rate which covers the loss of income that occurs from the land occupied by them. It has become common for landowners to charge a cash rent that is more nearly the economic cost of providing these facilities. This is particularly true of the smaller farm because of the proportionately higher cost per acre of providing an adequate set of buildings as compared to a larger farm. In the case of specialized structures such as livestock confinement buildings, a rental rate which at least covers the lessor's ownership costs is generally charged.

Pasture rates are generally established as a cash rental, based on a rate per acre. This is the easiest way to handle pasture rent, particularly if the acreage involved is agreed upon at the time the lease is made and the rent is stated in gross figures, such as $100 for the pasture.

The cash rental rate can be determined by the months of feed it will provide for mature animals. If an acre of pasture will carry a cow for 1 month, it is providing an animal unit month (AUM) of grazing. If it will carry an animal for 6 months, it will provide 6 AUMs of grazing.

Another way of obtaining income from pasture is to charge on a head per month basis for livestock grazing on the pasture. Generally, under this arrangement, the pasture owner looks after the cattle and maintains the fences. Where this is used, the rates are generally quoted on an animal unit basis. An animal unit is a mature cow with calf up to weaning, or one horse, or about 1,100 pounds of grazing animal.

Q. How is government land leased?

A. Both the state and federal government own land and lease some of it to private individuals. The majority of this land is pasture, or rangeland. Generally, it is leased on a cash basis at relatively low rates. In some cases, the rent is established by competitive bidding for a designated period of time, such as 5 years. In other situations the price per animal unit is established by the government agency handling the land, and landowners who have leased the land in the past have the right to continue leasing the land as long as they desire. In some situations, the right to lease adjacent lands becomes attached to private land and exists so long as the owner of the private land pays the specified rental charges. In these cases, this right to lease government land becomes an asset to a particular owner, and is a salable commodity, should he decide to sell.

Practically all land of this type has grazing limits put on it by the government. These limits are generally expressed as animal units to be grazed on the property during a designated period, or a stocking rate which cannot be exceeded. The degree to which these limits are enforced varies with the different agencies handling the land, and the relative damage that can occur to the land by overgrazing.

Q. *What is a direct operation?*

A. Large corporate or investor-owned farms may opt for an organization much like a manufacturing company, with management hiring all labor. Machinery and supplies are provided by the owner. Employees work on shifts, or a standard 8-hour day, plus overtime.

Many operations of this nature have been a disaster. Farming and ranching tend to be highly entrepreneurial businesses.

In theory, the advantages of such operations include:

1. Application of sophisticated financial and marketing expertise.
2. Massive buying and selling power.
3. Employment of trained specialists.
4. Availability of capital necessary to introduce latest technology.

The disadvantages of a direct operation are:

1. Loss of incentive of employees compared to owner/operators or lessees. Employees expect to get paid, regardless of the end result of a harvest. (Owners or share-tenants are motivated by results.)
2. Lack of skilled employees to operate expensive, technical machinery and equipment.
3. Fluctuation of labor needs due to vagaries of weather. Critical periods require massive overtime, yet slack periods still require at least minimum payment to retain employees.
4. Inability to compete with the rugged individualism and sacrifice most independent farmers bring to their task.

Most successful direct farming operations produce specialty crops such as vegetables and flowers, or tree crops such as fruits and nuts. Other operations which lend themselves to very systematic management, such as broiler or laying operations, are successfully run as direct operations.

Q. What is the basis of charge for custom farming?

A. Farm owners may contract for all or a portion of the field work to be done by custom operators. The basis charge for this type of contract may be by the acre, hour, ton, base, or bushel.

As an example, the contract for growing corn could include:

Function	Cost
Plowing	$ 7 per acre
Discing	$ 4 per acre
Harrowing	$ 2 per acre
Planting	$ 4 per acre
Fertilizing	$ 4 per acre
Cultivating	$ 5 per acre
Combining	$ 15 per acre
Miscellaneous	$ 7 per acre
Total	$ 48 per acre

Or, you might contract a custom package for $40 per acre.

Perhaps the most familiar custom operation involves the fleets of combines that start harvesting wheat in Texas, and gradually move northeasterly through Oklahoma, Kansas, Colorado, Nebraska and the Dakotas.

A sample of the "Custom Farming Agreement" is found in the last section of this chapter.

Q. Cattle feeding contracts—how do they work?

A. Under this type of operational contract, persons purchase cattle and place them with a feeder for fattening to finished weight.

Most of these agreements are weight-gain contracts or are on a cost-plus basis. If the contract is a weight-gain contract, the owner pays the yards an agreed upon fee per pound of gain, plus an additional charge for yardage and related maintenance. On the other hand, if it is a cost-plus basis, the yard agrees to provide care and feed for the cattle, and bills the owner on a regular basis for the cost of care and feed.

Another common practice is to place the cattle on a ranch wherein the rancher agrees to care for and maintain the cattle for a period of time for a stipulated amount. Generally, the agreement provides for the rancher to be paid an agreed upon amount per pound of calves weaned from the cowherd, plus costs for specific items.

Examples of a cattle feeding contract and a pasture contract are shown at the end of this chapter.

Grower or Producer Contracts

With the advent of the integrated livestock operation, processing companies entered into agreements with farm operators to grow broilers, produce eggs, grow pullets, or grow turkeys. The agreements are quite comprehensive and spell out clearly the obligations of each party. The grower is normally compensated according to: (1) A flat fee; (2) the feed conversion experienced; (3) a combination of feed conversion and market price; and (4) sharing of the profits. Each one of these agreements vary in the manner in which the compensation is paid, and somewhat as to the obligation of the parties. In certain instances, the grower has title to the poultry, and in others he does not.

As with the grower-processor contract, it is quite common to have grower-canner contracts, wherein a grower will produce vegetables, citrus fruits, deciduous fruits and tree nuts, and other specialty crops.

The types of contracts generally fall into (1) bailment, coupled with the contract to produce and deliver, and (2) contract to produce and sell.

A bailment contract, coupled with a contract to produce and deliver, means that title to the seed and resulting crop is with the canner. Actually, the bailment is coupled with an agreement to plant, cultivate, harvest, and deliver--being in that respect practically identical to the other category of contracts to produce and sell.

A contract to produce and sell is one in which title is with the grower but is later purchased by the canner. The agreements spell out some of the following: (1) acres to be grown; (2) exclusive sale to the processor; (3) the party to furnish the plants or seed; (4) fertilizer; (5) insect control; (6) planning date; (7) growing, cultivating and harvesting provisions; (8) dusting, spraying and soil testing; (9) the party to furnish the container and how it is to be charged; (10) delivery conditions; (11) hauling services; (12) grading of the produce; (13) grading defects;

(14) provision in regard to past acreage, which means that the canner will pass up acreage, or not accept produce from past acreage because of drouth, excessive rain, over-maturiy, or under-maturity, among other reasons. Normally, the canner would be required to compensate the grower to some extent for the amount passed over, (15) payment provisions, such as on a flat price per ton, hamper, bushel or hundredweight; (16) arbitration; (17) excuse for failure to meet the contract obligations, such as labor strikes, Acts of God, machinery breakdowns, fire, civil strife, labor shortages and transport troubles; (18) provisions in regard to cancellation, and (19) violations.

Here again, it would be advisable for the grower to have an attorney go over the agreement and explain any of the provisions that the grower may not understand. A sample broiler-grower contract is shown in the next section of this chapter.

Q. *What is the purpose of a deferred sales contract?*

A. It is common in many areas to sell livestock and grain under a deferred-sales contract. The primary purpose is to ensure that the seller will not be taxed on the proceeds in the year of the sale. For a cash basis farmer, a sale can be made stipulating that the proceeds will be paid in the next year, and for the specified amount. Producers may also use a deferred-sale contract to 'lock in' a particular price being offered some time in the future. A form that has been used by the Nebraska Feed Grain Dealers Association is shown at the end of this chapter.

Q. *Livestock leasing–what are typical provisions?*

A. Leasing of livestock has become popular primarily due to certain tax benefits that accrue to a lessor. A program that has been used in beef cattle leasing is one providing that an owner of the cows leases them to a farmer-rancher for a specified period of time. The farmer or rancher would pay either cash rental or give the lessor back a share of the calves. The farmer would be responsible for caring for the animals, risk of death, etc., during the period of the lease.

In the purebred business, cows are many times leased as the owner does not desire to sell the cows. He wants to retain them for his herd, but is still willing to let another party have the offspring for one or two years. In the grade beef cattle, normally, cash rental is paid for the use of the cows, and the lessee deducts the cost of the lease payments and thus obtains an animal after tax. Generally, in these types of leases, the lessee is an individual who is not directly involved in farming. His primary motivation is the tax benefits and the economic return that he may gain by being in the cattle business. The lessor would be the rancher who would lease the cows to the investor (lessee) for a stipulated amount and also provide care for the animals during the lease.

In a typical lease arrangement in the dairy business an individual owns and places cows on lease to a dairyman. The dairyman pays a cash rental and agrees to raise at least a portion of the offspring to an agreed-upon weight. The lessee would be entitled to the use of the cow and all of the milk from the cow and a share of the calves. One of the motivating factors of the owner is the tax benefits and the potential economic return from the lease. Normally, the owner would retain enough calves to maintain the herd.

The leasing of sows was once quite popular. The farmer paid either a cash rental or a share of the pig crop for the use of the sows. All of the care and maintenance becomes the responsibility of the farmer.

In all of the livestock leasing arrangements, the farmer has the advantage of lower initial capital requirements, compared with purchasing the animals. The farmer can lease the animals without any outlay of capital other than the lease payment. Lease payment is tax deductible.

A sample livestock lease is shown in the next section.

Q. *Can machinery be leased?*

A. In many areas machinery dealers and companies provide equipment on a lease basis. As with the leasing of livestock, the farmer or rancher leases equipment either on a periodic basis or a long term basis. The advantage to the lessee arises from not having to show the lease payments on his balance sheet and he does not need to have his capital tied up in the machinery and equipment. Most of the lease instruments are standard forms which are furnished by the leasing company. One is shown at the end of the next section.

SAMPLE LEASES AND CONTRACTS

Following are sample contracts showing typical provisions contained in some of the more common operating arrangements. It is advisable to seek legal counsel for interpretation of a specific contract in order to tailor provisions to conform to a given situation.

CUSTOM FARMING AGREEMENT

Farm Acres _____   Farm No. _____

Tillable Acres _____

Location _____

This agreement, made and entered into this _____ day of_____ ,
19_____ . by and between_____ of_____ ,
state of _____ , hereinafter known as OWNER, and _____ ,
of _____ , state of _____ , hereinafter referred
to as OPERATOR.

SCOPE OF AGREEMENT

The purpose of this agreement is to set forth the understanding of the parties
relative to the custom operations on the property described below and on the noted
terms and conditions. The property on which the services are to be performed is
situated in the county of _____ , state of _____ ,
specifically described as follows:

PERIOD OF SERVICES

The services to be performed are for the crop year from_____ ,
19_____ to_____ , 19_____ . OWNER reserves the right to
terminate this agreement at any time OPERATOR fails to perform custom work in
a manner consistent with good farming practices or OPERATOR does not furnish the
services as requested by OWNER. Upon such termination OWNER shall pay for
quality services rendered and all further obligations under this agreement shall
cease.

CUSTOM SERVICES

OPERATOR agrees to furnish all necessary labor, equipment and fuel to perform the following services for the total price indicated. Work performed on an
acre basis shall be considered tillable acres and as directed by OWNER, the following schedule shall prevail.

Type of Service	No. Acres	Per Acre	Per Bushel	Per Hour	Per Ton	Per Bale
Plowing						
Disking						
Disking with harrow						
Planting corn						
Planting corn with fertilizer						
Rotary hoe						
Cultivation						
Applying fertilizer						
Drill grain						
Field cultivator						
Field cultivator with harrow						
Harrowing						
Spraying						
Combining						
Grain delivery						
Mowing fence rows and lots						

OPERATOR shall perform the services as season, weather and good farming practices dictate. OWNER reserves the right to specify particular times for services to be performed and the general manner in which it shall be accomplished.

PAYMENT

Payment for services determined by the schedule above shall be _____ _____ ; the balance is to be paid after corn harvest but no later than _____ , 19_____. OWNER may demand evidence that OPERATOR does not have unpaid labor, gas or equipment bills which might create a lein on the property.

RELATIONSHIP OF THE PARTIES

OPERATOR is an independent contractor and shall be solely responsible for his employee's wages and payroll taxes. OWNER'S control over the work to be performed by OPERATOR is to the time the work is to be performed and the desired final results. In addition, OPERATOR agrees to indemnify and save OWNER harmless for any loss or claims arising out of OPERATOR'S service.

OPERATOR _____

Address _____

OWNER _____

Address _____

CATTLE MAINTENANCE AND FEEDING CONTRACT

THIS CONTRACT is between _____
whose address is _____
(hereinafter called FEEDER) and _____
_____whose address is _____
_____(hereinafter called OWNER).
OWNER has appointed Oppenheimer Industries, Inc., 1808 Main St., Kansas City, Missouri, to represent OWNER as OWNER'S Agent in the execution and performance of all the terms of this contract.

FEEDER AND OWNER HEREBY DECLARE AND ACKNOWLEDGE THAT THE ONLY AGREEMENTS AND UNDERSTANDINGS EXISTING BETWEEN THEM ARE THOSE WHICH ARE SPECIFICALLY SET FORTH HEREINAFTER.

1. CARE AND MAINTENANCE.

A. OWNER hereby agrees to place with FEEDER, and FEEDER hereby agrees to accept from OWNER the placement of _____head of feeder cattle, in FEEDER'S feedlot, to be fed by FEEDER in accordance with the terms of this contract. All or a part of said feeder cattle shall be placed on feed early in the program with the balance of said cattle to be placed on feed at a time to be determined by OWNER.

B. FEEDER agrees to receive OWNER'S cattle as delivered and to feed and care for the cattle in accordance with the standards of care and responsibility generally accepted as good animal husbandry practice. In this regard the practices, though not limited to the following, shall include:

(1) Vaccinations, implanting, worming, parasite control.

(2) Branding as to OWNER and to insure the cattle are not comingled in pens with cattle not owned by OWNER.

(3) Feeding an appropriate feed ration approved by OWNER.

(4) Overseeing the general health of the cattle and to document all hospital, veterinary, drug and medical expense.

(5) Removing sick and injured cattle from the feeding pens and placing them in separate hospital pens. All chronic and poor doers shall be reported to OWNER and marketed in the best possible manner.

C. OWNER agrees to pay FEEDER for feed, preparation of ration, yardage, vaccine, medicine and veterinarian services in accordance with the following schedule:

(1) OWNER agrees to pay FEEDER invoice cost for feed and feed ingredients.

(2) OWNER agrees to pay FEEDER for services
    (a) $ _____per ton markup on feed.
    (b) _____per cent markup on invoice cost of feed ration.
    (c) _____per head per day yardage.

(3) OWNER agrees to pay FEEDER cost plus _____% for vaccine and medicine, plus actual cost of veterinary services.

(4) FEEDER agrees to supply OWNER with a current breakdown of ration costs.

2. PURCHASE AND FURNISHING OF FEED

The feed for OWNER'S cattle will be furnished by OWNER and/or purchased from FEEDER. The furnishing or purchase of feed from FEEDER shall be as follows:

A. Feed/ration purchased from FEEDER shall be in accordance with paragraph 1C.

B.   Feed/ration or ration ingredients furnished by OWNER will be delivered to FEEDER'S premises for feeding to OWNER'S cattle. FEEDER shall acknowledge delivery of feed by kind and quantity. FEEDER shall provide OWNER with a monthly accounting and running inventory of feed consumed by OWNER'S cattle. OWNER shall provide cost or value of feed/ration or ration ingredients to FEEDER. Such cost or value shall be used in computing cost of services in paragraph 1C and feed conversion limitation in paragraph 6.

3. PAYMENT

FEEDER shall bill OWNER for purchased feed and services monthly and OWNER agrees to pay FEEDER within ten (10) days of billing.

4. INDEPENDENT CONTRACTOR

A.   The contracting parties agree that FEEDER is a independent contractor and not the agent or employee of OWNER. FEEDER hereby agrees to assume all responsibility for, and protect OWNER from any loss occasioned by, or any claim asserted for:

(A) FICA taxes, Income Tax Withholding, Unemployment Compensation, or any other taxes on or measured by wages paid to FEEDER'S workers; (B) Workmen's Compensation claimed by any of FEEDER'S workmen, employees, or subcontractors; (C) by third persons because of or growing out of any actions connected with the handling of OWNER'S cattle.

B.   FEEDER shall maintain a blanket liability insurance policy of not less than five hundred thousand dollars ($500,000.00) per person and one million dollars ($1,000,000.00) per accident for personal injury and one hundred thousand dollars ($100,000.00) for property damages. FEEDER shall furnish certificates of such insurance to OWNER to reflect OWNER'S insured interest.

5. SALE OF CATTLE AND HANDLING PROCEEDS

A.   FEEDER agrees to feed, and otherwise responsibly care for OWNER'S cattle for the period of time necessary to finish the cattle to an optimum weight and condition. When the cattle have attained market weight, FEEDER shall so advise OWNER of the condition of the animals and bids for purchase and upon OWNER'S concurrence FEEDER shall sell the cattle. FEEDER is to furnish or cause to be furnished to OWNER, weight tickets from a sealed and certified scale and sales documents on completion of sales.

B.   FEEDER is to direct that checks or drafts for cattle sales be payable to OWNER and remitted to OWNER, at such locations as OWNER may direct.

6. FEED CONVERSION LIMITATION

To provide an incentive for FEEDER to achieve optimum feed conversion, at the completion of the feeding of all cattle under this contract, the "feed conversion per pound" is set at a maximum ration of _____pounds of feed to one pound of weight gain. The determination shall be as follows:

A.   "Weight Gain" shall be an amount equal to the payweight of OWNER'S cattle at the time of purchase by OWNER (less the aggregate of the average purchase payweight of all cattle that die, however, such deduction shall not exceed 2% of the total purchase payweight) subtracted from the payweight of OWNER'S cattle at the time of sale. "Pay Weight" shall be defined as the net weight after shrink allowance, if any, upon which purchase and sale of OWNER'S cattle is made. The cattle shall be weighed on sealed and certified scales. The total "Weight Gain" on each pen of cattle shall be recorded and aggregated.

B.   "Feed Usage" shall be an amount equal to the total pounds of all ingredients fed to a pen of cattle from the time of purchase by OWNER until they are sold. The total weight of these ingredients shall be computed on an "as fed" basis. "Feed Usage" for each pen of cattle be recorded and aggregated.

C.   "The feed conversion per pound" is the quotient of the "Feed Usage" divided by the "Weight Gain."

D.   If over the length of this contract there is a "feed conversion per pound" greater than _____ : _____, the cost of the feed ingredients, plus all non-ration feed expenses set forth in paragraph 1C, shall be divided by the total pounds of the feed ingredients and the quotient (in cents per pound) shall be multiplied by _____ and this product shall be multipled by the "Weight Gain" of the cattle. This computation shall produce the maximum cost of feeding for the cattle fed under this contract.

E.   The maximum total cost of feeding, based on the computation in paragraph 6D, shall be subtracted from the actual cost of feeding over the term of this contract. The difference shall be considered a feed cost adjustment to be paid by FEEDER to OWNER within 10 days of billing by OWNER.

F.   In the event a particular lot, pen or group of steers are not sold after having been on feed 150 days (125 days for heifers), FEEDER shall secure current market bids for said cattle and submit such bids to OWNER with a 10 day written notice to sell said cattle. If OWNER does not approve the bid as submitted (or subsequent bids) within 10 days of notice date, said lot, pen or group of cattle will be omitted from feed conversion calculations as defined in this paragraph 6.

7. PERIL INSURANCE

FEEDER represents and warrants that it will insure all of OWNER'S cattle while in FEEDER'S feedyards against named perils, satisfactory to OWNER. The perils shall include, but not be limited to: fire, lightening, windstorm, theft, accidental shooting, drowning, collapse of buildings, vandalism or mischief and, smothering. FEEDER shall furnish OWNER with a certificate of insurance reflecting the above provisions. Insurance proceeds resulting from claims made on account of any such loss to cattle owned by OWNER in FEEDER'S feedyards will accure to the account of OWNER. Insurance premiums shall be charged to OWNER.

8. FEEDER'S RECORDS AND INFORMATION.

A.   This contract shall terminate automatically unless OWNER by written notice elects otherwise, if or when FEEDER does (if an individual), becomes bankrupt or insolvent, makes any assignment for the benefit of creditors, attempts to sell, mortgage, pledge, remove, dispose of or injure any cattle belonging to OWNER, or if any distress, execution or attachment is levied upon the cattle or any part thereof, or if any distress, execution or attachment is levied upon any premises, equipment or other asset belonging to the FEEDER which, in the judgment of the OWNER will render continued performance under the terms of this contract impossible.

9. TERMINATION OF CONTRACT FOR CAUSE.

A.   This contract shall terminate automatically unless OWNER by written notice elects otherwise, if or when FEEDER dies (if an individual), become bankrupt or insolvent, makes any assignment for the benefit of creditors, attempts to sell, mortgage, pledge, remove, dispose of or injure any cattle belonging to OWNER, of if any distress, execution or attachment is levied upon any premises, equipment or other asset belonging to the FEEDER which, in the judgment of the OWNER will render continued performance under the terms of this contract impossible.

B.   In addition, OWNER shall have the right to terminate this contract upon ten (10) days written notice to the FEEDER if the FEEDER materially violates any provision of this contract or becomes involved in any financial difficulty which, in the opinion of the OWNER'S banking connection, may impair his financial responsibility.

C.   In the event of termination of this contract under this paragraph, the FEEDER shall deliver possession of OWNER'S cattle forthwith in accordance with the directions supplied by OWNER and OWNER is hereby authorized to enter upon any premises where the cattle or any part thereof, may be found and take possession of and remove such cattle, and in addition to possession of the cattle, the FEEDER guarantees to OWNER the unconsumed prepared ration shall be made available for delivery or other disposition as directed by OWNER.

10. LOCATION OF CATTLE.

FEEDER agrees that during the entire period covered by this contract, to keep the OWNER'S cattle where they may be seen and inspected by OWNER.

11. TERM OF CONTRACT

The effective beginning date of this contract shall be _____ _____, 19 _____, and continue until all cattle being fed hereunder have been fed to finished weight and sold, or unless terminated in accordance with paragraph 9, whichever is sooner.

12. TITLE TO FEED AND CATTLE

Title to and ownership of the cattle and feed furnished or sold to OWNER shall be and remain with OWNER at all times. FEEDER shall have no assignable interest that may be subject to attachment, garnishment, execution or other proceedings and shall not in any way hypothecate OWNER'S cattle or feed for purpose of borrowings. FEEDER shall be responsible in case of loss for replacement of OWNER'S feed with feed of kind and quantity if a loss or destruction of feed occurs while feed is in FEEDER'S custody.

13. NOTICES

Any notice required or permitted to be given under this contract shall be sufficient if in writing and if sent by certified mail (return receipt request) to OWNER'S Agent, Oppenheimer Industries, Inc. at 1808 Main Street, Kansas City, Missouri 64108, and to FEEDER at _____ or to such other address as either party shall designate by written notice to the other.

14. DEATH LOSSES

FEEDER shall be liable to OWNER for the market value of cattle (determined at the time of death) that die due to FEEDER'S negligence. Such liability shall be in addition to all other responsibilities under this contract. FEEDER shall substantiate all deaths as they occur by providing OWNER with documentation in the form of veterinarian certificates of cause of death, disposal company receipts, or standard death loss slip from feedyard.

15. INTEREST AND COSTS

OWNER shall be entitled to interest from date of billing, at 10% per annum, on all amounts due under this agreement. In the event OWNER must resort to legal action to collect amounts due, OWNER shall be entitled to court costs and reasonable attorneys' fees.

16. AGENCY REPRESENTATION

FEEDER agrees that Oppenheimer Industries, Inc. has authority and power of attorney to represent and act in OWNER'S behalf in any negotiations, institution of legal proceedings in OWNER'S name, execution of legal pleadings for OWNER, or in any matters which may affect the OWNER'S interest in the contract. FEEDER specifically waives any objections to (1) the representation of OWNER by Oppenheimer in any of the foregoing and (2) the requirement that OWNER be physically present in any negotiation or legal procedding.

17. ASSIGNMENT

This contract is assignable only with prior written consent of OWNER.

18. ACCEPTANCE

In consideration of the mutual promises and obligations created herein, this agreement, when properly executed, shall be binding on FEEDER and the OWNER and their respective successors, executors, administrators, heirs and assigns.

Dated and signed this _____ day of _____ , 19 _____

at _____

| FEEDER | OWNER |

CATTLE PASTURE CONTRACT

This contract made this_____day of_____, 19_____ between Western Live Stock Company, a Wyoming Corporation, hereinafter called Rancher, and _____ of _____ hereinafter called Stockowner.

The Stockowner agrees:

1. To transport and deliver to Rancher_____ head of_____to be pastured by Rancher in an area immediately south of Casper, Wyoming. Cattle are branded _____.

2. At termination of this contract to transport said cattle from Ranchers property.

3. To pay Rancher_____ per head for a season's grazing to commence in _____ and terminate _____ weather and grass conditions permitting.

4. To make down payment of _____ which is acknowledged with this contract; another_____to be paid _____ ; and the balance when cattle are removed and contract terminated.

5. To pay for all veterinary costs except minor individual treatment.

The Rancher agrees:

1. To pasture said _____ in the manner customary to the area in which cattle are located.

2. To pay all labor connected in caring for said cattle during term of this contract.

3. To keep sufficient white block salt available to cattle at various places during pasture agreement.

4. To keep an accurate account of cattle at all times and advise Stockowner periodically. Further to furnish Stockowner evidence of loss through death by removing brand from animal carcasses. However Stockowner not to seek reimbursement for cattle lost through death or straying.

RANCHER   STOCKOWNER

_____   _____
Western Live Stock Company

SAMPLE BROILER CONTRACT*

THIS is an agreement entered into this _____ day of _____ , 19___ , at _____ , _____ , between _____ , hereafter known as the Producer, and _____ , hereafter known as the Company.

The purpose of this agreement is to have an understanding of the conditions that will exist and what is expected of each party in growing broilers.

Section I.   The Company and Producer jointly agree that:

1. The Company, in consideration of the agreements with the Producer hereinafter set forth, hereby furnishes to the Producer _____ number of chicks. The Producer, in consideration of the agreements with the Company, agrees to raise the chicks to a marketable stage.
2. The chicks are to be placed between _____ (dates) and are to remain on _____ farm located in or near (town or city) _____ , (county or parish) _____ , (state) _____ , until marketed by the Company.
3. The Company shall have full title to the flock placed on the Producer's farm, including title to the feed, medicine and other items supplied by the Company.
4. The terms of this contract in no way imply or constitute a partnership, joint venture or employer-employee relationship, but the Producer's actions constitute an independent operation.
5. The Producer shall insure for fire and windstorm damage to the buildings and equipment used in broiler production. The Company shall insure for fire and windstorm damage to poultry, feed or any other supplies furnished by the Company.
6. Neither will assign this contract to any person(s) or entity nor turn care of said poultry over to anyone else without written consent of the other party.

Section II.   The Producer agrees to the following:

1. That the Company be allowed full and complete right of ingress and egress to Producer's premises for supervision and control of the broiler production operation.
2. That he will provide the following equipment and supplies:

	Type	Rate
Feeders		
Waterers		
Bulk bin		
Litter		
Brooders		
Heat		

3. That he will provide adequate poultry housing and not keep more than one chicken per _____ square feet of floor space.
4. That he will furnish adequate labor at all times when birds have to be handled, such as vaccinations, catching or other handling.
5. That he will not nor will he allow others to have any other fowl on same farm as long as said poultry is there.   He will not visit poultry on other farms or let other persons come in contact with poultry on the Producer's farm.
6. That he will not use feed furnished by the Company for any other purpose than the feeding of chickens owned by the Company.
7. That he will provide a poultry disposal pit.
8. That he will follow the management program of the Company.
9. That he will maintain and keep daily records of feed consumption and mortality.
10. That he will immediately notify the Company of all emergencies, diseases or any important decisions.

---

* Maness, J.C. and E.P. Roy, Economic Integration in the Hatchery Industry, La. Agr. Exp. Sta. Circ. 301, Baton Rouge, La. Feb. 1962.

Section III. The Company agrees to the following:
1. To provide chicks from the best breeding obtainable and to advocate the best management and feeding program known to the Company.
2. To supply and deliver the following items:

	Type	Rate
Chicks		
Feed		
Medicines		
Vaccines		

3. To provide a serviceman for regular visits or for any reasonable amount of time for assistance in production of said broilers.
4. To establish and maintain an account of all charges as set out in Section IV, and provide a final audit of the project account.
5. To bear any loss after an audit of said account.
6. To have the right to terminate this contract if it is willfully breached by the Producer, and remove poultry and furnished supplies from the Producer's premises.

Section IV. Conditions of Payment:
1. Items considered as expenses will be:

Item	Terms	Conditions
Chicks		
Feed		
Medicines		
Vaccines		

2. All settlements shall be based on the weights that pass federal and/or state inspection and are paid for by the processing plant. These weights shall be used to calculate feed conversion and other efficiency data.
3. The conditions of place of weighing and market price shall be:
Place of weighing: _____
Market price: _____
4. The methods of payment shall be _____ and/or the following:

(A) FEED CONVERSION:

Feed Conversion	Price per Pound
1.90 - 2.09	
2.10 - 2.29	
2.30 - 2.39	
2.40 - 2.49	
2.50 - 2.59	
2.60 - 2.69	
2.70 - 2.79	
2.80 and over	

(B) MARKET PRICE:

Market Price	Plus or Minus Price per Pound
11.0 - 11.9	
12.0 - 12.9	
13.0 - 13.9	
14.0 - 14.9	
15.0 - 15.9	
16.0 - 16.9	
17.0 - 17.9	
18.0 - 18.9	
19.0 - 19.9	
20.0 and over	

(C) AVERAGE WEIGHT:

Average Weight	Plus or Minus Price per Pound
3.00 – 3.09	
3.10 – 3.19	
3.20 – 3.29	
3.30 – 3.39	
3.40 – 3.49	
3.50 – 3.59	
3.60 – 3.69	
3.70 – 3.79	
3.80 – 3.89	
3.90 – 3.99	
4.00 and over	

(D) POINT SPREAD (Average weight-feed conversion x 100):

Point Spread	Price per Pound
49 and under	
50 – 59	
60 – 69	
70 – 79	
80 – 89	
90 – 99	
100 – 109	
110 – 119	
120 – 129	
130 – 139	
140 – 149	
150 and over	

(E) A rate of $ _____ per thousand broilers.

(F) A rate of $ _____ per _____ pound(s) of broilers.

Section V. Arbitration Procedure:

1. Disagreements not reconciled between the Company and the Producer shall be referred to a board of three disinterested persons after giving three days' notice to the other party. This agreement to arbitrate is irrevocable and supersedes any other manner of claim. It is a part of the consideration flowing to and from each of the parties hereto, the same being a condition precedent to any action against the other for the collection of accounts or damages, whereas the right to resort to an action at law or equity is hereby specifically waived in favor of arbitration. Of the three disinterested persons, one shall be appointed by the Company, one by the Producer and the third by the two thus appointed. In the event that the Producer and the Company appointees cannot agree on a third party, the county agricultural agent domiciled in the county where the broiler house is situated (Section I, Paragraph 2) shall be requested to select the third party. The decision of these three arbitrators shall be considered binding by the parties to this contract unless a matter of law or a sum exceeding $ _____ is involved. Any costs of arbitration shall be shared equally between the two parties to this contract.

IN WITNESS THEREOF, The Producer has hereunto set his hand and seal and the Company has caused its hand and seal to be affixed hereto by and through its duly authorized officers.

Signed _____

DEFERRED SALES CONTRACT

a partnership

John Doe Grain Co., Anytown, Nebraska, a corporation, hereinafter known as Buyer,

an association

and_____, hereinafter known as Seller, covenant and agree as follows:

Buyer agrees to purchase from Seller approximately_____bushels of _____ at the agreed price of $_____ per bushel under the following terms and conditions to wit:

Seller shall deliver the above described grain within_____days to Buyer's elevator in Anytown, Nebraska.

Seller hereby warrants that title to the above grain is free from encumbrance of any nature whatsoever and that Seller has good and merchantable title, with the right to dispose of the same. Seller hereby authorizes the Buyer to contract for the sale or disposition of said grain for its own account either before or after delivery to the elevator above designated without further authorization from Seller except this contract and buyer shall not be required to account for or pay the balance of said purchase price until the_____day of_____, 19_____.

Seller hereby acknowledges receipt of the sum of $_____to apply on this contract and the balance shall not be due until the_____day of_____, 19_____, it being the intent of all parties hereto that said sale shall not be completed until final payment by the Buyer to the Seller and it is specifically agreed that Seller shall, under no circumstances be entitled to the balance due herein until the_____day of_____, 19_____.

Buyer agrees that it will pay the balance due without interest on the due date as fixed herein to the Seller.

It is further agreed by and between the Buyer and Seller that this contract shall be binding upon the heirs, administrators, executors of the respective parties and that this contract can not be assigned.

Dates this_____day of_____, 19_____.

JOHN DOE GRAIN COMPANY

_____   By _____
Witness   Buyer

_____   _____
Witness   Seller

LIVESTOCK LEASE AGREEMENT

THIS AGREEMENT, made this _____ day of _____ , 19___ , between Livestock Corporation, Champaign, Illinois, hereinafter referred to as LESSOR and _____ of _____ , hereinafter referred to as LESSEE.

WITNESSETH: For and in consideration of. the mutual promises hereinafter expressed, the parties agree as follows:

1. ANIMALS LEASED AND DELIVERY CONDITION
LESSOR agrees to lease to LESSEE, ____ females and ____ boars.   LESSEE shall have the opportunity to inspect the above animals at LESSEE'S place of business, and after delivery and acceptance it shall be conclusively presumed that all animals are of suitable quality and health. LESSOR agrees to have the breeding hogs immunized against cholera and erysipelas before delivery. Any gilt which proves to be a nonbreeder after the boar has been with her for at least sixty days may, at the option of the LESSOR, be replaced with a gilt of equal quality.

2. TITLE, PERIOD OF LEASE AND CONDITION ON TERMINATION
The LESSOR shall retain title to all leased animals and LESSEE'S interest shall be possessory for the period of the lease which shall be for twenty (20) months, commencing with delivery of the animals to LESSEE'S place of business, which shall be the _____ day of _____ , 19___ .   LESSEE agrees that on termination of the agreement all leased animals will weigh a minimum of 400 pounds.

3. CARE AND FEEDING
LESSEE agrees to follow established animal husbandry practices which shall include adequate sow feeding rations for female animals during gestation. LESSOR has permission to inspect animals at all reasonable hours.

4. LOSSES
LESSEE agrees to redeliver the leased animals at the termination of the lease or as provided in paragraph 3 above. In the event a female animal dies or disappears, LESSEE is guaranteed permission to substitute a 220-pound gilt of equal quality within 10 days of death or discovery of disappearance and such substitution shall be considered as satisfaction of delivery of original animal(s). In the event a male animal dies or disappears LESSEE SHALL _____

_____

_____

5. LOCATION OF ANIMALS
All animals shall be delivered to the premises designated by LESSEE and approved by LESSOR.   LESSEE shall move the animals only with permission of LESSOR.

6. DELIVERY FEE
LESSEE shall pay LESSOR $9.60 per head delivery fee at the signing of this agreement and an additional $9.60 per head for each replacement animal delivered, to be paid when the animal(s) is/are delivered.

7. LEASE TERMS AND PAYMENT
The total rental for the animals shall be $79.40 per head. The rental and payment schedule for the leased animals during the lease term are as follows:

1st - 10th month	$3.80 per head
11th month	$11.40 per head
12th - 15th month	$3.80 per head
16th month	$7.60 per head
17th - 19th month	$3.80 per head

Payment shall commence on _____ day of _____, 19____, and installments payable on the same day of the month until entire rental is paid. Payment shall be made to LESSOR'S place of business at P.O. Box 23, Champaign, Illinois.

8. DEFAULT

LESSEE shall be in default and this lease may be terminated in which case the unpaid rental becomes immediately due and payable without notice as liquidated damages and animals returned to LESSOR if any of the following events occur:

    a. Rental payments are not made within 10 days of due date.

    b. Failure to maintain and feed animals in the manner noted in paragraph 3.

    c. Failure to replace dead or missing animals within the period and manner as prescribed in paragraph 4.

    d. Actual or attempted disposal, passing of title or mortgaging of leased animals.

9. ASSIGNMENT

LESSEE shall not assign this agreement without written permission of LESSOR.

10. REDELIVERY

LESSOR is granted permission to enter upon LESSEE'S premises in the event of default as provided in paragraph 8 and repossess leased animals. LESSEE agrees to grant peaceful possession of the animals either in the event of default or at the expiration of the lease term.

11. COLLECTION

To further secure full payment hereof, LESSEE hereby irrevocably authorizes any attorney of any Court of Record to appear for him in any such court, at any time after default, and to confess judgment, without process, in favor of LESSOR for the full balance remaining unpaid hereon, together with all late charges and weight shortage of leased hogs as determined in this agreement, costs and reasonable attorney fees and LESSEE hereby consents to immediate execution upon such judgment and does ratify all that said attorney may do by virtue hereof.

12. LIABILITY

LESSEE agrees to hold LESSOR harmless for any damages the animals may cause to the property of LESSEE or third party or any personal injury caused to any person whomsoever, resulting or claimed to have resulted from actions of leased animals.

13. GENERAL

Wherever used herein, LESSEE shall mean each and all of the persons, jointly and severally, subscribing hereto as LESSEE.

This agreement is binding on the heirs, administrators, executors and assigns of the parties hereto. However, in the event of death or disability of LESSEE, LESSOR shall have the option of continuing or terminating this agreement.

LIVESTOCK CORPORATION, LESSORS

By _____

_____
LESSEE

EQUIPMENT LEASE AGREEMENT

This AGREEMENT, made and entered into at_____ this

_____ day of _____, 19_____, by and between_____

of _____, hereinafter called LESSOR, and_____

_____

_____ of _____, hereinafter called LESSEE;

WITNESSETH: That in consideration of the payments and rentals hereinafter provided for, and of the terms and conditions hereof, the Lessor hereby agrees to lease to the Lessee, and the Lessee hereby agrees to lease from the Lessor, the following described equipment belonging to the Lessor, to wit:

EQUIPMENT LEASED
(Kind of Machine, Make, Model, Serial Number, Description)

_____

_____

_____

_____

_____

_____

                                              Total Value $_____

F.O.B. Lessor's place of business, or _____   _____

Above equipment to be used in _____operations

on _____ at or near _____

_____ in the State of _____

TERM OF LEASE: The term of this lease shall be for a period of_____ months, beginning with the_____ day of _____, 19_____ and terminating the _____ day of_____, 19_____.

RENTAL RATES AND PAYMENT: The rental rates set forth in this contract do not include sales, use or occupational taxes. If and when such taxes are incurred by law, these amounts shall be added to the rental payments due under this contract.

A. If this equipment is leased on a monthly basis, the Lessee agrees to pay a total of $_____ in rental as follows: $_____payable with order and including first month's rental, receipt of which is hereby acknowledged by Lessor; and the balance payable in advance on the_____day of each month in_____installments of $_____each commencing with the month of _____ 19_____.

B. If this equipment is leased on a quarterly or seasonal basis, the Lessee agrees to pay a total of $_____in rental as follows: $_____payable with order, receipt of which is hereby acknowledged by Lessor; and the balance payable in_____installments of $_____each due and payable on

_____

Rental payments shall be made to Lessor at Lessor's address above set forth except that, if Lessee is notified to do so by Lessor or his assignee, payments shall be made to such assignee.

PRIVILEGE OF PURCHASE OPTION: Lessee is granted an option to purchase the equipment leased hereunder at the expiration of the lease period for the sum of $_____. Option to purchase shall not be deemed exercised until Lessee's (buyers) written notification to that effect is received by Lessor (seller) on or before the expiration of the lease period. The lease must be in good standing before the option can be exercised. The option is nontransferable.

Any alteration or modification of this Lease shall be in writing and signed by the parties hereto. Lessee acknowledges receipt of a signed copy hereof.

All conditions stated on the reverse side hereof are considered to be a part of this contract.*

In Witness Whereof, the parties hereto have on the day and year first above written hereunto set their hands and seals.

LESSEF _____   Accepted and Approved _____ , 19___.

BY _____

BY _____   LESSOR _____

WITNESS _____

WITNESS _____   BY_____

PHONE NO. _____

_____

*Conditions stated on reverse side of the contract are not included here for the sake of brevity.

CHAPTER 13

Tax Considerations in Buying, Selling and Owning Land

The success of investment strategy is measured in after-tax dollars. Proper tax planning in real estate can greatly affect the net result of a transaction, and frequently influence the decision of whether to buy or sell at a particular time.

Since it's not possible to turn one chapter of a book into a comprehensive tax guide, the purpose here is to identify situations that may result in tax savings. One correct maneuver can result in the realization of thousands of net dollars.

Land buyers often ignore the many options open to them. When "tax shelters" are mentioned, one thinks of oil wells, apartment buildings, breeding operations, and motion pictures. But land has its shelters if tax implications are considered. Some of the landowners' tax benefits are that:

1. Interest on borrowed money is deductible.
2. Property and other taxes can be deducted.
3. Accelerated methods of depreciation are available for the land improvements.
4. Land is investment property, and can be exchanged, thus deferring and sometimes avoiding taxes.
5. Investment tax credit may be available.
6. Some land improvement costs may be deducted or amortized.
7. Installment sales spread and thus reduce taxes.
8. The profit realized by selling land for more than cost is taxed at capital gain rates.

So use this chapter as a source of ideas . . . which should lead to better money management and result in more dollars to spend. Remember that tax laws change, and further research and examination will be needed to apply the suggestions herein.

ALLOCATING PURCHASE PRICE

Since land itself is not a wasting asset (unless you have something like a gravel pit or coal mine), the buyer is normally interested in writing off as much of his investment as possible annually through depreciation. For example, let's assume a $200,000 farm purchase. Isolate the items that can be depreciated:

Item	Value At Purchase	Years Of Remaining Useful Life	Depreciation Rate	Annual Deduction
House (if rented)	$30,000	20	5%	$1,500
Barn No. 1	22,000	10	10%	2,200
Barn No. 2	16,000	10	10%	1,600
Other Buildings	18,000	10	10%	1,800
Fences, etc.	8,000	7	14%	1,120
			Total	$8,220

This oversimplified example shows $8,220 depreciation and means that the 40% tax bracket buyer will have $3,288 more in his pocket the first year because of the buildings on the property. Be sure to allocate before the first tax return is filed.

There is no set method to use in the allocation. The buyer has an advantage if he can allocate more of the purchase price to items which will be sold quickly, such as crops or livestock that produce ordinary income. If growing crops are purchased with the land, the price allocated to these crops will be charged off as an expense against ordinary income.

A buyer acquiring property will want to allocate as much of the purchase price as possible to the rapidly depreciable property, and a lesser amount to property that depreciates slowly, so he can recover his investment as rapidly as possible. Similarly, a buyer of land and buildings should try to establish a relatively high cost for fences, structures, buildings, and other depreciable property; and a moderate price on the land and for the house if it is to be used for his residence. The more that can be fairly allocated to rapidly depreciating items, the better the buyer's tax position. Since this desire may be contrary to the best interest of the seller, allocation may become a matter of negotiation.

The seller may want to allocate differently. The more value a seller can apply to the land the greater the portion of the proceeds subject to the favorable capital gain tax rates. So allocation becomes negotiable, and may benefit one party more than the other, depending on the individual's tax rates. The best evidence of bona fide allocation starts with the documentation of the sale contract. IRS will frown on different allocations made by the buyer and seller.

INVESTMENT CREDIT RULES

The 10% investment tax credit is a very important aspect of an owner's income tax picture. Application was broadened considerably by the Revenue Act of 1978. In effect, the federal government allows a rebate of up to 10% of the cost of a wide range of qualified business investments made anytime during the tax year. It should be considered whenever the purchase of equipment and livestock is budgeted for proper timing.

Useful life must be at least 3 years for property to qualify for any investment credit, and must be the same as that used for depreciation purposes. If useful life of the property is:

3 years or more but less than 5 years	$33\frac{1}{3}\%$ qualifies
5 years or more but less than 7 years	$66\frac{2}{3}\%$ qualifies
7 years or more	100% qualifies

There is a $100,000 limit on the cost of used property on which the credit may be taken in any one tax year and there is no carryover of excess to following years. To maximize qualified investment in a year when you go over that limit, claim the credit on the longer-lived assets.

Investment credit is mandatory. It must be taken on eligible property in the year it is "placed in service." This means in the year that 1) depreciation begins under your depreciation practice, or 2) the property is placed in a state of readiness for its specifically-assigned function.

Eligible property includes depreciable livestock (except horses), and almost all other tangible property (except certain types of buildings) which is used in farming and can be depreciated. Purchased breeding and dairy stock, specialized livestock structures, grain storage, and machinery are the big items.

Most buildings and their structural components do not qualify. However, there are exceptions. Single purpose livestock structures and enclosures are eligible for investment credit. This includes confinement hog buildings, cattle finishing facilities, milking parlors, poultry houses, etc., if built specifically to house, raise, and feed a particular type of livestock. Also, such a structure must house equipment necessary to feed and care for the livestock. If use of the structure changes, the credit could be recaptured.

Work space used in caring for livestock is allowed, but other uses, such as selling of produce or storage of feed, supplies and machinery would be disqualifying. Greenhouses specifically designed, built, and used for the commercial production of plants also qualify for the tax credit.

Major improvements to a farm building (rehabilitation) made after October 31, 1978 are eligible for investment credit if the building has been in use at least 20 years and has not been rehabilitated for at least 20 years. The building must be used for production in your business and the improvement must not include enlargement or replacement of more than 25% of the exterior walls. Examples of rehabilitation are replacement of partitions and electrical wiring in a barn. A farmhouse does not qualify. There are other details which should be checked with your tax advisor.

Storage facilities qualify, even though they would otherwise be classed as buildings. The principal requirements are that : 1) the structure must be used in farming, 2) any work space within the structure must be quite small in relation to storage space, and 3) it must be used for the bulk storage of fungible commodities, such as grain. Most grain bins and silos will qualify.

Other depreciable property that qualifies, if it is used for crop or livestock production, includes:
- Fences, gates, and corrals to confine livestock or keep them out of cultivated areas.
- Drain tiles to irrigate or drain cultivated fields and pastures.
- Paved barnyards to keep livestock out of mud and to facilitate loading on trucks.
- Water wells and water systems for livestock, poultry, and irrigation--if outside of buildings. However, a water system in a single purpose livestock structure would qualify.
- Depreciable parts of dams and drainageways.

- Special lighting, signs, and other identity symbols.
- Gravel or paved roads, bridges, and culverts essential to farming.
- Replacement parts, machinery overhauls, and shop tools placed on a depreciation schedule.
- Business portion of depreciable property put to both personal and business use.

Business energy credit of 10% may be allowed on certain energy saving investments. This includes equipment which converts biomass (waste, sewage, grain, wood, crop residues, etc.) into synthetic solid, liquid, or gaseous fuel. After 1982, it applies to equipment that converts biomass to alcohol for fuel only if such equipment uses an energy source other than oil, natural gas, or a product therefrom. Related handling, storage, and pollution control equipment is eligible for the credit, too.

There's also a 10% energy credit for investment in equipment that recycles solid agricultural wastes, or that increases energy use efficiency, or cuts consumption in existing business facilities. And there is a 15% credit for investments made in 1980 through 1985 for equipment that uses solar or wind energy to generate electricity, to heat water, or to heat or cool a business structure. Examples of this type of investment are windmills, solar collectors, and heat exchangers.

All of the credits mentioned are on top of any regular 10% investment credit or the 10% credit for the cost of rehabilitating a building.

New vans are eligible for the full 10% investment credit if used for at least 3 years to transport employees. A van must have capacity for at least eight passengers and must be used at least 80% of the time to transport employees to and from work.

Maximum credit that can be taken in any one year is limited to the smaller of your tax liability, or $25,000 plus a percentage of your tax liability over $25,000. The Tax Reform Act of 1978 initiated a step-up in the limitation from $25,000 plus 50% of your tax liability over $25,000 in 1978 and earlier years, to 60% in 1979, 70% in 1980, 80% in 1981, and 90% in 1982 and thereafter. Unused credit may be carried back 3 years, then forward 7 years.

Recapture occurs when property is disposed of before the end of the useful life originally claimed. Your income tax in the year of disposal must be increased by the amount of the improperly claimed credit.

SELECTING DEPRECIATION METHODS AND RATES

A major technique for the recovery of investments in certain farming assets is use of a deduction for depreciation. Depreciation is an allowance for exhaustion, wear and tear, and obsolescence of property. To be eligible for depreciation, the property must be used in the trade or business or held for the production of income and must have a useful life of more than one year.

Allocation of purchase price establishes the depreciable basis of farm buildings, storages, wells, fences, drains, orchards, vineyards, groves, and also of depreciable personal property such as machinery, and dairy or breeding livestock.

Depreciation is not optional. Claim it on all property which qualifies. If you neglect to take depreciation when it is due, you are not allowed to recover that lost depreciation in a later year. You should establish reasonable depreciation schedules in the year you buy the item.

The four important elements in determining depreciation are:

1. Tax basis
2. Useful life and period of depreciation
3. Salvage value
4. Method of depreciation

The common methods of depreciation are straight line, declining balance, and sum of the year's digits. Without attempting to go into great detail, the straight line method has the advantage of simplicity and the others have the advantage of more rapid recovery of cost. A special 20% first-year additional depreciation allowance is available in many instances on machinery and equipment. Where this is available, it is a very useful tool in managing taxable income. The 20% special allowance can be taken on up to $10,000 of eligible property on a single return, or $20,000 on a joint return.

Generally, an owner benefits by rapid recovery of costs from fast depreciation methods and short life for depreciable property. Such procedures often have the effect of postponing tax rather than reducing it.

When a farm is purchased, the types of depreciation available are limited. Any existing buildings may only be depreciated on a straight line basis. In other words, if the useful life is 10 years, you may only depreciate at the rate of 10% per year. Depreciable real estate acquired new can be subjected to rapid depreciation, limited to the equivalent of 150% of straight line. Real estate is not eligible for the 20% first year special allowance. Land is never depreciable.

It is not always best to select the method of depreciation and length of life which will result in most rapid recovery of investment. Rapid recovery will usually be of most benefit when you expect less taxable income in the future than at present. On the other hand, if you expect to have more taxable income in later years, slow recovery may be most beneficial in the long run as it delays more of the deductions until higher income years. The value of saving extra tax dollars today and having them available for immediate investment should be considered, however. Another factor to consider is the recapture of depreciation taken in excess of straight line when the asset is sold. (Recapture is discussed in further detail later in this chapter.)

TAX CONSIDERATIONS FOR AN OPERATING FARM

While major tax considerations occur at the time of purchase and sale, there are many steps that may be taken during the period of ownership which will reduce and defer taxes and perhaps allow losses to offset income from other sources. These include:

- Accounting methods
- Conservation and land clearing expenses
- Farm operating losses
- Property lost from an involuntary conversion

Accounting Methods

Most farmers report on a calendar year basis. It is simpler to obtain information on rule changes and to obtain tax forms at the time you need them when filing on the calendar year basis.

Farmers may keep records and report their income on either the cash or accrual method. They make their choice when they file their first tax return. Having made the choice, they are not allowed to change without written consent from the Internal Revenue Service.

If you use the cash method, you report when income in cash or equivalent is received, and when expenses are paid. To illustrate the difference between cash and accrual reporting, assume that a farmer buys $100 worth of feed on December 15 but does not plan to use it until January. If he is on the cash basis, he can pay for the feed in December and lower his current taxable income by $100, or pay for it in January and reduce his next year's taxable income by $100. This gives him more flexibility in year-end adjustments. If he is on the accrual basis, the December purchase will not affect his taxable income for that year, because the feed will appear in his inventory at year-end.

Most farmers use the cash method of accounting because of the following advantages:

1. Simplicity. Fewer records need to be kept and inventories are not required.
2. If investing in and building up the business, you pay less tax currently because the increase in inventory is not recognized.
3. Under the cash method, there is more opportunity to make year-end adjustments to even out income, thus avoiding high tax brackets in some years.
4. Because raised breeding livestock has a zero basis when sold, the cash method results in less tax at time of sale. The cash basis reporter can convert more ordinary income to capital gain through raising breeding livestock than can the accrual basis farmer.

Conservation and Land Clearing Expenses

Expenditures made for soil and water conservation, as well as for land clearing, can be deducted for tax purposes as current business expenses. Soil and water conservation expenses may either be capitalized or written off as a current business expense. It is normally an advantage tax-wise to deduct such expenditures as opposed to depreciating them.

To qualify the expenditures, the taxpayer must be in the business of farming, use the land in farming, and the expenditure must be for soil or water conservation or prevention of erosion to the land. Generally speaking, qualified expenditures include eradication of brush, leveling, grading and terracing, contour furrowing, restoration of soil fertility, planting of windbreaks, construction, control and protection of diversion channels and drainage ditches, earthen dams, water courses, outlets and ponds, and flood control facilities.

The maximum amount of soil and water conservation expense that may be deducted in any one year is 25% of gross farm income. The excess can be carried over to future years. Land clearing expenses are limited to the lesser of 25% of taxable income or $5,000. The excess may be added to the basis of the land.

Land clearing expenses must be for land clearing operations and to prepare the land to make it suitable for farming. Qualified expenses include the removal of rocks, stones, trees, stumps, and brush; treating or moving earth; and the diversion of streams. Depreciable structures are not included. Depreciation on equipment used in land clearing must be taken as a land clearing expense.

Bear in mind that deductions previously taken as soil or water conservation or land clearing expenses will have to be recaptured according to the formula if the property is held for less than 10 years.

Farm Operating Losses

No one likes losses, but if they occur, the tax treatment may allow their use for maximum tax advantage. Transactional losses may result from sales and exchanges of capital items, casualty and theft losses, or abandonment, retirement, demolition or disease of business property. On the other hand, losses incurred in normal farming operations will appear in the year incurred as an excess of deductions over income from the operation involved.

When these losses taken together exceed the farmer's income from other sources, a net operating loss may result. This net operating loss is that amount of excess losses which may be carried forward, or carried back and then forward as a deduction to reduce taxable income in other years.

For operating losses to be deductible, there must have been profit motive. Hobby farms are under close observation by IRS and losses may be disallowed if the enterprise appears not to have been profit-motivated. If a farming operation shows a profit for any 2 or more years within a period of 5 consecutive years it is presumed to be a profit-motivated operation. That does not mean that you would not be able to qualify a farming operation that showed losses more consistently, but the burden is upon the taxpayer to prove that he is striving for profits.

In recent years limitations have been placed on the deduction of farm expenses. A farm loss is allowable only to the extent the taxpayer has an amount "at risk" in the farm operation. This rule was put in place by the

Internal Revenue Service to prevent abuses of borrowings being made on a nonrecourse basis to apply farm losses to other off-farm earnings. While these rules were aimed primarily at farm tax shelters, they may reach other operations where the borrower has no personal liability.

The calculation of the net operating loss is a complicated procedure, as is the carryback and carry-forward. The use of a professional account is recommended.

Involuntary Conversion

When a government agency using federal funds acquires land for public use, the tax treatment of the proceeds from the conversion is different than from an ordinary sale. While the gain or loss must be determined just as in a voluntary sale, if the entire proceeds are used to purchase replacement property within the specified replacement period, the tax-payer may elect to postpone tax on the gain.

An involuntary conversion is defined as destruction in whole or in part, theft, seizure or requisition, condemnation, or sale under threat or imminence of condemnation.

When property is substituted in kind as a result of an involuntary conversion, there is no gain recognized so long as the substitute property is similar or related in service or use. For example, if the state highway department condemns property and conveys a similar property in exchange, there is no taxable gain.

If money is received as a result of condemnation, gain will be recognized unless a special election is made to reinvest the proceeds. If the replacement property cost is less than the proceeds received, gain will be recognized to the extent of the unexpended proceeds.

Condemnation is the most common involuntary conversion. This refers to the process by which property is taken for public use without consent of the owner, but with just compensation. All condemnations of business property or property held for the production of income are involuntary conversions whether the transaction results in a gain or a loss. A sale under threat or imminence of condemnation is also treated as a condemnation. Threat or imminence of condemnation exists when a property owner is informed by a representative of the condemning authority that it has decided to acquire the property and the property owner has reasonable grounds to believe that the property will be condemned if he does not sell. The sale does not have to be made to the condemning authority. It may be made to a third party and the proceeds reinvested without recognition of gain.

Where the property is only partially taken, severance damages may occur. If they are separately assessed and stated, the proceeds may be separately treated. The damages are applied first to the cost of restoring the remaining property and then to reduce the basis of the remaining land. Or, they can be reinvested in other property of like kind. Gain results if the amount of severance damages exceeds the basis of the re-tained property.

The time period during which condemned real estate held for investment or business purposes may be replaced by like-kind real estate is through the end of the third tax year following the first tax year in which any part of the gain is realized. The period during which the taxpayer may ac-quire replacement property begins at the earliest date of the threat, or imminence of requisition or condemnation. It is possible, therefore, for the owner to buy replacement property before the actual condemnation takes place.

Like-kind property by definition is similar to that type of property which may be substituted in a tax-free exchange. Like-kind means pro-perty of the same general class, nature, or character, but need not be of the same grade or quality.

TAX CONSEQUENCES FOR THE SELLER

Proper and timely tax planning by the seller before an offer to purchase is obtained may save him substantial money when the sale is completed. One of the first considerations is the *basis* of the property.

Basis is the amount of the investment for tax purposes. More important, it's the amount you can recover tax-free when you dispose of the proper-ty. The original basis is the amount of the initial investment. It may be adjusted either up or down, depending on what has occurred since the time of purchase. However, the basis of an item of property depends first upon the manner in which it was acquired.

If the property was *purchased,* the original basis is the purchase price or cost. This includes the amount paid either in cash or other property plus commissions, legal fees, and other expenses which may have been connected with the purchase. The cost likewise includes the amount of debts assumed in connection with the purchase.

If the property was *inherited*, the basis is the fair market value at the time of the decedent's death.

If the property was *received by gift*, the basis is generally the same as it was in the hands of the donor. This could be affected by whether the property may later be sold at a loss, and by such things as whether gift tax was paid on the property.

If the property was acquired in a *"taxable exchange"* the basis of the property received is its value at the time of the trade.

If the property was acquired through a *like-kind or "tax-free" exchange,* the basis of the property acquired is the same as the basis of the property that was traded, adjusted for money received, gain included in income, and the cash paid.

As important as determining the basis is the examination of the property in its parts, including: land, depreciable real estate such as buildings, fences and tiling; and the house and site.

Even though a farm is sold as a package for a lump sum, the sale must be broken down. Sales price and basis must be determined for each item. The tax basis of the buildings and other depreciable items is usually the cost or other basis when acquired, plus the improvements less the depreciation. The house is a capital asset which would have an original basis plus improvements.

If the house is occupied by the owner, it is not depreciable except for that portion used in the farm business, and this has been severely limited under recent tax laws. If the house is occupied by a tenant farmer or a renter, it is a depreciable building. The basis is increased by soil and water conservation expenses that have been treated as capitalized items but have not been written off, and land clearing expenses which could not be deducted.

In summary, the following factors must be considered in establishing the tax basis of items or real estate:

1. Determine the original basis of acquisition.
2. Cost of improvements to the property increase the basis.
3. Depreciation taken will decrease the basis.
4. Casualty losses will decrease the basis.
5. Severance damages arising from condemnation awards or partial sales of the property will reduce the basis.

Sale Of The Farm Residence

Special attention and separate allocation for the residence is a must at the time of the farm sale. One who sells or exchanges a residence at a gain is not taxed if he reinvests the proceeds in another residence within 18 months, or if he bought a new residence within 18 months prior to the sale. Thus, if the new residence costs as much or more than the price received for the old one, none of the gain is recognized for income tax purposes. Consequently, it may be to your benefit to allocate a relatively high amount to the residence.

A special election is available to a taxpayer who attains the age of 55 years. If he has owned and occupied his home as a principal residence for a total of 3 years out of 5 years immediately preceding the sale, he may elect a one-time option to exclude all gain up to $100,000. The law applies to sales and exchanges after July 26, 1978.

Recapture of Depreciation on Buildings

If a farmer has used straight-line depreciation on his buildings, he will not have to be concerned with recapture unless the property has been held for less than a year and there is a gain on the sale, in which case any depreciation claimed would be converted into ordinary income to the extent of the gain. Some or all of the excess depreciation over straight line will be recaptured as ordinary income on sale, or other disposition of the property up to the amount of the gain realized. Depending on when the depreciation was claimed, different formulas apply to recapture.

Recapture Of Deductions

Tax reforms have added recapture provisions which convert to ordinary income some or all of the deductions claimed for soil and water conservation and land-clearing expenses to the extent of the gain realized on the sale or other disposition of land. Certain of these expenses may have been set up as capital items and depreciated, or they may have been deducted from ordinary income in the year when the work was done. If a farm is held for less than 10 years, part of the soil and water conservation and land-clearing expenses that have been claimed will have to be recaptured as ordinary income. The amount is gradually reduced, until after 10 years of ownership none of the expense is recaptured.

Depreciation taken on machinery which is later sold at a gain is to be reported as ordinary income. This can be a significant amount if an owner has used a rapid rate of depreciation.

Gain on the sale of purchased breeding animals up to the amount of depreciation taken after December 31, 1969, also has to be recaptured as ordinary income.

Investment credit has to be recaptured if the sale results in the items being disposed of before the expiration of the useful life for which the credit was computed.

Timing Of The Sale Is Important

A prime consideration in liquidating the farm business is the effect of timing of the sale on taxes. It may be possible to sell a portion of the assets, such as the livestock in the fall, machinery in the spring of the following year, and perhaps wait until the following year to sell the land, in order to spread the taxable gain over 3 years.

Suitable timing may also allow for proper time periods to have elapsed to avoid the recapture of such expenses as soil and water conservation.

Timing may also affect the gain from the sale of raised breeding animals. For example, breeding animals must be held for at least 2 years. Therefore, one should consider delaying selling a few months, if, by doing so certain animals will qualify for capital gains treatment as opposed to ordinary income.

Exchanging Farm Property For Other Property

If business property such as a farm is traded for other business property, all or part of the gain can escape immediate taxation. While such an exchange is frequently called a "tax-free" exchange, it is basically a method of deferring taxes and is more accurately titled a "like-kind" exchange. On the surface, the technique appears to be fairly simple. In fact, it can be complicated. It also involves serious tax consequences if conducted improperly.

The basic idea of the like-kind exchange is to allow the transfer of basis from one parcel to another and postpone any tax on the gain until the new property is sold. In order to qualify, it must, in fact, be an exchange as distinguished from a sale. Voluntary tax-free trades are not to be confused with condemnations and other involuntary conversions.

Many owners incorrectly believe that they can sell their farm outright and reinvest the proceeds from that sale on other farmland without being subject to capital gains tax on the profit. The only way most farmers can dispose of their farmland and avoid immediate taxation of any of the proceeds is through a qualifying exchange.

Many investors exchange not only once, but proceed to second or third exchanges in which case the taxable gains on all properties are postponed. The tax postponement continues as you repeatedly exchange properties until you sell the last piece exchanged. Then all prior postponed taxable gains are included when the tax is paid on the last ·sale.

A proper exchange must meet three tests:

1. It must be a true exchange and not merely a sale and a purchase.
2. The properties involved must be qualifying "like-kind" properties.
3. The property must be held for investment or business and not for resale.

Like-kind, however, does not require that the property be identical. For purposes of an exchange, the Internal Revenue Code speaks of "property of a like-kind to be held either for productive use in trade or business or for investment." It is proper to exchange vacant land for improved land; farm and ranch land for city rental land, vacant land, apartments buildings, or business buildings; leasehold with 30 or more years left to run for a fully-owned fee; cow for a cow; truck for a truck; tractor for a tractor; etc.

Examples of exchanges which will not qualify are farmland for tractors; farmland for farmland and tractors together; and an exchange does not include mortgages, stocks, bonds, promissory notes, or securities. It does include breeding livestock and farm machinery.

A practical problem in an exchange is the difficulty in finding a person willing to trade property for property. Consequently, most exchanges involve three parties. A buyer may have no property of a like-kind to exchange. The owner who wishes to exchange property must then find a similar property for sale at another location and ask the buyer to purchase it. Then they exchange parcels. If handled properly, this transaction results in a tax-free exchange for the two parties actually involved. A properly worded contract is imperative.

The intention of the parties at the beginning is crucial. The courts may overlook some errors you make in carrying out your exchange plan so long as it is planned from the beginning.

It is not necessary to locate and approve the land to be received before the exchange agreement is drawn up and signed. The written agreement should clearly state that you are planning an exchange. It is usually sufficient if the agreement allows for an outright sale with an option to exchange, if the buyer can find like-kind property acceptable to the seller.

The plan of exchange cannot be too loose. Arranging a tax-free exchange and the computation of taxable gain, if any, on such a transaction is complicated. It requires imagination and careful legal and accounting advice before you make the agreement.

If the trade is not even and cash is received, or if the property traded or received is mortgaged, part of the gain may be recognized and immediately taxable in an exchange. Examples follow:

An owner who trades a farm for an apartment house and pays additional cash includes the cash payment in the adjusted tax base of his farm when determining the tax basis of the apartment house, but has no gain to recognize.

If the owner receives cash for his farm in addition to other investment property (the apartment house), the cash received must be reported as gain, up to the amount of gain which has occurred on the farm.

If an owner trades his farm for an apartment house, with no cash involved, but in the deal the owner is relieved of a $10,000 mortgage on the farm, and assumes no mortgage on the newly acquired property, he is considered to have received $10,000 in money for tax purposes.

A transaction which involves a swap of property, plus cash or "boot", may qualify both as a nontaxable exchange, and as an installment sale.

Property traded away may result in investment credit recapture. A tax-free exchange is a "disposition" for investment credit purposes.

USE OF INSTALLMENT SALE BENEFITS

The desirability of the installment sale has been discussed elsewhere in this book, but because of the large percentage of land transactions handled on an installment basis, and the tax savings that often result to sellers, the key elements deserve further discussion.

Note: *As this book goes to press, Congress is considering a revision liberalizing the tax treatment of installment sales. Major elements of the proposed change include: removal of the 30% maximum for payments received in the first year; removal of the provision that payments must be received in two or more years; and a restriction that installment reporting of gains is not allowed if the property is sold to a close relative and that relative resells the property within two years.*

Buyer Benefits

1. Built-in financing.
2. Lower downpayment than conventional loan.
3. More favorable interest rate, generally.
4. Payments are often more flexible.

Seller Benefits

1. Capital gains spread over a period of several years, thus reducing the tax rate.
2. Higher price due to more buyers capable of buying.
3. Offering a lower rate of interest (which helps the buyer pay a higher price) results in less ordinary income and more capital gain to the seller.
4. More rapid sale of the property.
5. Money remains invested in familiar property.

Requirements Of An Installment Sale

1. Seller cannot receive more than 30% of the sale price during year of sale. (See note above)
2. Sale proceeds must be received in 2 or more years. (See note above)
3. If existing mortgage assumed by buyer exceeds seller's basis, the excess is considered to be part of the payment received in year of sale.
4. Interest rate on balance currently must be at least 6%.

Example Of Savings

Cash Sale: Assume seller has a buyer for his property at $200,000. His basis is $50,000, thus resulting in a capital gain of $150,000. Only 40%

of capital gain is taxable, or in this case $60,000. Assume that this gain, plus his other income puts the taxpayer in the 50% tax bracket, thus it results in a tax obligation from sale of this property of $30,000.

Installment Sale: From above, assume the same situation of a $200,000 sale price with a $50,000 basis. Instead of cash, buyer takes 20% ($40,000) first year, and 20% ($40,000) per year for 4 years thereafter. Instead of reporting a $60,000 gross income inclusion in one year, he reports $12,000 per year for 5 years. Assume this reduces his tax rate to 25%, the tax due to this sale is $3,000 per year for 5 years, or a total of $15,000.

Result:	Cash Sale,	$30,000 tax
	Installment Sale,	15,000 tax
	After Tax Savings,	$15,000

Caution: The above example is oversimplified and ignores several factors, including the alternative minimum tax which may apply. Consult with your tax advisor before proceeding.

Income Averaging Compared To Installment Sale

Income averaging permits a person to average a high income year with preceding lower income years. Thus, part of an unusually large amount of taxable income can be taxed at lower rates. If the seller needs cash beyond what an installment sale will provide, income averaging may be an acceptable alternative. The base period for income averaging is the previous 4 years.

If income in any year is a fifth more than the average income for the prior 4 years, and if the excess is more than $3,000, all the excess income will be taxed under the income averaging provision, at the rate that applies to the first one-fifth of the excess income. In effect, the progressive rate schedule is eliminated on the top four-fifths of the excess income.

The complexities of changing tax laws often discourage principals in a transaction from proper tax planning. Remember that a few hundred dollars spent for consultation with an accountant or lawyer specializing in tax matters may save thousands of dollars otherwise wasted.

CHAPTER 14

Land Transition: Rural to Rurban to Urban

Many years ago while doing an economic study of agricultural land values in Florida, the "most successful" dairy operator in the state was introduced to me. With a trace of a smile he explained that he had become wealthy despite the fact that he had been forced to move his operations three times due to urban encroachment.

First, his "little" 300-acre place on the outskirts of Miami had been purchased for an industrial park near the new airport. So he took part of his money and bought 600 acres for $500 per acre further north on the outskirts of the then small town of Ft. Lauderdale. Ten years and 250,000 incoming people later, developers kept pestering him until he "gave up"; sold it to them for $3,000 per acre; and decided to move to the country part of the state, southwest of Orlando. There he bought a "real spread" of 5,000 acres for $200 per acre. More bad luck! Along came Disneyworld, traffic and those noisy developers, pestering him to buy his corner property for $50,000 per acre; his good pasture for $5,000 per acre; etc., etc. Somehow I got the idea that he wasn't too concerned whether he got $5.00 or $15.00 per 100 pounds for his milk!

This example supports an earlier observation made after knowing many wealthy farmers: All of them have been owners–none have been tenants. Fluctuating prices that farmers receive for their products make farming a high risk business. But appreciation of land values has built the net worth of many farmers to six or seven figures. Every year, thousands of serious farmers become reluctant (some not so reluctant) sellers, unable or unwilling to pass up offers of incredible land prices offered by developers, entrepreneurs, builders, and speculators who have a different purpose in mind for the land.

Highest and best use is the theory. Land used for the production of food and forage has a lower level of value when compared to recreational, residential, commercial, or industrial uses.

Look at relative values of U.S. land in the early 1980s:

Least productive ranch or mountain country: $60 to $100 per acre.
Average Midwest pasture: $300 to $400 per acre.
Typical Midwest cropland: $1,200 to $1,500 per acre.
Best Corn Belt cropland: $3,000 to $6,000 per acre.
Suburban raw land for residential use: $8,000 to $20,000 per acre.
Urban improved parcels for residential use: $20,000 to $250,000 per acre.
Urban improved parcels for industrial use: $50,000 to $300,000 per acre.
Small urban commercial sites: $100,000 to $500,000 per acre.
Oceanfront property: $100,000 to $1,000,000 per acre.
Best major city commercial or office sites: $1,000,000 to $5,000,000 per acre.

Change is an ever-present dimension of our society. As changes occur, they are reflected in patterns of land use and, in turn, land prices. Many factors account for constant shifts in land use:

1. Population transfers from the northeastern industrial states to the southern and western portions of the country.
2. Increased leisure time in the last two decades.
3. A realized desire to flee the pressures of a fast-moving society.
4. Greater weekend use of beaches, golf courses, and resort areas.
5. The increased demand for resorts, second homes, beach cabins, campgrounds, and parks.
6. A continued trend by industry and populace to move away from the congestion of the inner city and into suburban and semi-rural settings.
7. Expectations and goals change from generation to generation. A recent trend indicates some young people have less desire for big cars, big houses, and the trappings of high income. A simpler and more basic lifestyle often translates to a rural life.
8. Reductions in fossil fuel availability and resulting higher gasoline prices may force the development of more "contained" communities, providing residential, commercial, and industrial development in one community.

Further change is inevitable, and the owner of land should be aware of the considerations affecting his property. Resist the tendency to think in terms of the past, or in local trends. An outsider to an area often recognizes trends more quickly, because he is not biased from being "too close" to a property or neighborhood.

SELLING TO A DEVELOPER

The landowner who was sufficiently farsighted, or lucky, to buy or inherit land in an area of expanding urban growth, must capitalize on his good fortune by dealing intelligently with developers who have special prerequisites for purchasing land. Unless a seller has some understanding of these unique considerations, the developer will likely acquire one of the neighboring properties instead.

Developers seek out land in a variety of ways. Some large companies have a land acquisition staffman who will specifically search for properties suitable for the purpose intended. Others rely on brokers to be aware of available land and submit properties to their attention. Still others operate very haphazardly, stumbling onto properties more by chance than choice. The prudent developer will follow certain guidelines, and develop strategies and objectives necessary to make an intelligent purchase decision. Before purchasing land a prudent developer will:

1. Conduct a market survey of all available land in his area of development interest.
2. Inspect and analyze all land sales to determine his competitive position in the market.
3. Analyze all housing products being sold to determine what price he can allocate to residual land.
4. Have a complete awareness of any unique problems inherent to the political subdivisions involved.
5. Investigate all costs of development, and availability of utilities.
6. Program a realistic development schedule.

Builder vs. Developer

A distinction should be made between the builder and the developer. A builder prefers to buy land fully serviced with water and sewer, with only a minimum of offsite improvements to install. (Offsite improvements are classified as improvements to roads, bridges, canals, waterlines, and sewerlines which are required to facilities off the property. Onsite improvements include similar items within the property, plus sidewalks, street lighting, grading, and other steps necessary.)

A builder typically prefers not to concern himself with the time lag or risks related to land development. He is willing to pay a premium for land that is zoned, site-planned, platted, graded, and ready to pull building permits on. He is generally unwilling to inventory land for much more than a year's demand, and consequently wants small parcels.

A developer is willing to buy raw land, or land which is zoned and platted but without any earth moved or site improvements installed. He may also be a builder, but often is willing to sell developed land to other builders, as a method of diversifying his revenues, and speeding construction on the site. A developer may purchase from 50 to 1,000 acres, or more, depending on the absorption rate of dwelling units in the community. A developer may anticipate a 10-year, or more, selloff schedule.

Terms of Purchase Preferred By A Builder

A typical builder wants to buy enough lots to establish continuity of construction in a community, but is limited in the amount of cash he has.

Let's assume a builder wants to buy 30 single-family lots at $15,000 per lot. A typical deal would be structured this way:

He buys three lots for cash. This gives him clear title to those lots, and allows him to acquire a construction loan from a lending institution to construct three model homes. The builder obtains options on the remaining lots at a set takedown schedule, based upon the initial price, plus interest; or a stepped-up purchase price based upon the time elapsed from closing. In the event he misses a scheduled takedown, he will forfeit his option contract.

Alternatively, other sellers of lots may require a certain percentage downpayment on the entire contract. Against the downpayment, some lots may be released at closing, or subordinated to construction loans.

ECONOMICS OF DEVELOPING RAW LAND

A developer of raw acreage is faced with many unknowns, and the farm seller must appreciate his development schedule, particularly as to time and cost of investigation.

Assume a developer has concluded a search for land, probably taking several months to scrutinize a number of parcels. He settles on a 300-acre raw land parcel as meeting his general requirements for location, soil conditions, utilities, zoning (or zoning probability), terms and price. Let's say the price is $14,000 per acre. Before any prudent developer commits to a purchase price of $4,200,000, he must satisfy himself to the elements of feasibility. A developer will give close study to the following factors.

Engineering feasibility. Tests must be made for soil conditions, including elevation, topography, soil borings, fill and grading requirements, presence of organic material or rock, availability of utilities, drainage, and a multitude of other factors.

Planning and zoning. No one wants property not capable of being used for the purposes intended. City, county, state and federal governments, in the name of consumer and public protection, have built multiple agencies with jurisdiction over development, any of which are capable of complicating or delaying construction to the point of nonfeasibility. Nearby residents of a proposed community may form activist opposition to additional development within their area, and elected officials may yield to their demands, compromising a well-designed plan of development.

Conditions that must be satisfied precedent to a closing of a large parcel of land may include any or all of the following:

- Approval by Environmental Protection Agencies (EPA) at all levels of government.
- Approval by zoning boards concerning land use and densities.
- Site plan approval.
- Plat approval.
- Approval of Corps of Engineers.
- Approval by local water management districts.
- Extent of impact fees or "voluntary" dedications and contributions that may be required by city or county for roads, parks, and schools.
- Developer's agreement with owners of utility companies or franchises, guaranteeing availability of sewer and water taps.
- Removal of restrictions that may have previously been placed on the land.

- Satisfaction of subdivision development ordinances and building codes governing building setbacks, height restrictions, master plan submissions, etc.
- Issuance of building permits.

Economic feasibility. Simultaneous with the investigation as to whether the land is physically feasible, and can be bought conditional to obtaining necessary approvals and permits, a market analysis is necessary.

Investigation of the market will necessarily include these factors:

- Location of competitive land available to builders, along with price and terms asked.
- Absorption rates of the area.
- Product demand and sales price. (For example, is the local demand for single family residences, townhouses, or apartments?)
- Setting aside a portion of the land for commercial use.
- Will the combination of raw land cost, development costs, and carrying costs leave a profit margin when the land is built out, or sold to builders?

The example given earlier was based on the purchase of 300 acres at $14,000 per acre, or $4,200,000. The path from initial contract through development and sale of the finished land could follow these steps:

1) **Buyer contracts with seller.** Terms of sale are:
   –90-day "free look" for buyer to do initial feasibility.
   –$25,000 paid at end of 90 days for additional 6-month period of investigation.
   –At end of above 9 months, buyer has option of closing on sale or forfeiting his $25,000.
   –Assume buyer closes with an acquisition and development loan of $3,200,000 plus $1,000,000 cash equity.

2) **Buyer completes master plan** of development over the next 12 months, resulting in a land use of:

Arterial and collector streets	30 acres
Parks, lakes, and common area	50 acres
Net buildable land	220 acres
Gross acreage, total	300 acres

3) *Net buildable land is allocated* to the following uses:

	Acres	Dwelling Units
Single family detached housing at a density of 4 dwelling units per acre	80	320
Townhouse, cluster, or villa housing at a density of 8 dwelling units per acre	80	640
Apartment land at an average density of 14 dwelling units per acre	50	700
Commercial land	10	—
Total	220	1,660

4) *Buyer completes engineering,* permitting, and land development, including installation of sewer and water to the property line, grading, filling, construction of lakes, and major streets.

5) *Money is spent to put land in condition* for sale in small tracts to builders:

Cost of raw land, 300 acres at $14,000	$ 4,200,000
Development cost, 300 acres at $12,000	3,600,000
Planning and engineering	400,000
Legal and processing	250,000
Carrying costs and overhead	1,600,000
Cost of semi-improved land or 220 acres at $45,700/acre	$10,050,000

6) *Probable sales price:*

Single family, 80 acres at $48,000/acre (equal to $12,000 per lot)	$ 3,840,000
Townhouse land, 80 acres at $56,000/acre (equal to $7,000 per unit)	4,480,000
Apartment land, 50 acres at $63,000/acre (equal to $4,500 per unit)	3,150,000
Commercial land, 10 acres at $80,000/acre	800,000
Total sales price	$12,270,000

7) *Expected profit:*

Estimated sales price	$12,270,000
Cost to produce	10,050,000
Expected profit	$ 2,220,000

The profit may look attractive for land development, but the risks are great:
- Initial investment is high.
- The opportunity for error in the planning and development stage is significant.
- Market swings due to housing and monetary cycles can be vicious.
- The time period from a raw land contract to finished land product is lengthy.
- Rule changes by government bodies can be disastrous.

LAND FOR COMMERCIAL USE

The sale of land to commerical users will generally fall into one of the following categories.

1. Small single purpose sites
2. Strip shopping centers
3. Neighborhood shopping centers
4. Community shopping centers
5. Regional shopping centers

Single Purpose Sites

Small site users such as service stations, banks, savings and loan associations, and fast food chains prefer corner locations, or heavily traveled streets with access from two directions. Size required is one to two acres, depending on parking requirements and need for a drive-in facility. Location is extremely important, and this type of user is willing to pay a premium to protect their share of the market.

Strip Centers

Located along busy streets, strip centers require from 2 to 5 acres. Frontage needs vary according to size of the center, and depth of the land should be 250′ to 300′, depending on municipal building setback requirements. Normally these centers have no "anchor" tenant. Rather, they are an assemblage of local stores, such as restaurants, dry cleaners, real estate offices, book stores, and convenience stores.

Neighborhood Centers

The principal tenants in a neighborhood center are a supermarket and a drugstore. Net leasable area in this type of center will range from 55,000 to 80,000 square feet. Land area required is 7 to 12 acres, depending on the location appeal to local stores. A corner location on two major streets is always preferred because it provides both maximum public exposure to the stores leasing space and easy access from more than one main road. The site plan will usually include 2 to 3 freestanding buildings for restaurants or financial institutions and 15 to 30 local stores in an L-shaped design.

Community Centers

Community centers are oversized neighborhood centers, that include a 60,000 to 100,000 square foot department or discount store of the variety type in addition to the supermarket, drug, and local stores. Area required is 15 to 20 acres, allowing 150,000 to 220,000 square feet of net leasable area.

Regional Centers

A regional center will include several major department stores, and essentially provide a major shopping area designed to draw from at least 10 miles in each direction. This type of center may require from 80 to 150 acres, offering up to 1,000,000 square feet of leasable area. Only major metropolitan areas are capable of supporting regional centers, which are typically of the enclosed mall type.

LAND FOR INDUSTRIAL USES

The use of real estate for industrial purposes spans a broad spectrum. While industry is commonly associated with large manufacturing plants near major cities, many companies are establishing small plants and warehousing facilities near towns of 1,000 to 50,000 population. In addition to fabrication, assembly, or distribution activities, industrial needs include research and development, stockyards, packing and crating, publishing, and many related services requiring a small but motivated and reliable work force.

Attracting Industrial Firms

Electric companies, natural gas companies, and other public utilities are often able to furnish special acquisition services to industry and the community. They may cooperate with community organizations such as the Chambers of Commerce, and development committees comprised of local leaders. Community promotion, including the publication of industrial development aids, are helpful in spotlighting an area for development.

State development agencies are among the most active groups involved in industrial promotion. Some sponsor research reports which give community data and include information on specific sites available for development. Owners of land near a community are well advised to cooperate in the inclusion of their property as potential sites.

The Site Selection Process

The industrial firm usually knows its general needs and wants. However, if the site owner, or the industrial committee with whom he is cooperating, is cognizant of the typical site needs, they may be able to enhance the attractiveness of the site to the user.

Factors affecting the location of plants include these:

1. Proximity to good highways.
2. Labor supply as needed.
3. Availability of suitable land, in size and shape, for expansion.
4. Proximity to markets.
5. Proximity to raw materials, supplies, and services.
6. Cost-reducing factors (taxes, wages).
7. Favorable leasing or financing available.
8. Abundant water supply.
9. Proximity to related industry.
10. Community's cultural-recreational assets.
11. Available vocational training facilities.

Land Requirements

Obviously, the size of site required will change infinitely for the various companies. Firms requiring less than 10 acres will include operations such as subcontracted job work, prefabrication, precision tools, optical instruments, electronic components, or specialty firms. They typically require no more than 200 square feet of floor area per employee.

In contrast, firms requiring over 100 acres are usually involved in activities with a relatively high capital investment like primary metals, chemicals or transportation equipment. They may require in excess of 1,000 square feet of floor area per employee.

The lack of available utilities–water, waste disposal, natural gas, and electricity–would constitute a serious limitation. Topography and load-bearing quality of the soil are also important factors. Uneven, sloping, or poorly drained soils may make development costs prohibitive.

Zoning must be flexible to allow the use required. Land use plans may require modification to enhance the availability of land in suitable locations.

Sale Terms To Users

Local industrial development committees often buy and hold land for future industrial use. Outright purchase assures the future availability for industrial use, and affords some control over the type of development that will occur. If limited financial resources prevent outright purchase, options should be procured to assure land availability.

Most industrial firms will require 6 to 12 months of study for feasibility purposes. Creative land leases, or build-to-suit proposals may be necessary to provide the final incentive to an industrial user.

THE SECOND HOME MARKET

Every year several hundred thousand families decide to realize their desire for a second house where they can spend leisure time, or look forward to retirement years. Areas with desirable climates such as Florida, California, Texas, Arizona, and New Mexico have been obvious targets of second home purchasers. Winter sports enthusiasts look to places like Colorado or Vermont for condominiums or mountain cottages.

Aside from obvious resort areas, many urban families seek out nearby retreats, developments with lake-oriented activities, or simply one to 10 acres in wooded and secluded areas upon which to build an A-frame, park a camper, or pitch a tent.

A relatively simple transaction will help demonstrate the opportunities that exist to capitalize on this constant demand.

A Development Example

A few years ago I acquired an 85-acre parcel of partially wooded pastureland in Missouri for $400 per acre, simply because I thought it was reasonably priced and had certain characteristics making it a relatively easy property to subdivide. It had a paved road on one side, gravel on another. A waterline was accessible along the paved road.

Not wishing to become involved in expensive and time-consuming engineering and development activities, I took the most simple approach to subdivision and had the property surveyed and platted as shown.

The lots ranged in size from 8 to 16 acres. All lots had a minimum of 440-feet frontage and were from 800 to 1,500 feet in depth. Over a 2-year period, a local Realtor sold all seven lots at an average price of $950 per acre, totaling $80,750.

The results were:

Gross sales price:.....................	$80,750	$80,750
Less selling costs:		
Commissions.........................	8,075	
Real estate taxes	800	
Surveying and platting	2,200	
Legal, title, and recording............	900	
Original purchase price	34,000	
Total	$45,975	45,975
Net profit before income tax		$34,775

Certainly not a fortune, but I had a loan on the property, with release prices on individual lot sales, and never had more than $10,000 equity in the property. So the return on equity invested exceeded 300% in a 2-year period.

The economic fact is that more people can afford to buy 10-acre properties than 85-acre properties, so the developer can subdivide and sell off smaller properties at a higher price per acre. The secret is knowing the value of property, and its salability at any given location.

GOLF COURSE COMMUNITIES

Probably 20 million Americans play golf once a month, or more, on about 15,000 golf courses. The sport has increased in popularity annually, and there is no reason why the growth should not continue.

Parcel As Purchased

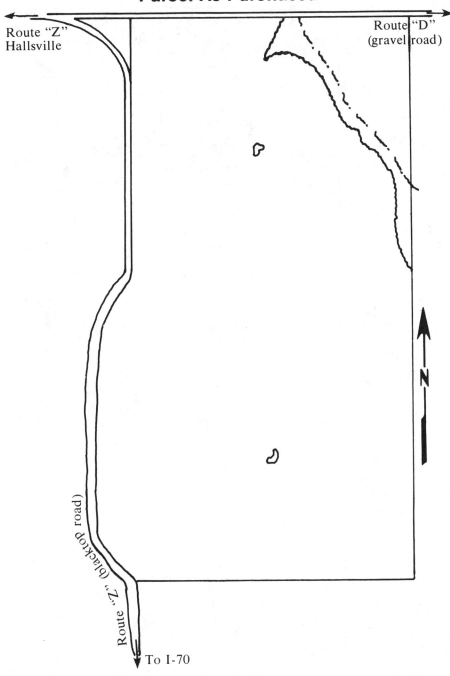

Parcel After Surveying and Platting

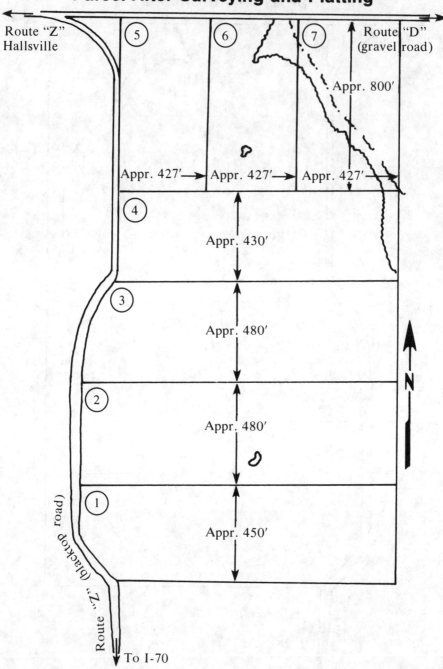

The economics of golf course developments are such that one of three events must occur for a golf course to be built:

1) For an 18-hole course, a minimum of 300 members (unless they are very wealthy) must decide that they want a private or semi-private course, and put up the money to build and own it.
2) A city or municipality must determine the esthetic desirability of having a golf course, convince the residents to support it with tax revenues, and probably subsidize the annual operations of the course.
3) As part of a residential community, a developer analyzes the cost-benefit ratio, and decides that a golf course in the development will sufficiently enhance the value of the land surrounding it to recover the cost, time, and responsibility involved.

Economics of Development

Assume a developer is considering a 600-acre property for a golf course community. Assume further that the zoning of the land is residential, 4 units per gross acre, thus allowing the construction of 2,400 dwelling units. Developing a plan to locate a golf course within the community will provide several economic benefits.

The governmental authority may agree to the construction of the golf course on 150 acres, and still allow 2,400 units to be built on the remaining 450 acres. Utilizing the greater density will provide a diversified mix of single-family homes, townhomes, and apartments.

A golf course is an attraction to home buyers, whether or not they are golfers. Homeowners are willing to pay substantial premiums for lake or golf course views. A single-family lot normally worth $20,000 may sell for $8,000 to $15,000 more with a golf course location. A typical condominium or townhouse will sell for $3,000 to $8,000 more when it has a golf course or water view.

In times of economic slowdown for housing, a golf course community is still a draw and may speed the rate of sales. The image of a community is enhanced by a country club atmosphere, and is thus more competitive in the market place.

A golf course within a community must be designed to give maximum residence exposure to the fairways. While good playing design normally calls for at least two holes to play side by side, a 7,000-yard course should still provide nearly 3,500 yards of frontage views.

General guidelines to the construction of an 18-hole course are:

Land cost	Offsite improvements - roads, etc.
Design and engineering	Clubhouse
Construction	Contingencies
Equipment and storage area	Carrying charges
Landscaping	Operating Fund

Obviously, the variables are so great as to initial costs and operating costs as to be only guideline figures. Development costs must allow for:

Area............................... 110 to 160 acres.
Development Cost..................... $15,000 to $30,000 per hole.
Land Cost .... variable by area.
Clubhouse .... $150,000 up.
Carts............................... leased.
Maintenance Equipment .... $50,000 up.

Normally, an 18-hole course cannot provide adquate playing time for more than 300 to 400 membership units. Depending on the type of member (social or serious), a club can only accommodate 200 to 500 rounds per day.

To give an example, if a foursome started every ten minutes off the first tee between the hours of 8 a.m. and 2 p.m., 148 players would tee off. Some increase in play is available if the course is doubled up by starting off both the front and back nine, but these players must be dovetailed with other starting foursomes.

Many types of golf courses can be built: 18-hole championship course; 9-hole executive course; pitch and putt "par 3" courses. The decision to build a course within a development community should always be governed by the economic feasibility dictated by the enhancement of land values for the dwelling units to be constructed.

CHAPTER **15**

Government Regulations and Property Rights

The right to own real property is one of the most revered of all American traditions. Not only has property ownership been the source of all great wealth . . . pride and strength flow from the security that individuals and families derive from owning a house . . . a farm . . . a country place of their own. Socialistic or communistic countries tend to view property as public, not private. In "The Communist Manifesto," Marx and Engles sum up the theory of Communism very simply: the abolition of private property.

The Constitution of the United States grants and guarantees the rights of free citizens to own and use property. The rights of land ownership extend beyond mere title. Economists commonly speak of "the bundle of rights," and include: *possession, control, quiet enjoyment, and disposition.* Since the early 1950s the rights of individuals to own and use private property have been steadily eroded.

In addition to the right of governmental bodies to place a tax on your real property, other governmental actions can influence your use and enjoyment of the land. Under certain circumstances, government can claim your property without your consent. Zoning ordinances and other regulations may severely restrict the uses and activities permitted on your property.

TAKING PROPERTY WITH COMPENSATION

Included in the constitutional guarantees is one that forbids the taking of private property without payment of just compensation. The right of the federal, state, or local government to take private property for public use upon just compensation is called the *right of eminent domain.*

Many landowners felt the effects of condemnation actions in the period ranging from the 1950s through the early 1970s. At this time, scores of state and federal dams and lakes were being built to generate power and for flood control. The Interstate Highway System was being constructed across the continent. Hundreds of thousands of acres were affected by these takings. Often the most productive land was taken for lakes as water was backed up across the "bottomland,"that fertile, alluvial soil laid down by siltation of top soil. Highways often split productive farms diagonally, reducing efficiency, and separating buildings from remaining land.

Owners learned that there was no recourse. Verbal battles were waged. Sometimes they became physical, as landowners fought to keep the land they had so carefully assembled, or the house where generations had preserved moments of personal history. The battles became legal for the most part, and when negotiations failed, were waged in the court rooms between the condemning agency and the landowner, each with one or more appraisers, attorneys, and other assorted expert witnesses to parade before the jury to state their case.

This author served as an appraiser and expert witness in a dozen states before state and federal courts, sometimes employed by the condemning agency, at others by the landowner. On occasion the landowners were fair -- more often biased -- but almost always outraged that their land was being "taken" from them.

The taking agencies, in turn, had varying policies. Some agencies, particularly early in their condemnation experience, made no secret of their intent to buy the land as cheaply as possible. Other agencies sincerely wanted to pay the owner every cent due . . . but not one cent more.

Justice was not always done . . . but at least an effort was made to pay "just compensation."

TAKING PROPERTY WITHOUT COMPENSATION

Police Power

Certain public powers over property fall within the premise of "Police Power." The most common police powers deal with ordinances or legislation imposed to protect the property, life, health, and safety of citizens; in other words, for the benefit of the public good.

An example of a police power to protect the public may be the erection of a median strip across a busy street to prevent left turns or crossovers. This action may restrict the flow of traffic to a commercial property, but is considered to be of public benefit and not compensable under eminent domain. The owner who is financially crippled certainly won't agree.

Zoning

Zoning is a traditional type of regulation which communities use to control the use that can be made of each parcel of land and to further regulate the type, density and occasionally the volume of building construction. Zoning, as the word implies, consists of dividing the jurisdiction into various use zones. Zoning is normally done through an ordinance passed by the city or county, but stems from the State's police power.

The purposes of zoning, if done properly, include:

1. To prohibit unsuitable or improper structures
2. To provide for better transportation and flow of traffic
3. To increase the safety of the general population
4. To increase the general health and welfare of the populace
5. To prevent the overcrowding of land
6. To establish orderly uses of land by designating the location of each
7. To control the height and area of a building by specifying the number of storys permitted; by setting front, side and rear yard set-backs of buildings, and by limiting the amount of ground that may be covered by a building
8. To insure that there is adequate parking for the uses provided
9. To help provide land for housing in appropriate categories

Zoning falls into two broad categories:

Planned developments. Planned Unit Developments (PUD) or Planned Community Developments (PCD) encompass areas large enough for a mix of uses. The development may embrace several thousand acres, including residential, commercial, and industrial uses.

One county describes the purpose and intent of their PUD ordinance as follows:

"The purpose of this provision is to encourage the accomplishment of a more complete living environment through the application of enlightened and imaginative approach to community planning and shelter design. This alternative should introduce a variety of architectural solutions, provide for the preservation of natural features and scenic areas, reduce land consumption by roads, separate vehicular and pedestrian circulation systems, originate approaches to a meaningful integration of open space networks and recreation areas within the development, establish neighborhood identity and focus, and ideally provide for the compatible co-existence of and with his environment."

Conventional zoning treats each use independently. Typical districts consist of:

1. Agricultural - minimum area of 5 acres per DU
2. Residential estate - minimum area of 2-½ acres per DU
3. Residential transitional, minimum lot area:
   a. With private well/septic tank: 1 acre per DU
   b. With public water, paved roads: ½ acre per DU
4. Residential single family - minimum area of 7,500 sq. ft. per DU
5. Residential multiple family, medium density, 8 DU per acre
6. Residential multiple family, high density, 12 DU per acre
7. Neighborhood commercial
8. General commercial.
9. Specialized commercial
10. Light industrial
11. General industrial
12. Preservation - conservation
13. Public ownership
    * DU = *dwelling unit*

Q. *When is zoning misused?*

A. Persons concerned with preserving private property rights view with alarm the extension of controls that are devised by governmental agencies in the name of public need, but at the expense of private ownership. Zoning is one control that public officials have abused. When zoning becomes an arbitrary approach to the control of property for particular interests, often political, courts must determine whether the invalid exercise of this police power results in the destruction of value or confiscation of property. There is no clearcut line that determines when zoning is arbitrary and capricious versus proper and beneficial.

Q. It is legal to "down-zone" property?

A. As certain segments of the public have become more environmentally-minded, elected government bodies who control the zoning may yield to public outcries for a decreasing construction activity. This has led to down-zoning. Until recent years, once property carried a certain zoning classification, such as "Multi-family, 12 Units per acre," it could not be down-zoned except with the consent or application of the owner. It is now a common occurrence in many parts of the country to see a city council or county commission down-zone a property without regard to the financial loss of the owner.

Let's say the zoning of a property is changed from 12 units per acre to 3 units per acre. The property owner will have suffered a serious loss of value since the land at lower density may only be worth half as much. He may have gone to great expense prior to the down-zoning to have the engineering rendered, site plans completed, commissioned architectural drawings, and otherwise pursued the development of his property. Thus, not only has he suffered the loss in value of his property, but out-of-pocket expenses as well. If there is an overwhelming public need to change the use of property, thus causing the owner a financial loss, the public should reasonably pay for this loss. The legality of down-zoning will undoubtedly receive more court testing.

Q. What is the appeal process available to an owner who feels he has been wronged?

A. The broad application of a zoning ordinance is certain to create unnecessary hardships on the owners of some parcels of land. An administrative board to review these grievances and make special exceptions may be called a *zoning board, planning and zoning commission, board of appeals, board of adjustment, or board of review.*

If the zoning restriction destroys the ability of the owner to use the property in a meaningful way, an adjustment should be made. Normally, the board will consider fairly the unique problems affecting a property and grant a variance. Officials may be reluctant to make changes, however, when a completely new ordinance goes into effect. They may reason that if they open the door slightly by making a few changes, an avalanche of applications for variances will pour into their office.

Professional planners, particularly those who have never owned property, are sometimes purists who feel that landowners have to suffer special indignities for the common good. Media may also rush in to criticize variances granted by appointive or elected officials, saying that changes must not be allowed. The developer, or landowner, is often suspect when he tries to protect property rights, expecially if they are his. When he complains that the change in zoning makes his 100 acres worth only $500,000, down from a million, he finds little sympathy from the public. Even if he owes $600,000 on the property and has suffered irreparable financial loss, he is often viewed as fair game for the "good" of the public. If all 3-bedroom homeowners were suddenly told that they could only use their homes as 2-bedroom units, the concept of down-zoning would be known to all. It all depends upon "whose ox is being gored."

Q. What is a non-conforming use, as applied to zoning?

A. Existing buildings and improvements that are in violation of the ordinance but in place at the time of passage of a zoning ordinance are said to be non-conforming.

Normally, the present use may be continued under certain conditions, such as:

1. Ordinary repairs are permitted, but no structural alterations or major improvements may be made.
2. If an owner abandons the use of his property, he may later be prohibited from going back to the non-conforming use.
3. A time limit may be placed on existing uses. The importance to a buyer lies in the possibility that he will not be able to use his newly purchased property in the manner in which he intended.

LAND USE PLANS

Prodded by the federal government, nearly all states, counties, and incorporated cities and towns have now devised a land use plan to govern and guide the use of land in the jurisdiction concerned.

The process normally involves the use of consultants or a full time planning staff, who will compile three basic maps for property within the area: an existing land use map, an existing zoning map, and a future land use map.

Guidelines for preparation of a typical land use plan may be as follows:

1. A number of factors provide the primary determinants for the future land use patterns embodied in the various plans formulated. First, and perhaps more important, are the desires of the citizens of a community with regard to its appearance, its functions, its facilities, and its growth expressed through goals and objectives emerging from the planning process.

2. Next are the existing natural and manmade constraints which determine the overall development profile of a community, neighborhood, or study area. For example, the location of a river or major public facility may impede the implementation of the ultimate transportation network, thereby restricting an area to a low-density profile in general.

3. Existing land uses and patterns provide an essential framework for reanalysis of current land use and zoning policies and practices. Detail and accuracy are expecially critical where major public facilities such as roadways are proposed for development or expansion. The study of such areas represents a large portion of the time allocated to the preparation of this land use element. Other determinants affecting the patterns and distribution of land uses recommended in the element revolve around the need to identify neighborhood businesses and parks which, in most cases, have not been identified in the plan.

The procedure used in Broward County, Florida, demonstrated how a county may go through the evolvement of a land use plan. A diagram of how the plan was prepared is shown on a following page.

In Broward county this process has resulted in the following land use categories:

1. Residential - seven ranges of density

Residential Density Range Title	Dwelling Units Per Gross Acre
Estate	1 or fewer
Low (3)	1 to 3
Low (5)	3 to 5
Low-Medium	5 to 10
Medium	10 to 16
Medium-High	16 to 25
High	25 to 50

2. Commercial
3. Industrial
4. Agricultural
5. Conservation
6. Commercial recreation
7. Community facilities
8. Parks and recreation
9. Utilities
10. Proposed parks

The land use plan, after approval, is often substituted for the previous zoning ordinance. Or, it may be used in conjunction with the zoning ordinance to determine what type of development, if any, will be allowed on a tract-by-tract basis.

Agriculture has historically been free from zoning controls. New regulations have changed this freedom, prohibiting such uses as feedlots in certain areas. Drainage from feeding areas may be restricted, requiring ponding areas for decontamination or treatment. The protection of streams and water supplies and the prevention of a "nuisance" is primary in the planners' minds. The emphasis placed upon controlling various types of pollution in recent years will be reflected in more stringent zoning regulations dealing with farming.

BUILDING CODES AND SUBDIVISION REGULATIONS

Building codes and subdivision regulations are related to zoning and land use ordinances. They must be studied prior to the purchase of any land because they affect how the property may be used.

Building codes have been adopted by most territorial jurisdictions. A single building code may cover a city, county, or region. For example, the Southern Building Code covers most of the State of Florida. The South Florida Building Code, however, covers Broward, Dade, and Monroe Counties.

The building codes were established to insure safety and reliability of construction. Depth of foundations for frost resistance and strength of roof trusses to withstand wind or snow loads are two minor examples of code applications. Codes have sometimes been responsible for increasing costs by failing to promptly recognize technological changes, such as the use of plastic pipe, or improved pre-assembled components.

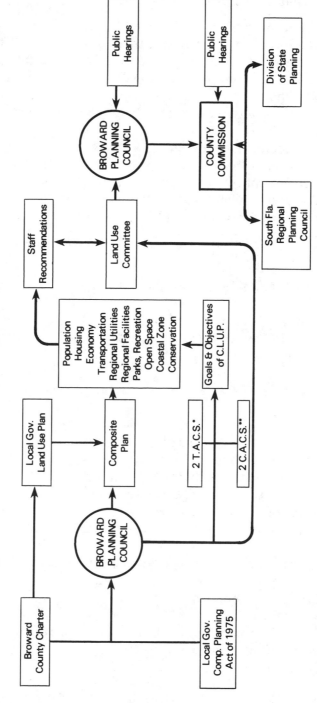

PREPARATION OF COUNTY LAND USE PLAN
REGIONAL ANALYSIS

*T.A.C. - Technical Advisory Committees
**C.A.C. - Citizens Advisory Committees

Q. What constitutes a subdivision regulation?

A. Subdivision regulations are designed to provide for proper and orderly development but often reflect the bureaucracy and red tape of government. The layers of government are illustrated by what a south Florida county proposes, as a very small part of its subdivision ordinance. Here is the review required of a new, proposed development. The following agencies must each review the proposal.

- The Engineering Department
- The Division of Planning and Administrative Systems
- The Department of Health and Rehabilitation Services
- The Division of Water and Wastewater
- The Environmental Quality Control Board
- The Water Management Division
- The Planning Council
- The Parks Department
- The Board of Public Instruction
- The Fire Protection Division
- The South Florida Water Management District
- The Florida Power and Light Company
- The Southern Bell Company

These agencies are directed to review the project for the following development requirements:

- Adequacy of regional transportation network
- Compliance with county design standards
- Conformity to the county trafficways plan
- Adequacy of grading and drainage plant
- Adequacy of portable water service
- Adequacy of wastewater treatment and disposal services
- Adequacy of regional parks and recreation facilities
- Consideration of impact on environmentally sensitive lands
- Adequacy of school sites and school buildings
- Dedication of improvements
- Local requirements
- Conformity to the county land use plan or a certified land use plan
- Adequacy of solid waste disposal service
- Adequacy of fire protection service

- Adequacy of police protection service
- Adequacy of local parks and recreation facilities
- Development presumed to have maximum impact permitted
- Procedures for depositing required fees

The incredible process of tracking a project through a bureaucratic jurisdiction can be frightening. Unfortunately, government does not always operate efficiently and some government employees are not responsive to the realities of time and economics. In many growing areas of the country, several years are now required to obtain approval of a residential development. The true victim is the homebuyer. Several thousand dollars per house are needlessly added to the cost of a dwelling in the name of "orderly growth."

Mandatory Dedications - Impact Fees

Mandatory dedications of property, or monetary contributions in lieu of property dedications, are sometimes demanded by city or county governments from the developer or property owner in return for granting development rights. The effect is to place an additional burden on the cost of new construction, compounding the difficulty of producing affordable housing. Fees commonly demanded include:

- Dedication of all on-site roads, even if servicing other areas
- Aid in construction of all roads touching the property
- Road impact fees for major streets several miles from the property
- City and county park, recreation, library, and other fees
- Sewer and water construction fees
- School site dedications, or money in lieu of land
- Aid in school construction
- Landscaping and maintenance fees in public rights-of-way

Q. *What are the typical steps a developer must follow to get a project approved?*

A. While the procedure may not be quite so involved in a more rural county, here is an example of what must be done in an urban area.

Land Acquisition. Developer has acquired a 20 acre property which is zoned to build five dwelling units per acre, or a total of 100 units.

Prepare Plat and Site Plan. Owner prepares his plan for development and layout of his lots, called a site plan/boundary plat, and submits this to the city along with a survey and engineering plans including but not limited to sanitary sewer plans; storm sewer plans; streets, paving and drainage; lighting; landscaping; fire hydrants; parking; and street signs.

City Agency Review. When submitted to the city, each department will look at the plans resulting in change, adaptation and delay, but hopefully they will give their approval and favorable recommendation to the City Planning Commission.

City Planning Commission. The next step is getting on the City Planning Commission agenda. The plans are presented to this elected or appointed body of citizens who may bounce the plans back to department level more than once. The end result will be a vote sending the project forward to the City Council with recommendations to approve or reject.

City Council. The City Council may hold one or more meetings on the project, or decide to schedule public hearings. They may table for further input from one or more departments. They may pressure the developer into donating land or paying fees for recreation, schools or parks. They may press for lower density. Let's assume city approvals are finally obtained by the developer. The project must be reviewed by still other agencies before final approval.

County Departments. Now come the county authorities. Each of the departments found in the city has one or more counterparts at county level. One county with which the author is familiar has more than twenty separate and individual agencies through which the developer must track his project. They may also consult with regional, state, and national offices such as Flood Control Districts, Departments of Environmental Regulation, Clean Air Commissions, and others.

County Planning Council. After each county department has made its mark on the plans, the project moves forward to the County Planning Council. This body will scrutinize and deliberate, and ultimately favorably or unfavorably pass the project to the last stop -- The County Commission.

County Commission. Most County Commissions are elected. Thus, most act in a political manner. One type of Commissioner may attempt to be a conduit between the people and government, without making any personal input. While this may appear to be the democratic way, much of the public feels that its representative should be better informed than the constituency, and is elected to seek out and study the issues, and then take the appropriate action. Other commissioners may obviously be pro-developer or anti-developer, regardless of the issues.

Q. Is it easier to build in a large or small community?

A. Many smaller communities in rural, non-industrial areas welcome growth represented by new housing, since it provides economic activity and new, attractive neighborhoods. Their county commissions tend to work with a developer to encourage his project.

Q. What causes a non-growth attitude?

A. Areas which have been experiencing rapid growth for years may find that the community has allowed itself to fall behind in services such as roads, schools, libraries, parks, and sewer and water treatment plants. Almost never is such a community blessed with officials who have the foresight to predict the scale of growth occurring. Suddenly traffic jams develop, schools run double schedules, and the quality of life begins to suffer. Instead of recognizing that county government is responsible and must now play "catch-up" with tax increases and bond issues to provide the necessary services, many County Commissioners may adopt the more politically popular position of "no-growth, slow growth."

Often, developers are accused of spoiling the environment and raping the land. In fact, every builder must meet the county regulations, and only acts in response to demand. A developer is almost never responsible for attracting people to an area of the country. Climate has generally been the great motivator of moves.

Commissioners oriented to non-growth will often attempt to slow development by adding layers of red tape and more regulations. They may use such tactics as: revising land use plans, down-zoning land parcels, or arbitrary rejection of building plats. In some cases impact fees or mandatory dedications are required by officials before plats will be approved. For example, our hypothetical developer may be told that he must donate 20% of his 10 acres for school and/or park sites; or, as an alternative, contribute an equivalent amount of cash to these agencies.

Legal Implications. Arbitrary impact fees and donated property have generally, but not always, been ruled unconstitutional when appealed to the courts. However, most small developers do not have the financial backing nor the desire to do battle in the courts. Instead, they yield and hand over their money or their land -- instead of losing their financial life.

It should be noted that many elected representatives engage in these actions with good intentions. They are trying to solve community financial shortfalls by extracting their pound of flesh from the developer who comes to them needing approvals. Still, it's important to remember that the United States Constitution prohibits the taking of private property without just compensation.

Often these officials are held out as environmentalists protecting the community. The irony is that they fail to recognize a major sociological problem of their own creation: the ultimate unavailability of moderately priced housing. Every delay, every requirement imposed upon developers adds to the cost, but not necessarily to the quality, of housing. Artificial scarcities of developable land are created, pushing up prices of the smaller supply of available land. It is not uncommon for land with an "approved" plat to sell for 50% more than identical land not so approved.

Thus an undeveloped but "platted" lot may sell to a builder for $15,000, versus $10,000 for the identical but "unplatted" lot. Add another $5,000 per lot for development. Since most builders respond to a 4:1 ratio benchmark of lot cost versus sale price of house and lot. This means $80,000 finished home prices, instead of $60,000.

AD VALOREM REAL ESTATE TAXES

Although the prime objective of taxation of real estate in this country has been to raise revenue, the effect has an influence on the use, tenure, and value of land. In some countries, taxation has been used to break up estates or force idle lands into use. Since the property tax in America is often the chief source of revenue to local and state government, the burden of the tax has continued to rise with the growth and increased cost of government services. As in the saying, "Nothing surer than death and taxes," there is little an owner can do to escape the tax. Even as land values rise and fall, the tax seems to stay, and steadily increase. The chief result of a tax on property is to reduce land values. Since most land is owned to produce revenue, and net income is capitalized into value, taxes directly reduce the value of land. For example, if an owner expects a 6% return on his investment, a $60 net income per acre would indicate a land value of $1,000 per acre ($60 divided by 6% or .06 = $1,000). An increase in taxes of $6 per acre would reduce the net income in this same example to $54 per acre. Again using 6% as the capitalization rate, the indicated value would be $900 per acre, a drop of $100 per acre.

Many a property owner has failed to maintain his buildings in a well painted condition because he felt the tax assessor would punish him by raising his assessment.

Assessment Procedures

Unequal assessments have plagued the collection of property taxes since these taxes were first levied. The property tax is based on valuations by local officials, realistically, few of whom have the training, facilities, or time to perform a complete appraisal of all property in their jurisdiction. That's not to say that dedicated city, township, and county assessors haven't applied their local knowledge to bring about fair assessments. However, since the methods of assessment vary greatly across the nation, property assessments commonly show substantial deviations from values as measured by sale prices. Some land may be assessed at a fraction of its value, while nearby parcels may be assessed near or even above the price at which they could be sold.

A common problem is that properties having a low value per acre are over-assessed relative to land of higher value. This is a result of ignoring differences in soils, location, topography, and other factors.

Farmland may often be overvalued relative to other nonfarm property, thus bearing a greater burden. Some states have "homestead exemptions," thus allowing owners of residences a big break in taxes, relative to landowners. States may also offer tax breaks to new industry. This again places a disproportionate burden on the owners of non-exempt property, meaning largely farm property.

Q. How can I be certain that my property is fairly assessed?

A. Be part of tax equalization. Whether locally elected or appointed officials have appraised the land, or tax equalization firms have been hired to inventory the property, the records of valuation are public and available for inspection and comparison.

Go to your assessor's office. Have a plat book showing owners of adjoining property with you. If you don't have a plat book, sketch out the properties within a 2 to 3 mile radius. From the assessor's records, note the following information of each ownership:

Total Acres _____ Value _____
Tillable acres _____ Value _____
Pasture acres _____ Value _____
Woodland _____ Value _____

Land classifications may be in more or less detail than shown above. Values shown will reflect appraisals, based on such criteria as "Fair Market Value," or "True Cash Value," or "Just Value." The assessor's policy, depending on the state, may then be to take a percentage of the appraised values to use as "Assessed Value." The final numbers will show the levy against the assessed value and the resulting tax.

Compare, insofar as possible, your assessment with that of all of your neighbors. Check average assessed value per acre. Check classifications and age and use of buildings. If the values are out of line and a reduction is called for, go to the assessor. If relief isn't granted, go to the next higher authority, such as the Board of Appeals or Board of Review. The courts are the last resort, and should only be utilized if gross inequities result in major over-assessments and loss of hundreds or thousands of dollars.

Q. *How is the tax levy applied to assessed value?*

A. It's important to understand how your tax bill evolves.

Each division of a community will budget the amount of revenue expected to be required for the coming year. The total need, less that revenue expected from other sources, results in the appropriation required from real estate taxes which, when divided by the assessed value, results in the rate or levy to be applied. The levy may be expressed as so many dollars per $100, or in mills per dollar. (A mill is a thousandth of a dollar, or a tenth of a cent. Thus a tax rate of 20 mills means $2 per $100 assessed value.) In addition to the tax by the governing body (city or county or both) other levels of government are permitted to levy taxes as well. These may include school board, bond issues, and special assessments. Tax rate limitations are often found in state laws.

Q. *What happens if I fail to pay my taxes?*

A. Real estate taxes are a lien on the land, and may be superior to all other liens. Failure to pay may result in a tax sale, or foreclosure. Normally the owner has a redemption period after such sale to pay the back taxes, plus penalties, and recover his land. Thus a tax title must be carefully studied to determine the extent of title.

CHAPTER 16 .

Under All is the Land

"Under all is the land" . . . those few words are the essence of what a book on land must address. George Santayana wrote, "Those who cannot remember the past are condemned to repeat it." And so the past weaves its way into projections of the future.

Predictions are only as good as the history in their making. History shows that certain factors have had a profound impact on land prices and ownership in the past fifty years. Inflation, population growth, technology advances in machinery, hybrids, fertilizer, and expanded incomes have transformed our approach to land and its value.

A hundred years ago most of the nation's population were farmers. As late as 1930, the ratio of farm power was 19 million horses and mules to one million tractors. By 1959, the animal numbers had dropped so low that the U.S. Department of Agriculture stopped counting them, and the number of tractors had increased six-fold. The next fifty years will surely bring as many changes as the last half century.

The purpose of this last chapter is to anticipate foreseeable trends, and the factors that will precipitate them.

Q. Is it likely that land prices will decline?

A. A long term downtrend is simply impossible. Short term reversals responding to depressed commodity prices may occur periodically. A monetary adjustment such as recall of the currency would affect all relative price levels, of course. But the most important overriding factor is that land produces food. Survival is the first law of nature. Food producers--farmers--will be paid whatever is necessary to continue production.

Look at it this way. Gasoline prices increased over 400% from 1975 to 1980. People paid the price and continued to buy gas to maintain their employment and life style. They made adjustments elsewhere. The price of corn, soybeans, cattle, chickens, etc., can increase 300% to the farmer—if that is necessary to maintain food production—and the consumer will find a way to pay the price. Land prices will keep going up.

Q. *Will farms continue to grow larger?*

A. Yes. The largest farmer is the most efficient producer and the most economically stable. Fifty years ago 2-row horsedrawn corn planters were the rule. Today, 12-row planters drawn at far greater speed are common. Using the same multiplier, is it possible to have 72-row planters in fifty years? Not likely, considering topography, but equally dramatic improvements will evolve.

The number of farmers will probably continue to decline. Less than one-fourth of the farmers now produce over 90% of the food. The economic base of the larger farmer is stronger. He has more equity, and can weather difficult times with greater ease. As land prices have increased, so has the equity of the owner. Since the largest landowner has the most equity, he can, and does, outbid the smaller neighbor for the land. And so it will continue.

Q. *Will energy shortages become a factor in food production?*

A. Possibly. The energy problem may become more critical before it's solved, but the need for food will keep farm equipment running, one way or another. The United States has only begun to address the energy crisis. Predictors of doom have always underestimated the ability of our people and industry to respond to crisis. But we're in a very early stage of converting farm crops to gasohol and other fuels. That conversion will become more efficient. Electric car development will leave more petroleum products for tractors. Power conversion from the sun, wind, and sea has enormous potential and merely awaits economically feasible application of techniques.

Q. *Will alternate food sources replace the demand for farm-grown products now in demand?*

A. Not in 50 years . . . maybe in 500. While some synthetic foods and nonfoods are penetrating traditional farm product markets, agriculture supplies the great majority of our basic food needs. Noncalorie sweeteners, nonleather shoes, synthetic fabrics, and imitation flavors are common examples of successful inroads. Most synthetics are additions rather than replacements.

The use of synthetics in foods will be limited in future years. Foods produced naturally are still cheaper than those synthetically produced. Consumers recognize that the nutritional qualities of agricultural foods are still a bargain.

While hydroponics research, ocean culture, and other forms of production changes will continue, farmers have always met the challenge of change, and land will continue to supply the vast majority of foodstuffs for the foreseeable future.

Q. Will investor, commuter, or foreign demand for land diminish?

A. No. Thousands of city residents now head for the country on weekends to enjoy their part-time home. In the future, they look for their country home to become their full-time residence, while they take an apartment in the city for their four or five working days.

Investors will continue to look for sophisticated vehicles which channel capital into land. Syndications and investment groups will be formed with greater frequency and larger dollar pools.

Foreigners have always viewed American land as underpriced. In southeast Florida, in 1979, nearly 40% of all large land sales were to foreign firms. As industry has yielded to foreign investment and ownership, so will a certain portion of land ownership. It should be noted, however, that state legislatures have placed severe restrictions on foreign ownership, and the 2% to 4% ownership now held by foreign interests is not likely to surpass 10% in the next fifty years.

Q. Where will the most dramatic changes occur in agricultural land use?

A. The mid-South probably has the most potential for innovative practices. Arkansas, Louisiana, Mississippi, Georgia, and Alabama have always had a lower productivity index than such traditional farm states as Iowa, Illinois, Indiana, Kansas, and Nebraska.

Major land clearing and drainage occurred in the Delta states in the period from 1960-68, bringing technological advances. But the productivity of the area based on the availability of moisture and a longer growing season has not reached its potential. Look for the capacity to double-crop this warmer area to greatly increase production, and thus land prices.

Other regions of the country will see innovations bring major adjustments. An example of what can transpire was seen in the introduction of sprinkler irrigation to the rolling hills of Nebraska and Colorado. Land selling for $200 per acre in 1970 went to $1,000 per acre in 1980–where water was available at reasonable depths. Alert national land buyers will focus on such conceptual changes to capitalize on big jumps in land values.

Q. *What about the effect of inflation?*

A. Inflation, triggered by government spending, will not soon come under control, in my opinion. I look for a minimum annual inflation rate of ten percent per year during the foreseeable future. The increasing burden of the nation's debt demands an increase in the money supply in order to service that debt with cheaper dollars. Land prices, from inflation alone, will follow the upward trend. While such assets as gold and silver get the headlines, serious investors know that land is unequalled as a long term hedge against inflation.

SUMMARY

America is a young country, still developing. Europe, a thousand years older in terms of modern civilization, provides some insight into our future. Our land will become more valuable; more sought after; more productive (though net return on investment will be lower); more tightly held by fewer owners; and continue as the major asset of our country.

Appendix A

CALCULATING MORTGAGE PAYMENTS

Mortgage payments may be structured in a number of different ways, subject to agreement of buyer and seller. Examples of several methods are shown, and tables are included for easy calculation.

Level Principal Payment, Plus Interest

The most simple (and probably most common) land mortgage is structured on equal annual principal payments, plus interest payable quarterly, semiannually, or annually.

Example:
Terms of Note: $100,000.00, payable in ten equal annual payments, plus annual interest of 8%.

End of Year	Principal	Interest	Total
1	$10,000	$8,000	$18,000
2	″	7,200	17,200
3	″	6,400	16,400
4	″	5,600	15,600
5	″	4,800	14,800
6	″	4,000	14,000
7	″	3,200	13,200
8	″	2,400	12,400
9	″	1,600	11,600
10	″	800	10,800

Level Principal, Plus Interest, Balloon At End

Commonly, a seller providing financing will want to keep his payoff period short, but to amortize the debt would put the annual payments higher than the buyer could afford. In this case, a "balloon" method is used with the buyer knowing he will have to refinance the note at the time the balloon is due.

Example:
Terms of Note: $100,000.00, payable $10,000 principal per year for

four years, plus annual interest at the rate of 8%, balance due in full at end of five years.

End of Year	Principal	Interest	Total
1	$10,000	$8,000	$18,000
2	10,000	7,200	17,200
3	10,000	6,400	16,400
4	10,000	5,600	15,600
5	60,000	4,800	64,800

Self-Liquidating Mortgage Payments

Equal payments, including principal and interest, may also be structured in debt reduction. The total amount due each period is equal, but as payments are made, the amount to interest decreases and the amount to principal increases.

The following tables illustrate annual, semiannual, quarterly or monthly payments required to liquidate a $1,000 mortgage.

Equal Monthly Payments To Amortize A $1,000 Loan

Interest Rate	Five Years	Ten Years	Fifteen Years	Twenty Years	Twenty-Five Years	Thirty Years
6.0%	19.33	11.10	8.44	7.16	6.44	6.00
6.5%	19.57	11.35	8.71	7.46	6.75	6.32
7.0%	19.80	11.61	8.99	7.75	7.07	6.65
7.5%	20.04	11.87	9.27	8.06	7.39	6.99
8.0%	20.28	12.13	9.56	8.36	7.72	7.34
8.5%	20.52	12.40	9.85	8.68	8.05	7.69
9.0%	20.76	12.67	10.14	9.00	8.39	8.05
9.5%	21.00	12.94	10.44	9.32	8.74	8.41
10.0%	21.25	13.22	10.75	9.65	9.09	8.78
10.5%	21.49	13.49	11.05	9.98	9.44	9.15
11.0%	21.74	13.78	11.37	10.32	9.80	9.52
11.5%	21.99	14.06	11.68	10.66	10.16	9.90
12.0%	22.24	14.35	12.00	11.01	10.53	10.29
12.5%	22.50	14.64	12.33	11.36	10.90	10.67
13.0%	22.75	14.93	12.65	11.72	11.28	11.06
13.5%	23.01	15.23	12.98	12.07	11.66	11.45
14.0%	23.27	15.53	13.32	12.44	12.04	11.85
14.5%	23.53	15.83	13.66	12.80	12.42	12.25
15.0%	23.79	16.13	14.00	13.17	12.81	12.64
15.5%	24.05	16.44	14.34	13.54	13.20	13.05
16.0%	24.32	16.75	14.69	13.91	13.59	13.45
16.5%	24.58	17.06	15.04	14.29	13.98	13.85
17.0%	24.85	17.38	15.39	14.67	14.38	14.26
17.5%	25.12	17.70	15.75	15.05	14.78	14.66
18.0%	25.39	18.02	16.10	15.43	15.17	15.07

Equal Quarterly Payments To Amortize A $1,000 Loan

Interest Rate	Five Years	Ten Years	Fifteen Years	Twenty Years	Twenty-Five Years	Thirty Years
6.0%	58.25	33.43	25.39	21.55	19.37	18.02
6.5%	58.97	34.19	26.22	22.43	20.30	19.00
7.0%	59.69	34.97	27.05	23.32	21.25	19.99
7.5%	60.42	35.76	27.90	24.23	22.22	21.01
8.0%	61.16	36.56	28.77	25.16	23.20	22.05
8.5%	61.90	37.36	29.65	26.10	24.21	23.10
9.0%	62.64	38.18	30.54	27.06	25.23	24.17
9.5%	63.39	39.00	31.44	28.04	26.26	25.26
10.0%	64.15	39.84	32.35	29.03	27.31	26.36
10.5%	64.91	40.68	33.28	30.03	28.38	27.48
11.0%	65.67	41.53	34.22	31.04	29.45	28.60
11.5%	66.44	42.39	35.17	32.07	30.54	29.74
12.0%	67.22	43.26	36.13	33.11	31.65	30.89
12.5%	67.99	44.14	37.11	34.16	32.76	32.05
13.0%	68.78	45.03	38.09	35.23	33.88	33.22
13.5%	69.57	45.92	39.08	36.30	35.02	34.39
14.0%	70.36	46.83	40.09	37.38	36.16	35.57
14.5%	71.16	47.74	41.10	38.48	37.31	36.76
15.0%	71.96	48.66	42.13	39.58	38.47	37.96
15.5%	72.77	49.59	43.16	40.69	39.64	39.16
16.0%	73.58	50.52	44.20	41.81	40.81	40.36
16.5%	74.40	51.47	45.25	42.94	41.99	41.58
17.0%	75.22	52.42	46.31	44.08	43.17	42.79
17.5%	76.05	53.38	47.38	45.22	44.36	44.01
18.0%	76.88	54.34	48.45	46.37	45.56	45.23

Equal Semi Annual Payments To Amortize A $1,000 Loan

Interest Rate	Five Years	Ten Years	Fifteen Years	Twenty Years	Twenty-Five Years	Thirty Years
6.0%	117.23	67.22	51.02	43.26	38.87	36.13
6.5%	118.73	68.78	52.68	45.03	40.73	38.09
7.0%	120.24	70.36	54.37	46.83	42.63	40.09
7.5%	121.76	71.96	56.09	48.66	44.57	42.13
8.0%	123.29	73.58	57.83	50.52	46.55	44.20
8.5%	124.83	75.22	59.60	52.42	48.56	46.31
9.0%	126.38	76.88	61.39	54.34	50.60	48.45
9.5%	127.94	78.55	63.21	56.30	52.67	50.63
10.0%	129.50	80.24	65.05	58.28	54.78	52.83
10.5%	131.08	81.95	66.92	60.29	56.91	55.06
11.0%	132.67	83.68	68.81	62.32	59.06	57.31
11.5%	134.26	85.42	70.72	64.38	61.24	59.58
12.0%	135.87	87.18	72.65	66.46	63.44	61.88
12.5%	137.48	88.96	74.60	68.57	65.67	64.19
13.0%	139.10	90.76	76.58	70.69	67.91	66.52
13.5%	140.74	92.57	78.57	72.84	70.18	68.87
14.0%	142.38	94.39	80.59	75.01	72.46	71.23
14.5%	144.03	96.23	82.62	77.20	74.76	73.60
15.0%	145.69	98.09	84.67	79.40	77.07	75.99
15.5%	147.35	99.96	86.74	81.62	79.40	78.39
16.0%	149.03	101.85	88.83	83.86	81.74	80.80
16.5%	150.71	103.75	90.93	86.11	84.10	83.22
17.0%	152.41	105.67	93.05	88.38	86.46	85.64
17.5%	154.11	107.60	95.19	90.66	88.84	88.07
18.0%	155.82	109.55	97.34	92.96	91.23	90.51

Equal Annual Payments To Amortize A $1,000 Loan

Interest Rate	Five Years	Ten Years	Fifteen Years	Twenty Years	Twenty-Five Years	Thirty Years
6.0%	237.40	135.87	102.96	87.18	78.23	72.65
6.5%	240.63	139.10	106.35	90.76	81.98	76.58
7.0%	243.89	142.38	109.79	94.39	85.81	80.59
7.5%	247.16	145.69	113.29	98.09	89.71	84.67
8.0%	250.46	149.03	116.83	101.85	93.68	88.83
8.5%	253.77	152.41	120.42	105.67	97.71	93.05
9.0%	257.09	155.82	124.06	109.55	101.81	97.34
9.5%	260.44	159.27	127.74	113.48	105.96	101.68
10.0%	263.80	162.75	131.47	117.46	110.17	106.08
10.5%	267.18	166.26	135.25	121.49	114.43	110.53
11.0%	270.57	169.80	139.07	125.58	118.74	115.02
11.5%	273.98	173.38	142.92	129.70	123.10	119.56
12.0%	277.41	176.98	146.82	133.88	127.50	124.14
12.5%	280.85	180.62	150.76	138.10	131.94	128.76
13.0%	284.31	184.29	154.74	142.35	136.43	133.41
13.5%	287.79	187.99	158.76	146.65	140.95	138.09
14.0%	291.28	191.71	162.81	150.99	145.50	142.80
14.5%	294.79	195.47	166.90	155.36	150.08	147.54
15.0%	298.32	199.25	171.02	159.76	154.70	152.30
15.5%	301.85	203.06	175.17	164.20	159.34	157.08
16.0%	305.41	206.90	179.36	168.67	164.01	161.89
16.5%	308.98	210.77	183.57	173.16	168.71	166.71
17.0%	312.56	214.66	187.82	177.69	173.42	171.54
17.5%	316.16	218.57	192.10	182.24	178.16	176.40
18.0%	319.78	222.51	196.40	186.82	182.92	181.26

Appendix B

COMPOUND INTEREST

For comparison of investments, it may be helpful to know what money on deposit will accumulate to, with interest compounding.

As an example in the use of the following tables, assume $10,000 is on deposit at 10% for 10 years. By following the columns, the indicated factor is 2.5937, meaning that the $10,000 deposit will become $25,937.

LAND VALUE CONVERSION TABLE

Land for commercial purposes may be valued on a square-foot basis, rather than per acre. The table on page 290 shows this conversion. One acre contains 43,560 square feet.

(Tables begin page 288)

Compound Interest Table

Number of Years	Interest rate					
	5%	6%	7%	8%	9%	10%
1	1.0500	1.0600	1.0700	1.0800	1.0900	1.1000
2	1.1025	1.1236	1.1449	1.1664	1.1881	1.2100
3	1.1576	1.1910	1.2250	1.2597	1.2950	1.3310
4	1.2155	1.2624	1.3107	1.3604	1.4115	1.4647
5	1.2763	1.3332	1.4025	1.4693	1.5386	1.6105
6	1.3401	1.4135	1.5007	1.5868	1.6771	1.7715
7	1.4071	1.5030	1.6057	1.7138	1.8230	1.9487
8	1.4775	1.5938	1.7181	1.8509	1.9925	2.1435
9	1.5513	1.6894	1.8384	1.9990	2.1718	2.3579
10	1.6289	1.7908	1.9671	2.1589	2.3673	2.5937
11	1.7103	1.8982	2.1048	2.3316	2.5804	2.8531
12	1.7959	2.0121	2.2521	2.5181	2.8126	3.1384
13	1.8856	2.1329	2.4098	2.7196	3.0658	3.4522
14	1.9799	2.2609	2.5785	2.9371	3.3417	3.7974
15	2.0789	2.3965	2.7590	3.1721	3.6424	4.1772
16	2.1829	2.5403	2.9521	3.4259	3.9703	4.5949
17	2.2920	2.6927	3.1588	3.7000	4.3276	5.0544
18	2.4066	2.8543	3.3799	3.9960	4.7171	5.5599
19	2.5270	3.0255	3.6165	4.3157	5.1416	6.1159
20	2.6533	3.2075	3.8696	4.6609	5.6044	6.7274
21	2.7860	3.3995	4.1405	5.0338	6.1088	7.4002
22	2.9253	3.6035	4.4304	5.4365	6.6586	8.1402
23	3.0715	3.8197	4.7405	5.8714	7.2578	8.9543
24	3.2251	4.0489	5.0723	6.3411	7.9110	9.8497
25	3.3864	4.2918	5.4274	6.8484	8.6230	10.8347
26	3.5557	4.5493	5.8073	7.3963	9.3991	11.9181
27	3.7335	4.8223	6.2138	7.9880	10.2450	13.1099
28	3.9201	5.1116	6.6488	8.6271	11.1671	14.4209
29	4.1161	5.4183	7.1142	9.3172	12.1721	15.8630
30	4.3219	5.7434	7.6122	10.5582	13.2676	17.4494
31	4.5380	6.0881	8.1451	10.8676	14.4617	19.1943
32	4.7649	6.4533	8.7152	11.7370	15.7633	21.1137
33	5.0032	6.8408	9.3253	12.6760	17.1820	23.2251
34	5.2533	7.2510	9.9781	13.6901	18.7284	25.5476
35	5.5160	7.6860	10.6765	14.7853	20.4139	28.1024
36	5.7918	8.1479	11.4239	15.9681	22.2512	30.9128
37	6.0814	8.6360	12.2236	17.2456	24.2538	34.0039
38	6.3855	9.1542	13.0792	18.6252	26.4366	37.4048
39	6.7048	9.7035	13.9948	20.1152	28.8159	41.1447
40	7.0400	10.2857	14.9744	21.7245	31.4094	45.2592

(Compound Interest Rate Table continued)

Number of Years	\	\	Interest rate	\	\	\
	11%	12%	13%	14%	15%	20%
1	1.1100	1.1200	1.1300	1.1400	1.1500	1.2000
2	1.2321	1.2544	1.2769	1.2996	1.3225	1.4400
3	1.3576	1.4049	1.4428	1.4815	1.5208	1.7280
4	1.5180	1.5735	1.6304	1.6389	1.7490	2.0736
5	1.6350	1.7623	1.8424	1.9254	2.0113	2.4883
6	1.8704	1.9738	2.0819	2.1949	2.3130	2.9859
7	2.0761	2.2106	2.3526	2.5022	2.6600	3.5831
8	2.3045	2.4759	2.6584	2.8525	3.0590	4.2998
9	2.5580	2.7730	3.0040	3.2519	3.5178	5.1597
10	2.8394	3.1058	3.3945	3.7072	4.0455	6.1917
11	3.1517	3.4785	3.8358	4.2262	4.6523	7.4300
12	3.4984	3.8959	4.3345	4.8179	5.3502	8.9161
13	3.8832	4.3634	4.8980	5.4924	6.1527	10.6993
14	4.3104	4.8871	5.5347	6.2613	7.0757	12.8391
15	4.7845	5.4735	6.2542	7.1379	8.1370	15.4070
16	5.3108	6.1303	7.0673	8.1372	9.3576	18.4884
17	5.8950	6.8660	7.9860	9.2764	10.7612	22.1861
18	6.5435	7.6899	9.0242	10.5751	12.3754	26.6233
19	7.2633	8.6127	10.1974	12.0556	14.2317	31.9479
20	8.0623	9.6462	11.5230	13.7434	16.3665	38.3375
21	8.9491	10.8038	13.0210	15.6675	18.8215	46.0051
22	9.9335	12.1003	14.7138	17.8610	21.6447	55.2061
23	11.0262	13.5523	16.6266	20.3615	24.8914	66.2473
24	12.2391	15.1786	18.7880	23.2122	28.6251	79.4968
25	13.5854	17.0000	21.2305	26.4619	32.9189	95.3962
26	15.0793	19.0400	23.9905	30.1665	37.8567	114.4754
27	16.7386	21.3248	27.1092	34.3899	43.5353	137.3705
28	18.5799	23.8838	30.6334	39.2044	50.0656	164.8446
29	20.6236	26.7499	34.6158	44.6931	57.5754	197.8135
30	22.8922	29.9599	39.1158	50.9501	66.2117	237.3763
31	25.4104	33.5551	44.2009	58.0831	76.1435	284.8515
32	28.2055	37.5817	49.9470	66.2148	87.5650	341.8218
33	31.3082	42.0915	56.4402	75.4849	100.6998	410.1862
34	34.7521	47.1425	63.7774	86.0527	115.8048	492.2235
35	38.5748	52.7996	72.0685	98.1001	133.1755	590.6682
36	42.8180	59.1355	81.4374	111.8342	153.1518	708.8018
37	47.5280	66.2318	92.0242	127.4909	176.1246	850.5622
38	52.7561	74.1796	103.9874	145.3397	202.5433	1020.6746
39	58.5593	83.0812	117.5057	165.6872	232.9248	1224.8096
40	65.0008	93.0509	132.7815	188.8835	267.8635	1469.7715

Land Value Conversion Table

Value per Sq. Ft. of Land	Value of an Acre	Value per Sq. Ft. of Land	Value of an Acre	Value per Sq. Ft. of Land	Value of an Acre
$ .01	$ 435.60	$ .42	$ 18,295.20	$ .82	$ 35,719.20
.02	871.20	.43	18,730.80	.83	36,154.80
.03	1,306.80	.44	19,166.40	.84	36,590.40
.04	1,742.40	.45	19,602.00	.85	37,026.00
.05	2,178.00	.46	20,037.60	.86	37,461.60
.06	2,613.60	.47	20,473.20	.87	37,897.20
.07	3,049.20	.48	20,908.80	.88	38,332.80
.08	3,484.80	.49	21,344.40	.89	38,768.40
.09	3,920.40	.50	21,780.00	.90	39,204.00
.10	4,356.00	.51	22,215.60	.91	39,639.60
.11	4,791.60	.52	22,651.20	.92	40,075.20
.12	5,227.20	.53	23,086.80	.93	40,510.80
.13	5,662.80	.54	23,522.40	.94	40,946.40
.14	6,098.40	.55	23,958.00	.95	41,382.00
.15	6,534.00	.56	24,393.60	.96	41,817.60
.16	6,969.60	.57	24,829.20	.97	42,253.20
.17	7,405.20	.58	25,264.80	.98	42,688.80
.18	7,840.80	.59	25,700.40	.99	43,124.40
.19	8,276.40	.60	26,136.00	1.00	43,560.00
.20	8,712.00	.61	26,571.60	1.10	47,916.00
.21	9,147.60	.62	27,007.20	1.20	52,272.00
.22	9,583.20	.63	27,442.80	1.30	56,628.00
.23	10,018.80	.64	27,878.40	1.40	60,984.00
.24	10,454.40	.65	28,314.00	1.50	65,340.00
.25	10,890.00	.66	28,749.60	1.60	69,696.00
.26	11,325.60	.67	29,185.20	1.70	74,052.00
.27	11,761.20	.68	29,620.80	1.80	78,408.00
.28	12,196.80	.69	30,056.40	1.90	82,764.00
.29	12,632.40	.70	30,492.00	2.00	87,120.00
.30	13,068.00	.71	30,927.60	2.50	108,900.00
.31	13,503.60	.72	31,363.20	3.00	130,680.00
.32	13,939.20	.73	31,798.80	3.50	152,460.00
.33	14,374.80	.74	32,234.40	4.00	174,240.00
.34	14,810.40	.75	32,670.00	4.50	196,020.00
.35	15,246.00	.76	33,105.60	5.00	217,800.00
.36	15,681.60	.77	33,541.20	6.00	261,360.00
.37	16,117.20	.78	33,976.80	7.00	304,920.00
.38	16,552.80	.79	34,412.40	8.00	348,480.00
.39	16,988.40	.80	34,848.00	9.00	392,040.00
.40	17,424.00	.81	35,283.60	10.00	435,600.00
.41	17,859.60				

Appendix C

MEASURING LAND

To compute the area of a field or farm you must know the lengths of the different sides in whatever units of measure you are using. For small plots, the foot or yard may be most convenient. For larger areas, the rod (16½ feet), chain (66 feet), or mile can be used.

The area of a rectangular field is found by multiplying the length by the width. If a field is 20 rods wide and 60 rods long, it contains 1,200 square rods. The same field would measure 330 feet wide by 990 feet long and contain 326,700 sq.ft., or 5 chains wide by 15 chains and contain 75 square chains.

The number of acres in a field is determined by dividing the number of square units by the number of square units in an acre.

$$(1) \text{ No. of acres} = \frac{\text{Area in sq. ft.}}{43,560}$$

$$(2) \text{ No. of acres} = \frac{\text{Area in sq. yds.}}{4,840}$$

$$(3) \text{ No. of acres} = \frac{\text{Area in sq. rods}}{160}$$

$$(4) \text{ No. of acres} = \frac{\text{Area in sq. chains}}{10}$$

$$(5) \text{ No. of acres} = \text{Area in sq. miles x 640}$$

Doing The Measuring

Make measurements in a straight line and keep an accurate record of all distances as well as corners and odd shaped boundaries. Make a rough sketch of the field before you start, if possible, or as you go along. Label each side as soon as it is measured. A surveyor's chain (66 feet) is the best unit of measure on field-size or larger tracts. The number of square chains in an area, divided by 10, given the number of acres. Two men are required to carry the chain. A set of 11 wire (No. 9) marking stakes are used to keep a tally. One stake is placed at the start. The leading man sets a stake at each 66-foot interval. When the rear man has gathered up 10 stakes, the distance covered by the front man is 10 chains.

Fields of Different Shapes

Rectangular or square-shaped fields are the easiest to measure. Find the area by multiplying the length times the width.

L x W = Sq. Area

A trapezoid is a figure of four sides having two, and only two, sides parallel. It is figured the same as the rectangular field, except that you use the average of the two parallel sides for the length figure.

$$\text{Area} = W \times \frac{L_1 = L_2}{2}$$

Right triangle fields are three-sided fields having one square corner. To find the area, figure as if it were one-half of a rectangle. Thus ½ of the length (base) multiplied by the width (height) will give you the area.

$$\text{Area} = \tfrac{1}{2}H \times B$$

Other triangular fields not having a square corner can be figured as the right triangle, but height must be measured square from the base line (at right angles to it.) Thus ½ the height times the base gives the area.

$$\text{Area} = \tfrac{1}{2}H \times B$$

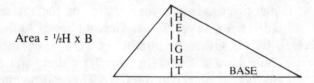

Many-sided fields. Those with more than 4 sides or with 4 unequal sides can usually be measured by using one or more of the methods already discussed. The trick is to divide the fields into triangles or rectangles that can be easily measured. A good rule is to measure from one corner to an opposite corner, dividing the field into more easily measured plots. Find the area of each of the new plots by using the formula for rectangles or triangles. Here are some examples of how fields may be divided for easier measurement.

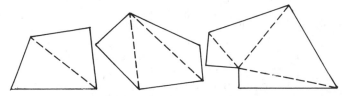

Curved boundaries. Where contour farming is practiced field measurement becomes somewhat more complicated. The best method is to measure off a straight base line near the center of the field. At equal distances take a number of measurements of the field width. Make these measurements square across (at right angles to) the base line. Find the average of these width lines and multiply this average by the length of the base line. This gives the area of the field. If the base line does not meet the ends of the field square (at right angles) you will have to figure the area of the small triangles A and B separately.

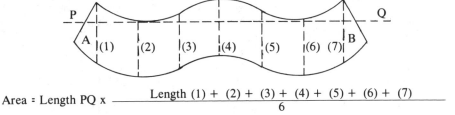

Area = Length PQ x $\dfrac{\text{Length (1) + (2) + (3) + (4) + (5) + (6) + (7)}}{6}$

When fields are curved too much for a straight base line to be drawn as above, do this: Measure a base line down the center of the field or as near the center as practical. Let it curve as the field curves. At equal distances, measure the width of the field. Make these measurements as square across the base line as possible, then use the same method of figuring area as used with a straight line base.

STANDARD MEASUREMENTS
Measure of Length (Linear Measure)

12 inches = 1 foot
3 feet = 1 yard
16½ feet = 1 rod
5,280 feet = 1 mile
1,760 yards = 1 mile
320 rods = 1 mile

Measure of Surface (Area)

144 square inches = 1 square foot
9 square feet = 1 square yard
30¼ square yards = 1 square rod
160 square rods = 1 acre
43,560 square feet = 1 acre
640 square acres = 1 square mile
36 square miles = 1 township

Surveyor's Measure

7.92 inches = 1 link
25 links = 1 rod
4 rods = 1 chain
10 square chains = 160 square rods = 1 acre
640 acres = 1 square mile
80 chains = 1 mile
1 Gunthers chain = 66 feet

METRIC MEASUREMENTS
Length

Unit	Number of Meters	Approximate U.S. Equivalent
Myriameter	10,000	6.2 miles
Kilometer	1,000	0.62 mile
Hectometer	100	109.36 yards
Decameter	10	32.81 feet
Meter	1	39.37 inches
Decimeter	0.1	3.94 inches
Centimeter	0.01	0.39 inch
Millimeter	0.001	0.04 inch

Area

Unit	Number of Square Meters	Approximate U.S. Equivalent
Square kilometer	1,000,000	0.3861 square mile
Hectare	10,000	2.47 acres
Are	100	119.60 square yards
Centare	1	10.76 square feet
Square centimeter	0.0001	0.155 square inch

Glossary

Abstract of Title - a written history in condensed form of the chain of title reflecting all transactions affecting the property since the original title was granted and bringing it up to the present date.

Acceleration Clause - a provision in a mortgage, note, or deed of trust which states that, upon default of the payment due, the balance of the entire principal shall become due and payable. If the borrower misses a payment of principal or interest, subject to the acceleration provisions, the lender can demand immediate repayment of the unpaid balance.

Access - the right to enter and leave a parcel of land from a public right-of-way. Also referred to as ingress and egress of an owner to his property.

Accretion - the addition or buildup of land by natural causes, usually due to the shifting of a stream.

Acknowledgment - the declaration by a person executing a legal document that his signature is a voluntary act. This act provides evidence of the genuineness of a person's signature and is normally done before a notary public. Documents can generally not be recorded unless they are acknowledged.

Adverse Possession - the right by which a person other than the owner makes a claim against land by virtue of possession that has been actual, continuous, hostile, visible, and distinct for a statutory period. Squatter's rights fall within this category.

Affidavit - a sworn statement in writing before a proper official, usually a notary public.

Agent - a person who legally represents another based upon authority received from that person.

Amenity - beneficial aspects of a property brought about by its desirable location because of features such as a tennis court, golf course, park, etc.

Amortization - gradual reduction of debt by a schedule of installment payment.

Appreciation - an increase in value over a period of time--the reverse of depreciation.

Assessed Value - the value placed on the property by a governmental agency for the purposes of taxation.

Assignee - the person to whom a transfer of interest is made, such as a contract, mortgage, or agreement.

Assignment - the transfer of property or rights from one person (the assignor) to another (the assignee).

Assumption of Mortgage - assumption of an obligation, normally by a purchaser, taking on the primary liability for payment of an existing mortgage or deed of trust.

Backbone - refers to the major improvements system necessary to develop a property. Includes grading, filling, and major street, sewer, and water connections.

Balloon - refers to a mortgage or a payment due at the end of a certain period of time in the form of a lump sum where the periodic principal and interest payments have not fully amortized the loan.

Binder - may refer to a deposit paid to evidence good faith on a real estate contract or a preliminary title insurance agreement which provides that upon meeting the requirements stated in the binder, a title insurance company will issue the specified title insurance policy.

Blanket Mortgage - refers to a lien that covers more than one parcel of real estate which makes it useful in the development and sale of one parcel and two smaller parcels.

Bona Fide - acting in good faith without fraud or deceit.

Capitalization - a means of determining value by dividing the net income of a property by a percentage that represents the rate necessary to attract capital to investment. May also refer to the amount of money invested in a company or project.

Caveat Emptor - "Let the buyer beware."

Cash Flow - the amount of money thrown off after the payment of operating expenses and debt service.

Chattel - personal property.

Cloud of Title - a claim or encumbrance on real property that interferes with good title to a property.

Closing - the conclusion of the real estate transaction where documents and money are exchanged.

Collateral - security given to help guarantee the repayment of a note or mortgage.

Common Area - that portion of a property which exists for the benefit of more than one person, such as all owners in the case of a community swimming pool or common ground.

Condemnation - the taking of private property by a public or quasi-public agency under the right of eminent domain.

Conditions Precedent - refers to those requirements which must be met before a contract will close.

Constructive Notice - notice given as recorded by public records.

Contiguous - adjacent or joining.

Contract - in real estate, an agreement between parties to purchase and sell, based upon specific conditions.

Covenant - a written enforceable promise contained in a deed or mortgage specifying the performance or nonperformance of certain acts or uses.

D/B/A - abbreviation for, "doing business as."

Debt Service - the amount necessary to amortize a loan, being the principal and interest payments.

Deed - a written document conveying the ownership of land from one party to another.

Default - the failure to abide by the terms of a contract, note, or mortgage, resulting in a breach.

Deficiency Judgment - the gap between the debt sued for and the price realized at a foreclosure sale.

Density - the number of dwelling units allowed per acre of land.

Depreciation - the decline in value due to physical wear and tear or an economic change.

Earnest Money - a deposit accompanying a contract.

Easement - the legal right to cross upon another's land for a specific purpose such as a utility easement.

Economic Life - the probable future life in which a property will earn a return.

Eminent Domain - the right of a public body to take private property for public use upon payment of "just compensation."

Encroachment - an improvement that is illegally placed upon another person's property.

Equity - in real estate, the difference between the value of the property and the debt owed.

Equity of Redemption - the right to redeem property during the foreclosure period.

Escrow - in real estate, may refer to money deposited in the hands of a third party who holds the funds in trust for the buyer and seller, or may refer to a procedure in which documents or money are deposited with a disinterested third party such as a title company who will make disbursements under the escrow agreement instructions.

Escalator Clause - a provision in a contract or mortgage providing for the upward or downward adjustment of such items as rent or interest rates.

Exculpatory Clause - a provision in a note or mortgage holding the debtor harmless from personal liability in the event of default. May also be known as a waiver of deficiency.

Fee Simple - the absolute ownership of real property not limited by restrictions.

Foreclosure - the legal procedure for terminating the mortgagor's interest in property covered by a mortgage.

Forfeiture - the loss of money or rights under a contract as the result of failure to comply with requirements of a contract.

Front Foot - a common measurement of property fronting on a main road and according to local custom may extend for a depth of 100′ to 300′. Prices for this type of property are expressed in a certain amount of dollars per front foot.

Gap Financing - an interim loan used to finance the difference between a construction loan and permanent loan until conditions are finalized.

Grantee - the person to whom real estate is conveyed.

Grantor - the person who conveys the real estate.

Gross Income - the total amount of income before the deduction of any expenses.

Ground Lease - a lease for the use of the land only, separate from the improvements placed thereon.

Highest and Best Use - that use which will produce the greatest amount of net income over a certain period of time.

Homeowner's Association - an organization, usually non-profit, formed to maintain and provide community facilities for the common enjoyment of the residents within that subdivision.

Ingress - the right of entrance or accessibility.

Injunction - a court order prohibiting certain acts.

Joint Venture - an association between two or more parties to enter into an ownership, business, or development. Its legal form may include partnerships, corporations, or other.

Junior Mortgage - a lien that is inferior to claims of mortgages placed ahead of it, as a second mortgage to a first mortgage.

Lease - a contract, written or oral, under which the possession and use of property are given to another person by the owner for a stated period and consideration.

Lessee - tenant.

Lessor - landlord.

Leverage - the use of borrowed money to purchase property.

Liquidity - the degree to which property can be converted to cash.

Lis Pendens - a pending suit, usually recorded so as to give constructive notice of pending litigation.

Mechanics Lien - a statutory lien for the benefit of contractors who have furnished labor or materials to a construction job.

Merchantable Title - acceptable title in a transaction. Free from encumbrances or defects affecting salability.

Metes and bounds - land description by direction and distances using angles and reference points.

Monument - a reference point in a description, either set by a surveyor, or a natural landmark.

Mortgage - the pledge of property as security for a note or debt.

Net Lease - a lease where the lessor receives a specified rental and the lessee or tenant pays all of the operating expenses including taxes, utilities, and insurance.

Net Listing - a listing wherein the owner states the price that he wants to receive and the broker must add on the amount of his commission.

Non-Recourse Note - requires the lender to look to the property only as security for repayment. The borrower has no personal liability.

Open Listing - where an owner gives a broker the authorization to attempt to sell his property, but any other broker or the owner himself could sell the property without payment of commission to the open listing broker unless he is the procuring cause of the sale.

Option - the right to buy or lease property for a certain period of time at a designated price.

Percolation Test - a soil test to determine the capacity of property to drain.

Plat - a map of a subdivided parcel showing lots with streets, easements, boundaries, and dimensions. Usually is the final document necessary to be recorded before a subdivision is begun.

Police Power - the constitutional right of government to take whatever rights or actions are necessary to protect the "health, safety, and promotion of general welfare." Rights under police power, such as zoning, are generally considered to be outside of the area of eminent domain and just compensation, even if an owner's property is damaged in value.

Power of Attorney - authority for another person to act on one's behalf as an agent or attorney.

Prepayment Privilege - the right of a borrower to pay a debt prior to its maturity. The right of prepayment may or may not include a penalty or other restrictions on behalf of the lender.

Quiet Title - a legal action brought to remove a cloud on the title and establish rightful ownership.

Realtor - a copyrighted word used to designate a member of the National Association of Realtors and their affiliates.

Redemption - the right of a mortgagor to recover property upon payment of the debt, or the right of an owner to recover his property if it has been lost under a tax sale.

Release Provisions - a provision in the mortgage or deed of trust allowing a portion of property to be released from the lien upon the satisfaction of certain conditions or payment.

Restrictive Covenant - a clause placed in a deed which limits the use of a property in accordance with the conditions imposed.

Right-Of-Way - an easement over land allowing those other than an owner to use the property for such things as a road, or public utility.

Riparian - refers to water such as a river, stream, waterway, or other water-related rights. Often affects irrigation and the use of a stream.

Second Mortgage - a mortgage inferior to an existing mortgage and placed on the property at a later time.

Setback - the distance from the property lines that a building must be placed.

Sheriff's Deed - a deed given under court order where a property has been sold to satisfy a judgment.

Specific Performance - a requirement in a court of equity for the defendant to carry out the terms of a contract.

Statute of Frauds - a legal element of contract requiring that real estate documents must be in writing to be enforceable.

Subordination - taking a secondary position, normally in relation to a mortgage or lease.

Survey - a map delineating a parcel of land, or the process by which this map is developed. Results in a depiction of size, location, and physical description, including reference markers and their locations.

Takedown - may refer to the advance of funds by a lender under a loan agreement--the rate at which land must be purchased under an option contract.

Takeout - a commitment to make a loan at a future specified time, usually a permanent loan after construction of improvements are complete. Construction lenders may require a developer to have a takeout loan before they will advance construction funds.

Topography - the lay of the land, including contour, slope, and delineation of hills, valleys, streams, etc.

Tort - the commitment of a wrong which allows another to take action.

Unilateral Contract - gives one party to the contract specific rights without giving the other party consideration for these rights.

Usury - an interest rate higher than the legal rate allowed to be charged.

Vacancy Rate - an allowance for a reduction in gross income due to less than 100% occupancy by tenants.

Water Table - the depth from the surface of the ground at which water is found.

Zoning - action taken by a governmental jurisdiction which specifies the use to which land or property may be put.

Index

Italicized page numbers and phrases throughout the index refer to illustrations. Boldface page numbers reference the main discussion of a given topic, as opposed to its minor references. The standard abbreviation q.v. (which see) appears after certain subheadings to refer the reader to the same entry as a main heading.

OTHER AGRICULTURAL BOOKS
AVAILABLE FROM DOANE

Estate Planning for Farmers–A 248 page Doane guide to help you make sure your estate--the money and property you've worked a lifetime to build--isn't hit by thousands of dollars of unnecessary estate taxes, probate and settlement costs. Estate Planning for Farmers shows how to transfer your farm to sons or daughters in an equitable way; how to cut federal estate taxes; how to organize your farm business to assure worry-free retirement years; how to use wills, trusts, insurance as estate planning tools; and much more.

Facts & Figures for Farmers–Here's a complete reference that brings together all the facts, calculations, tables and charts you need in the everyday operation of your farm. It's full of facts to help you calculate inputs, measure land, figure silo capacities, balance rations, calibrate sprayers, analyze budgets, estimate space requirements, machinery costs and capacities . . . to name just a few. Contains 348 pages of concise, easy-to-use information.

Farm Management Guide–The soft-cover, bound version of Doane's famous Reference Volume. Contains 336 pages, packed with valuable production, management and marketing information. Thirteen detailed chapters cover: types of farming; acquiring the farm; records, planning and financing; taxes and insurance; soils and crop production; forage production; livestock production; dairy production; livestock feeds and feeding; agricultural chemicals; buildings, equipment and machinery; water and irrigation; marketing. Makes an excellent "carry around" farm reference guide, or a wonderful gift.

Field and Equipment Record Book–A 160 page record book to aid in crop planning and production analysis. It's designed so that six years of cropping information, on up to 26 fields, may be kept, along with data on machinery, buildings and farm tools. Included are maps for plotting overall farm and field layouts, plus forms for recording fertility data, seed variety and rates, tillage work, pest control practices, crop progress, harvest and yield information for each field. The book is wirebound, with large 8½ x 11 inch pages for easy record entry.

Doane's Tax Guide for Farmers–A 330 page book that stresses tax management as a farm financial tool. Covers how proper planning and timing of transactions can reduce taxes . . . how to manage income and expenses from a tax standpoint. Also covers land and depreciable property, social security taxes and benefits, tax aspects of farm business organization, tax cutting suggestions as applied to gifts, property transfers, and retirement plans.

DOANE®

Doane Agricultural Service, Inc.
8900 Manchester Road
St. Louis, Missouri 63144
314/968-1000